Here Comes the Son

First published in 2020 by Pat Maloney
with What's Your Story, an imprint of
New Life Publishing, LU4 9HG
Reprinted 2020

British Library Cataloguing in Publication Data
A catalogue record for this book is available
from the British Library

ISBN 978 1 912237 26 5

Front cover image created by Hugh Byrne

Typesetting by New Life Publishing,
Luton, UK www.goodnewsbooks.co.uk
Printed and bound in Great Britain

Here Comes the Son

Pat Maloney

for James ...

The Tramp

Today I saw a tramp. I could tell that he was an intelligent man as he had positioned himself on the pavement, next to the cash machines outside of the bank. As I watched him from across the street, I noted that he avoided making eye contact at all costs, as if to do so might turn him to stone. This was despite the fact that he engaged all who passed in conversation.

'Excuse me, got any change'? 'Spare some change please'?

Most people who passed the tramp appeared to regard him, at best, with disdain. Some pretended he was invisible, while others pretended it was they who were invisible. Some even crossed the street to avoid him.

The man was the epitome of a down and out. So dishevelled was he, that it was impossible for me to hazard a guess, with any degree of accuracy, as to his age. His hair was a wild chaotic tangle which seemed to have a will of its own and sprouted out in all manner of directions. His beard was so large and so thick that as a man I could not help but be impressed by it, even if it did resemble an opened bail of wire wool. It was, I imagined, the type of beard that would make the perfect habitat for a host of small creatures to thrive in. Or, perhaps, for a human being to hide behind.

The tramp's clothes were as you might expect, filthy, tattered and torn. He looked like he had not taken a bath in months, maybe even years. In fact, he was so dirty he had a rusty red glow about him. The look on his face told me he carried the weight of the world on his shoulders. It was the painful expression of a man who knows he is beaten. So infectious was his shame, that even from across the street, I could feel it burn.

Had I seen the tramp twenty years ago, I probably would have been disgusted and annoyed that I had to witness such a disgrace whilst going about my business.

Ten years ago, I might have angrily thought, 'Get a grip and sort yourself out, there's no need to live like that.'

However, when I saw the tramp today. The only thought that kept going through my mind was, 'We're the same you and I, ... only I got lucky!'

A Life Worth Living

Are all lives worth living? What if you have lived a terrible life in which you have done terrible things?

Or, perhaps you are a good person, but you have had to endure a life-time of constant pain and suffering; a harrowing existence! Are these still lives which are worth having been lived? I suppose the question I really ask is - has my life been worth living?

There have been times when I did not think so. There have been times when I struggled to justify the point of my very own existence. There were times when I welcomed death, times when I actively encouraged it.

When I look back on my life, I can now see that I expected too much. I think I believed life was going to be some sort of magical roller-coaster ride of an adventure. When in fact for the most part, it is just mundane repetition, a series of hurdles and tragedies to overcome.

I don't mean to be morose; I am just trying to make sense of something beyond my grasp, something beyond my understanding.

I think perhaps, it may all come down to love. I am a human being; (fundamentally) I need to love and to be loved. Even if that love is only brief or fleeting. Is it the ability to love (or not to love) that makes me human?

There were times in my life when I had love, but I failed to recognise it. Times when I had love, but I pushed it away, because I did not believe I deserved it, and times, when I did truly love but it was not reciprocated. But still I had love. Only a life without love can be a life not worth being lived. A life that has no real worth or value.

All you need is love; but I think you have to start with yourself.

CHAPTER ONE

I HAVE JUST HAD A STUFFED CRUST PIZZA FOR MY DINNER (the frozen kind), it's raining outside and there's nothing on the telly. I live on my own in a one bedroom flat and sometimes I feel very lonely. I have family and I have friends, but I don't tell them that I am lonely, because I am ashamed of, and embarrassed by it. I am not moaning; I am just stating fact.

The truth of the matter is this, compared to five years ago, I have a fantastic life. Unfortunately, this does not mean that my life, is now fantastic.

Sometimes when I am by myself, I wonder what happened to the old me, the person I use to be. What happened to that happy go lucky young boy I once was. Who have I become?

I walk out to the kitchen and place my plate in the sink, with the other plates. I promise myself; I will wash them tomorrow. I make my way to the bathroom and as I enter, I stare at my reflection in the mirror. I look at my grey hair and the lines upon my face. I wonder what has happened to the sparkle that has now gone from my eyes. Where did all that time go! As I turn to leave the bathroom, I stare in the mirror and blow myself a kiss, knowing this is the only kiss I will be getting tonight and the next night and the next. These are quiet times indeed. But it wasn't always like this. In fact, it used to be very different. This is my story.

I was born on the 7th day of the fourth month in the year of our Lord nineteen hundred and seventy two. I was the baby of the family and for the most part, I was a happy and contented child. I seemed to have been born with a naturally cheery disposition, I had also been born with two different coloured eyes, one green and one brown. I have been told that as a small boy, I had a cheeky grin which would produce dimples whenever I smiled and that I had the loveliest mousy brown hair, which my sisters would comb and blow dry into the various fashionable styles of the day, whether I wanted them to or not.

I was a podgy boy and hence, was given the nickname, 'Pudsey Hockey', although my father always called me 'Plike'. Things were often quite difficult at home but despite everything, I was 'nearly' always smiling.

My father was a big man. Not so much, as in height, but as in stature. He was barrel chested with big strong arms and hands like shovels. He had jet-black hair which he would meticulously Bryl-cream to perfection. I can recall there was always a distinctive red and white tub of the stuff on the bathroom windowsill, next to his shaving brush and old-fashioned razor. I remember being totally fascinated by my father's razor. It was an excellent example of a 20th century piece of precision engineering. I would sneak into the bathroom when no one was around and take it down from the windowsill. I can remember the weight and the coolness of its brass handle in my tiny hand. I would slowly turn the steel nib at the base of the brass handle and watch in awe as the stainless-steel head would open up like the cargo doors on a Lancaster bomber to reveal a single Wilkinson Sword blade. I would then turn the nib at the base of the handle in the opposite direction and watch as the 'cargo doors' closed again with meticulous accuracy.

My father was a well-groomed man. He was also a good-humoured man, who liked to crack jokes and have fun. I think it only fair to say that he was, at his core, a decent man. He too was 'nearly' always smiling. That is until he took a drink, as he often did. The change in him was not only noticeable but also instantaneous; unfortunately, he was not a happy drunk.

My mother was a good woman who lived solely for her children. She had about her, that downtrodden look of a woman who is just about managing to keep her head above water. She was an attractive woman, but she rarely wore make up and never went to the hairdressers or beauty salons. As a small boy, I can recall her hunched over the kitchen sink dying her hair with a towel across her shoulders. My mother always looked tired and as if she were about to 'snap'.

My mother was the main caregiver in our house, she was also the main breadwinner. She dished out the 'slaps' as well as the dinners! She was always quite quick to lash out, sometimes for the most trivial of things. A wrong look could be enough to warrant a torrent of abuse or a slap. 'Stop crying or I will give you something to cry for'! She would also use language that would make a navvy blush.

My dad, when sober, was actually a bit of a softy in comparison to my mother. We all knew we could take liberties and push it a bit with him. But not so with my mum. One stern look from her was enough to put the fear of God into you! If my mother told you to do something, you didn't question, you didn't argue, you just did it, or else! She was 'nearly' always not smiling.

My parents were Irish economic migrants, who arrived in Britain (separately) in the early 1950s. Like thousands before them they sought employment and opportunities that were not available to them in their native homeland. Given the history of the two nations, I think for many it was a bittersweet transition. However, perhaps that's a story for another time. Like all of us, my parents were a product of their environment. Their expectations, needs and wants were basic. They lived a simplistic existence and hailed from a time when life was much slower. Unlike most today, they did not harbour grandiose ideas above their station. They knew their place! They were part of the 'tip your hat' brigade, taught to respond to a uniform and bow to authority. In short, and by today's standards, my parents were very old fashioned.

I don't know much about my father's upbringing, as he rarely spoke of his childhood or his life before 'us'. What I have learned has tended to be snippets of one sided, second-hand accounts that I have had little choice but to believe to be true.

He was born in 1930, in a little fishing village in County Kerry. I believe it to be a truly beautiful part of the world, although, I am still yet to visit. Naturally having grown up by the coast my father had a love of seafood. I recall him coming home from the pub one lunchtime, a little worse for wear and slapping a fish that appeared to be the size of a tuna onto the kitchen table, which he then expected my mother to prepare for him? I remember the very pleased look falling from his face when my mother told him exactly what he could do with his fish! (I also remember the fish eye winking at me, or so it seemed!)

My father loved winkles (molluscs) which looked like tiny snails. You could buy them by the 'pint' in those days. I can see him now, sitting in his armchair, newspaper on the floor at his feet, as he uses a safety pin or the like to remove the membrane from the shell of the winkle before digging out the small sandy snot like creature, and then eating it... what a treat!

It amused my father to encourage me to eat them too! Five years old, I would be standing in front of his chair by the fire, grimacing and chewing the gritty, rubbery pieces of snot, while he laughs and as I think to myself, 'I'm sure other kids get Mars bars'! I don't like seafood!

I never met my paternal grandparents and know nothing of my grandfather. He died when my father was 14yrs old, leaving his mother to bring up seven young children, my father being one of the middle children. I once saw a photograph of my grandmother; it was a black and white photograph that looked like it had been taken some time in the early 1900s. My grandmother is sitting beside a large wooden table in a ramshackle cottage. In the background, pots and pans hang from a stone wall above an old-fashioned range. Remarkably, she is wearing a fox around her neck. Not just a fur, an actual fox, with head and tail still attached! (I believe it is called a stole). My grandmother's left hand is resting on the table and sports a huge gold ring that can clearly be seen on her finger. She has an air of authority about her, which is undeniable. The photograph leaves no doubt that she is clearly a powerful woman, I would also suspect, she was highly revered within the local community. Not the sort of woman you would want to mess with! Her stern face told me as much.

From what I have gleaned over the years, she was not the type of mother who openly showed love and affection to her children, and certainly not my father. By all accounts, she was a cold-hearted woman who ruled with an iron rod. If any of her children were going to get it, it was him (I think there is one in most families, perhaps there is one in yours?).

For reasons unknown, my father was singled out to be the main recipient of her wrath. Did he remind her of the man who had abandoned her in death?

'young blood must have its course',
and, 'every dog his day'.

The story goes that at the tender age of 16 and after years of suffering abuse at the hands of my grandmother, he finally snapped and swung her around their kitchen... by her hair! I don't know if he hit her, but I would like to think he did not. However, what I do know, is that in 1950s rural Ireland, it must have caused ...'quite a stir'!

Immediately after the incident, my father left for England. He never wrote, he never phoned and in the next forty years; he only ever went back once, and I think that was long after his mother had died. I will not attempt to make excuses, for anyone to hit their mother is clearly a terrible thing. An unforgivable thing. But... if you get up every morning and walk out into your backyard and kick your dog, and then one morning you walk out into your backyard, kick your dog and it then turns around and bites you.... well it's not the dog's fault is it!

This is difficult, and will probably sound terrible, I certainly do not wish for you to get the wrong idea, but I admire him for it! I have only ever seen a photograph of her, and I felt intimidated, it must have taken great courage to stand up to her. I think what I am trying to say is, 'no one', has the right to abuse you, to ridicule, mock or scorn you. Regardless of whether it is your mother or not. I hope that makes sense. There have been times when I wished I were more like him! (But, not often).

I know virtually nothing of the circumstances surrounding my father's arrival in Britain. Did he stay with friends or family or was he alone? Either way it could not have been easy for a young boy a long way from home. I do know he found employment working in construction and became a digger driver. Apparently, he had always had a fascination with machinery and engines. I have been told that he was very good at his job and commanded great money, but like many of his countrymen, having worked hard by day, he played hard by night. I think left to his own devices and away from the confines and restrictions of home his disastrous love affair with alcohol began to take hold.

I know more about my mother. My mother was born in 1932 in the west of Ireland in County Mayo. The youngest of seven children she had an idyllic childhood growing up on the family farm. Her family was, I think, considered by the local community as, 'well to do', as they owned, rather than rented the small piece of land they farmed and the two stone dwellings that stood upon it, one being for the livestock and the other being 'home' for my mother's family. The thatched roofed stone building my mother lived in had only two rooms, no electricity, no gas and no running water. It was heated by burning turf (peat) from the bog in an open fire and was lit by kerosene lamps. Their water was collected from a well about a mile away. As I write this. I am reminded of one of my mother's sayings,

'You never miss the water till the well runs dry'!

Now it makes sense! It was I think, a hard existence, but none-theless a good life!

I never met my maternal grandfather as he died the year I was born, and I only ever met my maternal grandmother once, so again, I know little about them. However, my mother once told me a very charming story about them both.

When my grandparents were 'courting', my grandfather would go to meet his young 'Colleen', who lived several miles away in the next village, on horseback!

I smile whenever I think of this, it is not lost on me that in the space of three generations it has gone from my grandfather; making hay, checking teeth and inspecting shoes (and probably quite concerned about his horse too!) to me worrying about motor insurance, road tax and the legal depth of tyre treads! It's not the same is it? Where's the romance gone?

My mother had two sisters and four brothers and, being the youngest, she was by all accounts thoroughly spoilt! As it was in those days all of her siblings, except her youngest brother, left for England to find employment. My uncle Pat (like me, named after his father) stayed behind to help run and eventually inherit the farm which was his by birthright. As it also was in those days, all of her siblings sent money home to their parents. My mother once told me with a grin, that her brother Mike, had sent some money home. Upon hearing the good news she had immediately began to pester her mother into taking her to get her hair done (a perm); my grandmother eventually relented but told her not to mention it to Mike; as she would not want him thinking the money was going on hair do's! Apparently, when he did come home a week or so later, my mother wore a scarf around her head for the duration of his visit!

When the time came for my mother also to leave for England, her eldest brother, Matty, sent her the boat fare (£6). She has always maintained that she came to England due to health reasons as she had asthma and the damp climate of Ireland exasperated her condition. But I don't believe this to be true, I think like any young person she was excited about the possibilities of a new life in a new country, I think the 'asthma' story was a way of trying to ease her conscience at her 'perceived' abandonment of her beloved parents. In short, I think she felt guilty for leaving them!

I think for my mother the excitement of a new life in a new country was short lived. Having arrived in England, she went to stay with her brother and his wife Magdalene, in a little place called Wythenshawe, where she effectively became their children's nanny. My poor mum, she had arrived full of excitement and wonder only to be left at home all day looking after the children. She once told me she could see the tops of trees over the brow of a hill from her bedroom window, the scene reminding her of home. She said she was so homesick that she use to cry herself to sleep every night and would try to stifle her sobs with her pillow so as not to be heard. She was only nineteen, in a foreign land and as green as the grass she had just left behind.

She also told me that one day, not long after she had arrived, my uncle Matty asked her if she knew the facts of life! Even as she recalled this conversation, she looked embarrassed. She said she was horrified to think a brother of hers would ask her such a thing and remembers, 'wanting the ground to open and swallow her up'! Her brother was clearly only trying to protect her, she was no longer living in the quaint little village, 'back home'! She was now living in post war Britain, where things were very different to the life she had once known.

An Officer and a Gentleman! Uncle Matty was already living in Britain when the second world war broke out and like (nearly) all men, had immediately signed up for service. He enlisted in the army but failed to mention it to his parents. Presumably, this was so as not to worry his mother, or to enrage his stout Irish father, whom I am guessing would not have been too pleased that his son had joined the British army, war or no war!

While off fighting the 'Hun', uncle Matty kept up the ruse, that he was in fact, 'simply' working in England, by sending letters home to his mother from the battlefield, via his landlady in London. Whom in turn, would open the letters, re-address them and then post them on to Ireland. What I would give to read those letters?! I wonder what they didn't say!

My mother's brother was shot and wounded on three separate occasions. He fought at the battle of Dunkirk, was awarded medals for heroism and bravery and served throughout the entirety of the Second World War. And all without his parents ever finding out!

I don't think they make them like that anymore! A man brave enough to stand up and fight for what he believed in, but not brave enough to tell his father he was doing it.

I never had the opportunity to meet my uncle Matty, but I think I would have liked too. He died of cancer in the early 70s, (he was not an old man!). My mother has always kept a photo in her purse, which appears to have been taken some time in the late 1960s. He is standing in front of an open fireplace, which has a rifle mounted on the wall above it. He stands proud, hands clasped behind his back, wearing a blazer showing off his war medals. His hair is oiled, and slicked back. He is wearing dark horn rimmed glasses and sports a thick well-maintained moustache that any military general would be proud of. He has a confident smile and a sparkle in his eyes. He is every bit the English gentleman!

After a year or two of being a house-bound nanny, my mother eventually found employment (and her feet so it would seem), working for a small independent car manufacturer, she said she enjoyed good pay, but her female colleagues where unkind and constantly made fun of her, due to the fact she was a naive 'biddy' from Ireland. She told me she remembers the two-minute silence at work when the King died. (George V1, not Elvis!). She also said she remembers being sent to the bakers for a... Durex loaf!

Now she was out of the house more and had her own money she slowly developed a social life. One evening her and a friend, the 'new' Irish girl at work, went to a local pub for a drink, something neither of them would have been allowed to do back in Ireland as only a woman of ill repute would dare venture into a pub unaccompanied by a man! She and her friend were sitting at a table and had not been in the bar long when the door opened and in walked a handsome young stranger with jet-black wavy hair. He was wearing a pin stripped suit and had impeccably clean shoes.

It would seem my mother had caught his eye and they began talking before agreeing to go on a date!

My mother was to meet this young man outside of Colchester park gates at a predetermined time. My mother turned up for the date as agreed, but as she stepped down from the bus, was horrified to see the young man rolling around on the ground, 'scrapping' with some bloke outside the park gates!

So there you have it. The spoilt little girl from the well to do family and the bad boy! Clearly, the bad boy was my father. She said the first time she saw him she thought he was 'gorgeous'! As their child, I find it hard to believe that my father was ever... 'Gorgeous'!

In 1955, and after 'holding hands' for only three months they were married. Strange, but there are no wedding photos.

They were young and naïve, thrown together by chance and left alone to get on with it the best they could. I would like to think they were happy to begin with. However, I suppose as time went by and as her concerns about his drinking turned into constant nagging, they began to resent one another. Perhaps loving turned to loathing, irritability and then rage, but in 1955 when you said 'I do'.....you did!

For the first few years of their marriage, they enjoyed the unbridled freedom afforded to most childless couples. However, all that changed in 1959 with the birth of their first child, my sister Kathleen. It is said that 'A rolling stone gathers no moss'! My parents were no exception, now having settled in a small industrial town a little under 30 miles outside of London their family grew. Kathleen was quickly followed by Evelyn, then came Connor, next it was Bridie and then finally it was me, Pat.

CHAPTER TWO

MY MOTHER WAS 40YRS OLD WHEN SHE HAD ME. So, I'm guessing it was not a planned pregnancy. I suspect I may have been somewhat of a surprise!

Like my sister Bridie, I had been born at home. Home being a three-bedroom council house, which I can only assume, like most council houses in the 1970s, it didn't have much in it!

It was a somewhat simple affair of woodchip wallpaper and lino! We had basic furniture (the heavy brown type), we had a television (rented – not always colour), which when you put coins into, allowed a predetermined amount of viewing time and a well-worn settee, which we all hid behind when the club man came knocking. In the kitchen we had an old-fashioned gas cooker, a small fridge and (as my parents called it) a wireless! There was also an overhead washing line on a pulley system attached to the ceiling and that was about it. Our home was void of gadgets. We did not even have a telephone!

In the winter months when I awoke in the morning it was so cold, I would see my breath as I exhaled. There was no central heating. I would stick my toe out from under the blanket to assess whether it was warm enough to get up! There was no double glazing either, so if I happened to take a look out of the window, I ran the risk of tearing the net curtains, because they were usually stuck to the glass. As I write this, I can picture myself as a small child looking at the patterns of ice on the inside of the bedroom window, like a snowflake under a microscope! Dare I lick it? Quite magical now I think of it!

We lived at number 5 Tanglewood Close. Even by the standards of the day, our close seemed different to other places. Situated directly in the centre of a large estate and with no through traffic it often felt as though we were separate to and cut off from the rest. It was in many ways, like living in a bubble, a community within a community. As if someone had given the orders to circle the wagons and the Tanglewood residents had all huddled together in the middle, living side-by-side, cheek by jowl. As a result, we knew our neighbours well. These were the days when it was still okay to borrow a cup of sugar, a needle and thread or even a couple of quid from the people next door!

These were also the days when 'all' kids played outside. As such, our Close was always full of kids playing out on the greens in front of the houses. A safe place to play, and hence a magnet for kids from 'down the road' or 'just around the corner'. We were forever in and out of each other's houses and back gardens, building dens and generally running riot.

Red Rover, Kerby, and if you were feeling particularly brave, Knock Up Ginger, were among our favourite past-times and would keep us entertained for hours. With the daylight fading, we would be so engrossed and having such fun that the games would only end when we heard the first call of a parent beckoning their child. Our young hearts sinking because we knew the cry of, 'Come in now it's getting late', would surely start a chain reaction as other mothers followed suit.

I strongly suspect I am viewing it through rose-tinted glasses, but it was of a time when kids were allowed to be kids and even the adults seemed to possess more character, than those of today!

At the top of our Close was a block of 8 low rise flats, reserved exclusively for old people. There was Mrs Pepperpot, an ancient looking woman who, if you banged on her window, would give you sweets, (to piss off, presumably!) There was Percy, a confirmed bachelor with snow white hair, always chewing gum, always impeccably dressed and who would let you keep the change if you went to the shops for him. A true gentleman.

And then, there was old Reg. A dirty old git who kept budgies and lived in absolute squalor! However, Reg was a harmless old soul, who, regardless of the weather, always wore his trademark black trench coat and black trilby hat. What colour they may have been originally I have no idea; all I know is they were so dirty they shone. Old Reg pretty much kept himself to himself most of the time, but every now and then, old Reg would take a notion... to go visiting!

Our house, like many houses back then, was of the type that always had the back door open, so people would just wander in and out! I recall as a family we would be sitting in the living room watching television (and hoping there was enough money in it to see the end of Bullseye, or the like!), when you would hear someone come in the back door. Not one of us would get up from our seat to investigate; instead, we would simply wait for the living room door to open to see who it was. More often than not, it was Bridget Murphy, from across the road at number 2, but if it were old Reg then we would all moan and grimace behind his back!

Being so dirty, Reg had his very own teacup, one that my mother had put aside especially for him. It was very distinctive from all the other cups in our house, just to be certain that there was never any confusion and that you might accidentally drink from it! Sometimes however, we would have many visitors to the house. On occasion, more visitors ...than cups!

A tense atmosphere would build between those in the know, as a cup-like game of Russian roulette would ensue in our kitchen, resulting in some poor unsuspecting guest inevitably ending up with Reg's cup! Bringing much hilarity to us kids, as every time the unsuspecting visitor took a slurp of tea, we would all divert our eyes to the floor and try to stifle a giggle.

We were fortunate enough to have good neighbours; I can't help but wonder if they felt the same. To our left lived Mr and Mrs Gentle. Gentle by name and gentle by nature. A nice old couple who were pleasant and courteous in an old-fashioned sense. Like most back then they kept their gardens pristine. In the spring and summer months, Mrs Gentle would spend hours tending to her flowers and the hedgerows that encompassed their house. Therefore, the Gentle's, had my mother's approval and respect as decent (and clean) people, as she has always maintained in a rather harsh and criticising tone, 'untidy garden – untidy house'!

With seven of us living under one roof, there was often a lot of noise coming from our house. In fact, It was sheer bedlam at times, but they never once complained, I think Mr Gentle may have been a little fearful of my father!

To our right lived the McGuires who, as the name suggests, were Irish. Thus, they had my mother's respect and approval regardless of whether they kept their gardens nice or not (which incidentally they did). Mrs McGuire and my mother, having both hung out their respective washing, would spend hours gossiping over the garden fence, 'Did you hear about this one and did you hear about that one'!

The McGuire's had a daughter called Ruth, a year or two younger than me. I have a very stark and lasting image of Ruth; she is standing the other side of the stick fence that separates our back gardens. It is summertime and she is sporting pigtails, and wearing knee high white socks, which have pictures of Mickey Mouse on them. Ruth is screaming hysterically!

This is because Bridget Murphy's dog has managed to get into 'Fluffy's' hutch, (Ruth's rabbit) and has shred the poor animal to pieces! Ruth's screaming has brought everyone out of their houses. I think they must have thought there had been a murder! Which, I suppose, technically there had. Despite her dog, out of all the residents in Tanglewood Close, Bridget Murphy was by far my favourite. I loved Bridget like a dear aunty.

I once heard that gypsy's dunk their new-born babies in a bucket of ice-cold water to toughen them up and give them 'that' harsh look! Obviously, I now know this is not true (and racist), however it does (if unfairly), kind of describe how Bridget looked! Bridget was indeed 'hardy looking' and as mad as a box of frogs, although contrary to her appearance she was very loving and kind. She was a 'hard' woman not to like.

She had been born partially deaf; as a result, she had not learned to form certain sounds and words correctly. Some people mistook this to mean, along with her accent, that she was not, 'the full shilling'! However, this was not the case, Bridget was as sharp as a tack, could run rings around the best of them, and often did. Bridget's husband, Thomas was a carpenter by day and a heavy drinker by compulsion. Poor Bridget (just like my poor mother) suffered terribly at the hands of her violent husband. 'Ironically', my father had to go over to their house on a number of occasions when things had gotten particularly 'ugly'! It must have been a difficult and delicate situation for my father to walk into, as getting involved in domestic 'situations' involving husband and wife was not really the done thing back then!

Maybe that's why I don't ever recall anyone intervening when it was kicking off in our house!! That and the fact no one wanted to confront the mad Irish man at number 5!

After such incidents, Bridget would repay her husband's cruelty by starving him! She would hide food from him or 'take it' with her, if she was going to stay at her sisters, when also knowing there was no money in the gas or electric. 'Now, we sees how da... barsh stud likes dat', she would say while tipping her head as if to add 'good enough for him'!

Then the next time Thomas got drunk, he would beat her up again. Bridget's daughters (Isabelle and Amelia) were about the same age as me. We often played together in each other's houses, I remember the frightened looks on their faces, when their dad would come home drunk and start on their mum, that being my cue to go home! It was a look I knew all too well!

On happier occasions the three of us would go round to the shops and buy 10p mixtures, bring them back home and set up shop in the coal shed at the side of my house or theirs and then re-sell and barter the sweets. However, with the two sisters working together as a team, I always got short changed!

'Blacky' the rabbit killer! Blacky was as wild as Bridget was mad. The mongrel dog was not only a master at despatching rabbits, but also an excellent and expert milk thief! Every morning after the milkman had done his round, Blacky would visit each doorstep (almost everyone had their milk delivered in those days) and would carefully remove the silver foil from the top of the bottle with his tongue and then lap out the first two inches of milk from the bottle and without ever knocking one over! If you were to line all the bottles up next to each other in the close, the levels would all be the same. As a result, Bridget Murphy was forever marching round to the local shops to buy milk for the irate residents of our close.

Next door to Bridget lived, Frank and Eunice Edwards. Frank was the second person in the close (after Mr Gentle), to own a car, but unlike Mr Gentle he never bothered to acquire a licence or motor insurance. You could get away with it back then. Frank always referred to, 'er indoors', as the 'old battle axe', which was very unfair as Eunice was in fact a lovely lady. She worked at the local DHSS offices and could have 'grassed up' half the estate if she wanted to, but she never did (at least I don't think so!)

The Edwards had a wayward son called Rick. Probably just in his early 20's back then, Rick had long jet-black hair, a beard to match and a habit of dressing like an Arab. He also enjoyed taking copious amounts of hard drugs! Despite these afflictions, he was a very likeable fellow, even when he would be out in the Close taking flying kicks at his father's or Mr Gentle's car!

Bridget's dog sensed what we all knew; Rick was a fucking head case. Every time Blacky saw Rick, his hair would stand up on end, he would begin to snarl and bare his teeth, and then go for him, and vice versa!

One afternoon when Rick was higher than the Empire State Building, he knocked on Bridget Murphy's front door and told her matter of factly and in no uncertain terms that the next time the dog went for him he was going to kill it and leave it on her doorstep!

'Ah dats great, lovely, ya ya. Okay so den'! Said the bewildered Bridget, not quite understanding what the long-haired lunatic in the flowing smock was saying, as she simply shut the front door on him. Rick never did kill the dog, and Bridget continued to buy milk for everyone in the close.

Behind closed doors, I do not think there was anyone in the Close who could cast aspersions on anybody else, (less say Mr & Mrs Gentle!). One way or another everyone seemed to be dealing with some sort of crisis or mess. However, as contradictory as it may sound, it was still of a time when people had manners and respect for one another. Being a small child, with no other point of reference, I upheld (as I still do!) the belief that Tanglewood Close was a good place to grow up. I could run wild. I could play out until it got dark. I could avoid being bitten by blacky (or Rick!). In short, I had the opportunity to learn important social skills.

I think most people (my age) would agree the 1970s was the golden age of childhood. I feel sorry for today's kids; I don't think they have the same freedom or innocence that I enjoyed as a child. I think it was for most a more, simple, innocent time, of course that is as long as you didn't write to, or worse, receive a reply from JIML FIX IT!

There was often chaos and violence at home, but despite this, I consider myself 'lucky'! This is because I was born into a 'loving' but dysfunctional family. My parents and those around me instilled in me (not always intentionally) a strong sense of morals and a code of conduct second to none. The cloth from which I am cut! I had manners, I had respect and I had compassion. I was also aware that other people had it a lot worse; it was real character-building stuff.

CHAPTER THREE

MY EARLIEST MEMORY DATES BACK TO WHEN I WAS JUST 4YRS old. My sister Kathleen is leaving home. I think it is the tense atmosphere that has cemented the memory securely in my mind and has made me sense that something is wrong. Intuition should not be dismissed, even at the age of four! I can still picture the scene.

Kathleen is standing in the hallway by the front door. Her bags are packed; and laying beside her on the floor. She is wearing a fur coat (which I assume is fake) and she has tears in her eyes. My mother is crying and pleading with her to stay. My dad stands silent. He looks hurt and is at a loss as what to do.

Being so small I can remember being in and around their legs, but they hardly notice me as I stare up at their faces in an attempt to read the situation. Poor Kathleen looks torn, she too is now crying, and keeps reaching out for the door. Just 16yrs old, her fragile exterior and timid demeanour hide the fact that she is an extremely strong-willed girl. She has made up her mind and 'they' are not going to stop her.

I think being the oldest; Kathleen had witnessed the worst of our parent's relationship. I can only assume she had simply had enough of all the fighting and arguing and could not wait to get as far away as possible.

I remember the stone-cold silence in the hallway after she closed the door behind her and walked out of our lives.

I didn't see my sister much after that day in the hallway, so I pretty much grew up without her. It's sad, but as time went by, she became more like a distant aunty than a big sister. I remember she had a David Soul, poster stuck to the purple wall in her bedroom. It was a constant reminder that Kathleen was gone, I think that's why my mother took it down.

I think it was difficult for my mum after Kathleen left; maybe that's why she kept me (the baby) close. For the next few years, I was never far from her side. My mother's style of parenting was the old-fashioned thinking, 'spare the rod, spoil the child' which I am sure she believed affirmed her status as a good mum. As a result, I tended to do as I was told.

If she went visiting, then I was forced to tag along, and if, whilst out visiting, I were asked if I would like a drink of orange for example. I would look at my mother before I answered. If she smiled... I would say 'yes please'. If she frowned.... I would say 'no thank you', regardless of whether I wanted the glass of orange or not!

Likewise, if my mother went to the shops, then I had to go to with her. Going to the local shops could take hours, as my mother would constantly be stopping to gossip with every housewife she meet along the way. For a young boy it could be a very restless, long, drawn out, boring affair, especially if there were no sweets at the end of it. On one such excursion I had seen a plastic policeman's helmet (the tit shaped ones!), for sale in the local newsagents. It cost £1.40. I had begged my mother to buy it for me, but she said she did not have enough money. I was only little, and even then, I never asked for much. I think I may have struggled to hide my disappointment. However, I did not intend to give up on my prize. It was a long shot, but I would try my father. My father rarely worked anymore; but it just so happened that he had obtained a few 'shifts', So that evening I patiently awaited his return. Even at the age of five, I knew it would be a long wait, as he would surely be coming home via the pub, but fingers crossed!

I got lucky! He had come home from the pub drunk, as expected, but unexpectedly, in an unusually pleasant and placid mood, so I wasted no time in excitedly telling him all about the policeman's hat that I had seen for sale in the local paper shop. My father was grinning, and to my astonishment, started handing me £1 notes, whilst saying, 'is that enough to buy it, plike'? And so on, until I held, in the palm of my tiny hand, seven £1 notes! I couldn't believe my young eyes! I had never had so much money. That night I went to bed the happiest little boy alive!

I awoke at 2am to absolute Bedlam! It sounded like a full-scale riot was taking place on the landing outside my bedroom door. I could hear, crashing and screaming, my mother pleading, I could hear my brother and sisters shouting. But above it all I could hear my dad, roaring like a lunatic, 'where's my fucking money'! 'I want my fucking money'!! .... 'Give me my fucking monee...y'!!!

Just five years old, alone and laying in the dark, listening to it all kicking off! Full of fear, imagining the scene outside my door. I didn't know what to do, I didn't know how to react. So, I lay perfectly still in my bed, ...I didn't want to part with my seven pounds. I wanted my hat.

Eventually with tears streaming down my face I ran out onto the landing and shouted, 'here's your money', and threw the seven pounds at my father. I never saw the money again; and needless to say, I never got the policeman's hat.

I was not to know, that my mother and my sister Evelyn used to steal my father's money from under his mattress while he was asleep.

Presumably, without taking their eyes off him, one would gently lift the mattress, while the other slipped their hand in and took a chunk of the money Not all of it, that would have been madness, but just enough so we wouldn't go hungry. They had to do it. Because if they didn't, he would have drunk every penny.

Kathleen had been the apple of my father's eye, the blue-eyed girl. Evelyn on the other hand was the complete opposite of Kathleen. She was feisty, she spoke her mind without fear of reprisal, and if you backed her into a corner, she would always come out fighting. As far as our father was concerned, she could do no right! Evelyn was 10yrs my senior, and out of all of us, I think she suffered the worst cruelty of all.

Nearly every time my father got drunk, he would accuse my mother of being a whore and would say Evelyn was not his. I can assure you none of his vile accusations were true. How could he say those things to a child? Had she been singled out because she refused to show him love and respect? Did she remind him of his mother?

Needless to say, there has never been any love lost between them. As my sister grew, she became bolder and more defiant in her response to his repugnant and unfounded accusations. 'Good. I'm glad I'm not yours, because I wouldn't want a 'cunt' like 'you' for a father anyway'!

My sister's chides were like a red rag to a bull, fuel to the fire, a flame to the already smouldering touch paper. He would erupt, and fireworks would ensue, it was often spectacularly brutal.

Evelyn was a Christmas baby. Born on Christmas day 1961, how special, what a wonderful gift!

My sister Bridie and I have always been close. She is four years older and when things 'erupted' into violence as they often did, it was her job to look after me. Sitting together on the bottom step of our stairs, she would hug and reassure me as we both cried, while all hell broke loose around us. The shouting and the chaos that ensued has forever remained etched in my memory, but now as an adult, when I think back and try to envisage the fighting (which was often fierce), it is only that of a swirling cartoon cloud with protruding arms and legs and a series of whistles and bangs!

I suppose it's only natural that a child's young mind trying to process these events, creates a manifestation of a 'comical' cartoon cloud? The fearful internalisation of a five-year-old!

When things got really nasty, it was also Bridie's job to run to the phone box two streets away and phone the police. Just 9yrs old, in her pyjamas and having to run through the darkened streets in the middle of the night. Terrified and alone, with tears running down her cheeks. Sobbing so hard she can barely explain to the anonymous adult on the other end of the line that her dad is hurting her mum and wrecking the house. When all the while she should have been safely tucked up in bed, with a favourite teddy! I can feel the anger rising within me as I write this. I knew it was not right, but I was just a kid, I had no experience of the world beyond our house and Tanglewood Close. I had no comparison; so, in that respect it was normal. It was also normal for the police to turn up and take my dad away. I cannot remember how many times as a small boy I watched out of the window as my father was manhandled and bundled into the back of a Black Maria (police van) or squad car; whilst shouting and roaring for all the neighbours to hear! He was not the sort of man to go quietly.

On one such occasion he had arrived home the next day covered in bruises, sporting a black eye and a fat lip. He had clearly 'not ' co-operated' down at the station, and 'they' weren't having any of it and had given him 'a bit of a slap'! But that's okay ...because it was the 1970s.

It is strange, but we (the family) did not like it. We didn't like the idea of these burly police officers beating our dad up! He was after all, our father! Isn't it strange how loyalties and emotions can become confused? Here's a man who gets drunk and terrorises his wife and children, a bully, aggressive and vile and who by anyone's standards deserved a piece of his own medicine. A mother and her children, terrified, emotionally scarred, and all powerless to do anything about the situation. Each one living in their own fear, of his making. The police step in, he gets what he deserves... and we don't like it! Because he is, our dad and we love him... sort of!

Although the baby of the family, my father did not bother with me much. There was none of the father and son 'bonding' stuff like nowadays. He never once kicked a ball with me (at me perhaps!) or encouraged me to take part in sport. He never attended any of the school parent evenings. Nor did he ever enquire as to how my studies might be coming along. It wasn't personal! He did not bother with any of us.

Perhaps judging him by today's standards is a little harsh, however, all I ever got from my dad was, 'get out and play' followed by a tut! For my Brother Connor's sixteenth birthday, my father gave him a black eye! No card, just a black eye!

Connor was more of a father to me than my dad ever was. I hero-worshipped my big brother. He was 7yrs older than me, and much more thoughtful than my father. I was in junior school when my brother took me into town to Taylor & McKenna's toyshop and told me to pick whatever I wanted! (He was still at school himself but had a part time job working as a pop boy (glass collector) in a local social club). With so much choice I deliberated my decision for some time, before finally settling on a toy, 'driving simulator'. A late 1970s early 80s, child's 'driving simulator'. I do not believe there is a kid around today that would even give it a second glance, but to me, it was the best thing ever, the best toy anyone had ever bought me!

It comprised a dashboard and steering wheel (all plastic), which had a long arm that protruded from the front of the dashboard, on the end of which was a magnet. This sat under a large round plastic dish which had roads and bridges moulded into it. A matchbox car also having a magnet on the under carriage was placed on the dish directly above the magnet on the long arm. Thus when you turned the key in the ignition to 'start it up' the round dish would begin to rotate and as you steered left to right you drove the little car around the roads and over the bridges. It was super cool, and I loved it! I know I was in the junior school, because for some reason or other (end of term perhaps?), we were allowed to bring a favourite toy to school... which I did... and some little scrote broke it! It had cost £15, a lot of money back then, especially for a young lad to spend on his little brother. He was my hero.

It was unfair, the responsibility that had been heaped on my brother's young shoulders. From the age of ten, he had become my mother's protector (and my saviour), jumping in between my parents when things got out of hand. I think my father felt threatened by his oldest son (jealous even). Connor was quickly becoming a man. Deep down at some subconscious level, my father knew he was losing his place as Alpha male, it would not be long before he was no longer 'Man of the house'! This often-made things difficult for my beloved brother.

*****

When I was six my father took to his bed and refused to come out of his room. For almost two weeks he stayed in the room and drank day and night, only emerging to use the bathroom and then shuffling straight back into the room. There was no shouting or roaring or any of the 'antics' that normally accompanied his bouts of drunkenness. He was worryingly quiet! I was warned by my mother, to leave my father alone and not to go into his room. I can remember creeping past the bedroom door and wondering what was going on inside, I can remember the distinct whiff of stale alcohol and tobacco emanating from the darkened room. Occasionally I would hear him rambling and muttering to himself! Although she didn't say as much, my mother was very worried about him. At a loss as what to do about the situation, and being a good Irish Catholic woman, she eventually, sent for the parish priest. My mother was close to tears as she explained the situation to Father Crowe. The priest went into the room to see my father and emerged again almost immediately! I think he may have received 'short, sharp, shrift'! The red-faced priest, gently said to my mother, 'I think you should call for a doctor'.

My father was admitted to the 'St Jude ward' of the local hospital for drying out. Despite being only six years old, I knew it was the loony bin!

With my father safely out of the way, my mother went into his room, drew back the curtains and opened the windows, she stripped the bed and sprayed the room with air freshener. I remember seeing the light spilling back into the room and being thankful that the stale smell was now gone. It was as if a dark cloud had been lifted.

A few days went by and then my mother announced that we were going to visit him at the hospital. My mother gave me a bath, and my sister Bridie, was ordered to blow dry my hair. I think she fancied herself working as a stylist for, 'Vidal Sassoon', because I soon resembled a young, Donnie Osmond. Evelyn had recently bought me a new beige duffel coat, which had large peg style fasteners, running down the length of the front, (Paddington bear style). I remember feeling very smart as my mother, Bridie and I boarded the bus for the hospital, Evelyn and Connor, refused to come.

As I sat next to my mum on the bus, I was aware that this was a special visit! In my small hands, I clutched a packet of 'Jammy Dodger' biscuits, a gift for my father. My mother clutched a plastic container of 'Boiled Bacon and Cabbage', a gift for her husband, whilst Bridie, pretended to stare out of the window, but was secretly admiring her own reflection and tousling her hair (a gift to the world!).

As we entered the hospital ward, I saw my father sitting at the far end in an old fashioned, high backed leather chair. He smiled in acknowledgement when he saw us. As we made our way towards him, I took in my surroundings, pale hues covered the walls and by each bed, I saw the same vacant expression on the face of each, and every patient. To a young boy it was a very strange and intimidating environment.

As my mother spoke with my father in low hushed voices, he kept lowering his head and diverting his eyes towards the floor. He looked different somehow. I was too young to recognise it then, but I now know, that what I saw, was shame.

My father stayed in St Jude's, for a total of eight days before he discharged himself. He did not come home; instead, he headed for the nearest pub. When he did eventually arrive home later that night, he was very drunk and very angry! It was all my mother's fault that he had been belittled into going to that 'fucking place'. It was her fault that he had been made to look like a fool in front of his children and his friends. I am sure it was a difficult night for my mother! Despite all that I have told you, it was not all bad, *he* was not all bad!

When I was six, I also had to go into hospital! To have my tonsils removed, or 'yanked out with a big pair of pliers, while I was still awake', as Bridie constantly informed me prior to the procedure!

The Children's Annexe was housed in an oppressive and somewhat dilapidated looking Victorian building near the town centre. I knew 'it' was 'serious' because my mother and I arrived by taxi, and we never took taxi's! I remember walking up the steep concrete steps towards the huge wooden Gothic style doors, while holding my mother's hand.

In my free hand, I clutched my overnight bag, which contained new pyjamas, slippers, a dressing gown and a toiletry bag. I was aware that I would be staying on my own for a few nights and that my mother would be going home without me. I had never been away from the family home or my mother before.

My mother had looked reluctant to leave me, so I put on a brave face to show I wasn't scared, 'Don't worry mum, it'll be all right,' I smiled. I was six years old and I was trying to reassure 'her'!

There were ten other children on the ward. I assumed they too were having their tonsils, 'yanked out'. As an adult, I now know this was not the case. Some of the children were very ill indeed. I don't think I noticed it at the time, because like most kids we all just wanted to play and have fun. The ward, like the building it was in, was very old fashioned. Large old industrial radiators were fixed to the brick walls under huge sash windows. Thin white cotton sheets with a green 'hospital' stripe running horizontally along the top, covered my bed and at the end of the ward was a mountain of well-used, soft toys and games, which I made a beeline for. However, I soon discovered most of the games were incomplete. 'Connect three anybody'?

When I awoke after the procedure, my throat was very sore and I felt groggy, I wanted my mum! However, I soon forgot about my mother when the ice-cream was brought round! I think the policy was give 'em as much as they want as it helps soothe the throat. Bowl after bowl of mint choc-chip ice cream! It is still my favourite! At visiting time, my mum, Connor, Evelyn and Bridie all came to see me and made a huge fuss of me, ruffling my hair, and telling me how brave I was. My dad did not show up.

When visiting was over and all the parents and families had left, all of us children were ordered back into bed to rest. I was just beginning to doze off when I heard talking at the end of the ward, I lifted myself up on my elbows and saw my dad standing in the doorway. Smart pinstriped suit, polished shoes and hair Bryl-creamed to perfection. He was smiling and I instantly knew that he had been drinking. My dad, being the big softy (when he was not insanely intoxicated), that he really was, went around the whole ward, hugging and ruffling the hair of every kid in there before he got to me! All the kids thought it was great!

My father bear hugged me and with his huge shovel like hand ruffled my hair. I could smell the alcohol on his breath and remember the end of my bed dipping as he unceremoniously plonked himself down. 'How you doing plike', he asked, as he produced from his pocket a white crumpled paper bag containing a quarter pound of chocolate 'toffee' drops, which he then gave to me! He told me I was a good 'goss-ein', (boy), and that I would be home before I knew it. 'And are they looking after ya'? 'They are dad'. 'Ah, that's good' he said, as he stood and ruffled my hair once more before turning to leave, saying that he had to go. It was a very short visit!

I knew that having fulfilled his obligation, he was now heading back to the pub. Nonetheless, he 'had' come to see me. He had even brought me sweets, though it was impossible for me to eat them. All the kids on the ward agreed that my dad was very funny. His visit, all though a little unorthodox, had lifted everyone's spirits. It had made me feel special and I was glad. There 'was' love. He loved us all. It is just a pity; we had to look so hard to see it!

My poor mother put up with a lot over the years. She suffered at first hand the full effects of my father's drinking. She lived every minute of it. She remembered the bits he couldn't! Black eyes, and bruises and that is just the physical stuff. A lesser woman might have walked. A lesser woman might have buckled under the pressure, might have broken. But she didn't. I dread to think of the consequences if she had! Thank God for our mother. She is truly a remarkable woman.

But then, we all had it hard, she seems to forget sometimes when she is, 'harking' on about the past and how tough it was for her, that we were all there too, we lived it as well!

****

They were more simple and innocent times. I slept in the same bed as my mother up until the age of 8 or 9! I began to worry my friends at school would find out and think I was a sissy. The reason being, my mother had long stopped sharing a bed, 'with that bastard'! (her words not mine). Growing up, I never saw any displays of affection between my parents. I don't think I 'ever' saw them hold hands, let alone share a tender kiss or an embrace. As such, the sleeping arrangements at our house differed from time to time.

Connor had the box room, which everyone aspired to, my mother included! Mum and I shared the double bed in the middle bedroom with Bridie beside us in a single bed, while my father slept alone in the big bedroom where I had been born. Sometimes if he had been drinking, my mother would insist I slept in with him, as he was less likely to kick off, if I (the baby) was in beside him. I hated it because he would stink of cigarettes and alcohol, and he didn't mind letting one off now and again (although he was usually polite enough to try and disguise it with a cough!).

Sometimes it was okay; if he were in a good mood, he might tell me stories (making them up as he went along). I fondly remember one in particular, about how he had become lost up in the mountains of Kerry.

The story goes; when he was a young boy he went for a walk, alone up in the mountains. Being so high up the weather was prone to change quickly and without warning. This particular day whilst up in the mountains a dense heavy fog descended all around him, leaving him disorientated and confused. No longer was he sure which way was up, and which way was down. Unable to find his way he was sure he would perish, and the mountain would claim him!

He had all but given up hope, when out of the gloom he spied a faint light in the distance. So, with his hands held out high in front of him, he began to inch his way along as he followed the light through the cold and the damp. After some time, he stumbled upon the source of the glow that had guided him to safety. It had come from a tiny little house standing alone in a clearing.

Relieved, he called out, but no answer came. Desperate, but cautious he entered the small lodging and once inside found a roaring fire, welcoming, as it burned fiercely in a stone hearth. In front of the fire lay a little black dog all curled up and fast asleep. He looked around the single room and saw a table had been set, upon which sat a meal, steam rising in swirls beckoning and inviting. In the far corner of the room was a bed, freshly made with heavy blankets and soft pillows; but the little house was void of any persons!

Cold to the bone, he warmed himself in front of the fire. Then when his hunger had got the better of him and he was forced to put his manners aside he sat down at the table and ate the hearty meal. Now satisfied, he began to relax, but was soon overcome with weariness. Then, as if in a daze, he wandered across the room and climbed into the bed where he succumbed to a deep sleep.

When he awoke in the morning, he found the fog had lifted, the little house was gone, and he was under a tree! It was the 'fairies'! They had saved him from certain death!

Even at the age of six, I knew it was complete bollocks... however, I still liked it. I would huff and puff and gesture that I knew it was all lies, but I would be lying there in the dark with a grin on my face! I suspect he had a grin on his face too! Despite everything I was just a little boy, I knew he wasn't all bad. I loved my dad.

My fathers 'condition' had 'thankfully' rendered him virtually unemployable. The reason being, as soon as he had been paid; then he was no longer fit for work! Everyone was in agreement that this was a good thing. It also meant that his drinking was now, (usually) confined to every other Wednesday, as this was the day he received his Giro (dole money). I hated every other Wednesday.

As it grew near, I, and everyone else in the household, would be full of dread, it was always horrific. You also had to be mindful not to invite anyone to the house because you never knew what state he might be in. I remember one such Wednesday!

It was a warm summers evening. Connor had just turned seventeen and had recently bought (in anticipation of passing his test!), his very first car. A gun grey, 1600 E, Cortina, which was square in shape and had a walnut dashboard, it was his pride and joy. I'm sure that today it would be a classic and worth quite a lot of money. Connor, had it parked up, council estate fashion, on the grass in our front garden.

My father had fallen in the door at around six, extremely drunk and very abusive. He began goading my mother and anybody else within spitting distance. Fearful things were going to turn ugly my mother herded Connor, Bridie, and me together and ushered us all out of the front door. Then as if as an afterthought, defiantly shouted back in behind her, 'I hope you die roaring you fucking bastard', before slamming the door shut, thus creating the ruse that we had left! Only we had not left, because we had nowhere to go! We stood for a moment in silence, our eyes darting between one another, as each one in turn weighed up their options, before seemingly all coming to the same conclusion. Everyone looked over at my brother's car; so, we got in. But still, we had nowhere to go as Connor had not yet passed his test!

So, there we sat in the front garden, in my brother's car, listening to the sounds of my dad going berserk inside the house. How embarrassing the whole family just sitting in the car, in the front garden on a summers evening, what would the neighbours think! To pass the time and to try to drown out the noise of my father we made small talk.

About 30 minutes into our 'journey', we noticed a carefree young figure striding purposefully down the path towards our house. My sister groaned aloud as if in pain! It was her school friend Jenny from around the corner. Oblivious, she made her way to our front door. A wave of panic swept through the vehicle as the young girl lifted her arm, poised and ready to knock on the door! As quick as a flash, Bridie had the window wound fully down and hissed, 'psst' '...Jenny over here, quick get in'! Startled, the poor girl compliantly followed orders and squeezed herself into the back of the car between my sister and me. (Bridie had insisted Jenny sit in the middle because she wanted the window seat!). 'why are you all sitting in the car'? She enquired innocently!

There followed a brief silence before we all burst out laughing at the sheer absurdity of our situation. After a few minutes the 13yr old Jenny said, 'erm... actually... I think I have to go home now.... I'll see you at school tomorrow, Bridie, yeah'! I could see my sisters face turning red with embarrassment.

It was another hour before eventually the house went quiet, his spree had run its course, he had finally passed out. We could now recapture the house. I can remember sneaking about as he lay star shaped on the living room floor, 'Do you want tea'?, 'Do you want toast'?, we whispered to one another as we went about our normal routines in near silence so as not to wake the sleeping monster.

The next day my dad would be hungover and probably had no recollection of the previous day's antics. He would be sitting in his armchair, shaking from the drink, full of remorse and shame. Then it would be my mother's turn. She was nothing short of brutal!

She wouldn't dare say anything to him when he was drunk, but the next day when he was sober, she would let him have both barrels. 'Call yourself a man! You're nothing but a fucking wanker'! 'You're no fucking father'. 'I wouldn't piss on you if you were on fire, you fucking cunts bastard'! 'I hope you fucking die roaring'!

My father would sit silent in his chair, staring at the floor, like a little boy, like a mouse! Not a word. He would just take it all.

My sister Evelyn was harsh and would do the same as my mother and call him every name under the sun. Connor, not so much. Bridie was the only one who would stick up for him and say, 'that's enough now, leave him alone'. Me, well, I was just the baby of the family, but I would still throw him a look of disgust as I went past his chair!

I wonder what was going through his mind on those occasions. I wonder what he felt. He must have truly hated himself.

Listening to my mother as she spat all those awful names and abuse at him was unbearable. I understand why she said the things she did, but to witness and be part of it as a small boy was just as bad, if not worse than the night before when he was drunk and wrecking the place.

What did I learn from this? That drink is a curse and all men are bastards? I will be a man one day!

The only good thing to come from this, was now we had almost two weeks before we had to do it all again. This pattern of events played out throughout my entire childhood. As a young boy my life was marred by these experiences of extremity. Brief moments of calm and order followed by more episodes of chaos, disruption and upset.

I dread to think what it must have been like when they (mum and dad), were in their thirties, still young, vibrant and full of energy and passion (I'm talking about hate!)

I am aware I have been painting a rather bleak picture of how it was for my family and me, but I will say it again...it wasn't all bad. There were good times too. I enjoyed school and I even briefly owned a cat!

Chapter Four

We had a black and white cat. I say 'we' it was in fact Evelyn's cat. She was just a little girl when she had found the tiny kitten abandoned in the gutter at the side of the road. Defenceless, cold and hungry he had looked up at her with pleading doleful eyes. Shaking and barely able to stand his pitiful cries immediately endearing him to her. She had begged my mother to let her keep him and in a rare moment of tenderness, my mother had buckled under the weight of Evelyn's tears and said yes!

I truly loved Tibby, and what's more, Tibby loved me. Well as much as a surly, dismissive 'snob' can do! Maybe it was because for a short while we were about the same size, I was the only one in the family, who was 'at his level'. Connor was seven years older than me, and Bridie, well she was a girl! So Tibby was the closest thing I had to a playmate and a dangerous playmate at that. On many occasions, I recoiled in pain having been scratched, or clawed after having become 'too familiar'.

As a little boy, I had a habit of laying on the floor in front of the fire while watching children's television (The Flumps & Chorlton and the Wheelies). Arms resting on elbows and with my head in my hands, Tibby would take this as an invitation to climb on to my back, pushing and pressing his claws into me; before finally settling and curling up into a ball. Now in his elevated position in front of the fire (affording him all the heat), he would purr contently before going to sleep. I would not move; I would lay there for ages not wanting to disturb him. While my mother enjoyed the peace!

When Evelyn was sixteen she, too, left home. Maybe it was because of the memory of Kathleen leaving, that I became upset and tearful. In an attempt to cheer her little brother up, she told me that Tibby was now mine! I can remember feeling instantly happy and elated that I now 'owned' the family cat! The cat that had been around longer than I had! 'That's my cat'!

Less than two weeks after Evelyn had left, Tibby died. I was inconsolable. The sad affair was made all the more traumatic because it was 'my' cat!

My dad buried Tibby at the bottom of our garden in a little ceremony I had insisted upon. He had lent on his shovel, with his head respectfully bowed in silence as I recited the Lord's Prayer. Then when I was finished, he filled the hole up with earth, lit his roll-up and then ruffled my hair with his gigantic paw like hand before saying, 'C'mon, Plike', as he turned, and I followed him back up the garden! It was the first time I had ever experienced loss.

****

School was a godsend, literally! That is because I went to the local catholic school not far from our house. There seems to be a lot of controversy surrounding 'faith' schools nowadays, mainly Islamic ones. However, back then, I never considered my school to be a faith school, but that's exactly what it was. Nor did I realise that having Irish Catholic parents made me different from the rest of the population. But I found out as I got older that in certain situations it did. Nonetheless, I liked school.

I have an image in my mind of my first day. I am not sure if this is an actual memory or if somewhere along the way I have seen a photograph of myself in my uniform and the two have become merged. The image is this; short grey trousers (above the knees), a green itchy jumper, a white starched shirt with massive collars, a red tartan tie and plain black plimsolls. I fondly remember the tie had elastic at the top (to go around your neck). Funny, and a little embarrassing, but I still struggle to do up a tie. In this image/ memory, I am standing at the bottom of our close, beside a white picket fence. I have a beaming smile and I am looking very proud.

It is obviously a big day for me. However now as an adult whenever I recall this image, I am also forced to recount what was going on in our house at that time. It then becomes quite a haunting, almost sad image, as I can't help but pity the hopelessly optimistic smiling little boy in his school uniform. It reminds me, that although things have changed for me, how many other little kids are going through 'difficult' times, even as I write this?!

Religious education was (clearly) a big part of the curriculum at my school, although I recall little of what we were taught. I remember the priests coming to our junior school and talking to us about Lent. They wanted all the children to attend the local church at 6 30am every morning during lent for extra religious education regarding the meaning of lent and the lessons to be learned from it. I also remember being disappointed that my mother wouldn't let me go!

My parents although Catholic, were not what you might describe as 'practising' Catholics. My father never went to church (for fear of bursting into flames perhaps), and my mother only occasionally. In fact, despite there being a large Irish Catholic community in our area, we were rarely a part of it! However, my mother did send us kids (without her) to church on a Sunday.

I have a friend, Neil Duncan; when he was a kid his mum used to give him 50p for the collection plate. When the little wicker basket was passed around and would arrive at Neil's lap, he would study the contents of the collection, before dropping in his 50p and would then rummage 'loudly' through the coins and take 30p change for sweets! He is still a very careful man.

Even as a child I never liked going to church, it was always something that was forced, rather than something I wanted to do. However, some of my classmates seemed to really enjoy church. We even had a really cool priest who used to put on discos, just for the kids! His speciality was an ice-cream float, (a glass of coke with a scoop of ice-cream in it). Everyone loved father Breehan, he was involved in all sorts of activities and always encouraged the kids to take part. Then one day, he mysteriously vanished! It was a few years before anyone saw father Breehan again, which was when he appeared on the BBC's Panorama programme. He was in America, and on the FBI's most wanted list.

I sincerely hope he is still rotting in a prison cell somewhere. Personally, I think he should have got the death penalty! After all, ...it's not as if he is going to go to heaven!

After the programme had aired, there were rumours, that he may have abused kids in our area. I heard rumours of distraught parents going to the Bishop (but not the police?). I even heard an alarming story about a man who had been abused by a priest in Ireland, only for his son to be abused by a priest here in England! It's true these were only rumours, but still I can't help but think, 'blind' faith is a strange thing.

I have no desire, nor do I have the right to use this as an opportunity to 'stick the boot in' against the Catholic Church. I know the vast majority of its parishioners are fundamentally good, God-fearing people. It's just that when a 'man' tells me he is God's chosen representative on earth, I find it 'difficult' to believe. I am therefore uncomfortable with organised religion.

I have a friend whose parents are devout Catholics; he thinks it's comical that his dad has an imaginary friend! He told his dad, it was pure luck that he was not abused as a child, having been sent on so many trips with the church. He also added that, if he belonged to a swimming club and then found out that the bloke that ran the swimming club was a paedophile, then he would then no longer belong to that swimming club! A fair comment.

To be fair to the Catholic faith (rather than church) I recall watching a Sunday morning discussion programme about this subject. Most of the studio audience were attacking the Catholics and calling the Pope the king of the paedo's, when to my surprise, a young Muslim man said that he thought the Catholic church should actually be applauded, because they were the only religious organisation, open enough to even acknowledge or discuss the matter. Basically, if it's happening in the Catholic church, you can be sure it's happening in every other organised religion too. Power and control, I don't like it.

Nonetheless, I have always maintained a healthy respect for an individual's 'personal' beliefs and faith. I sometimes wonder what kind of world we live in, I try to comfort myself with the fact, that I believe good always wins over evil, because if it didn't, then surely nothing would exist?! It would be very arrogant of me to dismiss the idea of a God. After all, when the shit hits the fan, and all else fails, what do you do? Yeah.... So, do I!

Religion aside, I enjoyed school, it opened up a whole new world to me. A world away from Tanglewood Close and my family. I was beginning to grow and develop as a person. I was becoming an individual in my own right.

I remember the first time I was allowed to walk to school unaccompanied. An honour my mother had bestowed on me after

I had promised not to dilly-dally or deviate from my path, 'straight there and straight back', she had warned. I think I remember it so vividly, in part because it was a particularly cold, damp, foggy morning, I recall feeling very 'big' and very grown up (I was seven and a half !) but not so grown up that I could actually see over the top of the bushes and hedgerows.

As I walked along, I noticed spiders' webs swaying and glistening with dew drops in the hedges, whilst also being mindful not to step on the cracks between the paving slabs beneath my feet. I skitted through shallow puddles and avoided the deeper ones, then as I reached and began to make my way past 'the' scruffy house I, as did most kids, held my breath until I was totally clear! I was happy with my new-found independence. I was also as snug as a bug in a rug. Thanks in part to my snorkel jacket!

In 1980, I think almost every kid on the estate was wearing a green snorkel jacket complete with an orange lining and a grey fur lined hood. When the zip was securely pulled all the way up, 'and out' to the front, my vision (along with every other kid) was totally blinkered. There would be whole troops of children descending on the school gates, each one resembling a small green, fur-lined periscope! There was a real concern about the children's safety due to a lack of peripheral vision. So much so that my school issued a road safety warning one morning during assembly:

'When crossing the road with your hood up children, make sure you turn your head 'fully' to the left, and then again 'fully', to the right before attempting to cross'. There was even a demonstration on stage, of how to do it correctly! I think the school was genuinely worried that one of our number was going to get run over.

The cause of the snorkel jacket phenomenon was all down to a bloke called Dennis Galvin, who had obviously managed to get his hands on a job lot of the coats. He had been tirelessly working his way around our estate, going door to door and knocking them out to all the mums. I think you could pay weekly! I don't believe he was ever aware of the furore that he was creating. The 'gag' between us kids at the time, was this, Dennis was going to appear on Mastermind, specialist subject; Snorkel Jackets ...1099 to 1399!

I began to make friends, but you know how fluid childhood friendships are, best mates with him for a couple of weeks and then best friends with someone else for a couple of more weeks and so on. In the beginning, there was John Duffy, Robert Gill and although I didn't know it then, my life-long friend Jim Sweeny.

John Duffy was a pitiful looking kid. He was scruffy and wore glasses. He also wore a constant pained expression. It didn't help that the poor boy was constantly getting caned by the nuns for being late to school. I can see him now, returning to his chair with tears in his eyes. Even at the age of eight, I could see it was not his fault for being late all the time. I don't know what was going on at his house, but I don't think it was anything good. I would like to think if I were the teacher, I would not have caned the boy for tardiness. Instead, I would like to think I might have pulled him to one side and gently asked if everything was okay at home! I remember, John and I won the three-legged race on sports day. I can remember him grinning in delight. Perhaps I remember it, because it was rare to see the boy genuinely happy! We did not stay friends for very long: no reason, just you know how kids are. John was obviously a tortured soul because at the age of seventeen he hung himself from a tree in our local park. Shame because he was a really nice kid.

Robert Gill also wore glasses. He was skinny and nerdy and the type of snotty nosed kid who would look scruffy in a pair of swimming trunks. Looking back, he was a very strange kid. There was an incident once, involving us both when I was about 8 years old. My mother had sent me to the local shops for 20 Woodbines (her fags), and half pound of Corona (butter). I had taken my 'speedway' bicycle, which had a number 6 on the front of it. I had also 'installed' some plastic strips cut from an empty juice bottle, via clothes pegs, into the spokes of the wheels, so it sounded like a motor bike when I peddled! (Most excellent!).

When I got to the shops, Robert was there with some other kids, and as I rode past them, he made some insulting remark. Immediately outraged, I 'slammed' on my brakes and dramatically skidded to a stop, before dropping my bike to the floor and confronting him! 'What did you say!' I demanded. There was no way I was taking any crap off specky faced nerdy Robert. So, in a show of bravado I motioned to hit him! I did not intend to actually do it; it was just a scare tactic! However, being the little weasel that he was, he immediately brought his knee up in a defensive flinch and caught me right in the knackers! Ouch!! It shut me up.

Nor could I ride my bike home, instead I had to push it! I was in agony and close to tears as I inched my way back home. Despite the pain, my pride would not allow me to tell my mum that, 'nerdy' Robert had hurt me (in my special area). I did my best to present myself as normal, as I quietly and ever so slowly made my way upstairs, then once in the sanctuary of my room I closed the bedroom door behind me. Now alone, I dropped my pants and had a look in the wardrobe mirror. I can still see the disbelieving look of horror on my face and my wide eyes staring back at me. I couldn't quite believe what I was seeing. I was in shock, my left testicle had ballooned to the size of a watermelon (well, perhaps walnut! I was only eight!) what's more it was multi-coloured! I became seriously worried, but still, I didn't want to tell my parents. My mother however noticed something was up (no pun intended!). Perhaps it was the unusually quiet mood, my strange gait or the simple fact I had tears streaming down my face! She asked, 'What's wrong'?

Through muffled sobs, I told her what had happened. Then to my horror she made me 'get it out'! Upon seeing it, she gasped and reeled back in shock, which did nothing to ease my discomfort. 'Right that's it I'm going round there, I'm not having this', she cried! Did I just hear right? 'No mum... Please' I protested.

However, it was no good, she grabbed me by the hand and painfully marched me round to Robert Gill's mum's house. I actually thought she was going to make me get my 'balls' out on their doorstep! Robert's mum made him apologise, but I never forgave the specky faced twat ...or my mum!

****

As I neared the end of junior school and as innocent as I was, I had, like most young boys begun to 'notice' girls. It was at about this time that I experienced my first crush.

On more than one occasion I had caught Angela McAvoy staring at me from across the classroom and had thus 'leapt' to the conclusion that this meant she liked me. My good friend Jim Sweeny suggested I should buy her some sweets (he always gave me bad advice!), as a way of letting her know that I liked her too, so I did. With my fifty pence pocket money I bought Angela a massive bar of Bourneville chocolate. I was pretty cool about it too. Brimming with confidence I walked past her seat and without saying a word, casually placed the chocolate bar on the desktop in front of her. She, then, also without saying a word, got up from her seat, walked to the front of the classroom and 'casually' placed it in the bin! To say it was a crush is absolutely correct, for crushed I was. Oh, the hurt! Oh, the rejection! Oh, my fifty pence!

To add insult to injury an eagle-eyed boy spotted the bar of chocolate going in the bin and brought it to the attention of our teacher, the 'unfortunately' named Mrs Duckett, (sounds a bit like?), who stood 5ft nothing and had the most ridiculously enormous breasts you have ever seen! So enormous in fact, she looked like an impossibility!

Mrs Duckett, made a big song and dance about the wanton waste of the chocolate bar, retrieved it from the bin, broke it into small chunks and gave a piece to everyone in class, including Angela, (and Sweeny!). Red faced and still reeling with embarrassment from Angela's rejection, I refused to accept any of the chocolate.

When I got home from school, I told my brother about my humiliating experience. Older and wiser he just smiled and said, 'Yeah, don't worry about her, what you want to do is, go up to the best-looking girl in school and use the old aftershave trick'! Puzzled, I looked at him and said, 'What's the old aftershave trick'? He grinned, lent forward and whispered in my ear!

The next day at school, and for all to see, I walked straight up to Lola Moylett, who was standing with a group of her girlfriends and said, 'All right Lola, wanna smell my brother's aftershave'?

As I said it, I tilted my head to the left while slightly pushing my exposed neck forward and gestured towards it with my right thumb. Lola instinctively lent in to smell my neck, as she did this; I turned my face towards her and planted a kiss on her cheek. She shot back in astonishment but was grinning from ear to ear at my audacity. She could not stop smiling! While all her friends whooped in delight.

It went around the school like wildfire, that I, Pat Delaney had kissed the top girl, Lola Moylett. Making me an instant and absolute legend! Now I think of it, Angela McAvoy, might have had a slightly lazy eye!

MOLLY

Steven Molloy or 'Molly' to his friends, was every bit the stereotype. Short fat and ginger! A somewhat troubled but good-natured boy. We had become good friends after he had sat next to me in class and I had discovered that he had a sense of humour way beyond his years. From that moment on we were inseparable, two happy innocent little souls who were always laughing!

Molly was an only child, and as such, his parents had spoilt him rotten with all the latest toys and every gadget going. As a young boy, seeing all that he had, I was never envious nor was I ever jealous, as I genuinely liked Steve, however, I think it reminded me of what I didn't have! I got little in the way of material things, and by comparison, if I had a pound, then Molly had ten!

Molly's house was on the edge of the estate and had the added bonus of backing onto some fields and woodlands, which made for an excellent playground for two young boys. In the summer months, we would be gone all day, building dens in the woods, or even better finding somebody else's. Sometimes Neil Duncan, Jim Sweeny and another lad Paul McGillicuddy, would join us and we would play TAG! (you're it!). A game could last all day. Especially if you were chasing after Sweeny. He was impossible to catch, powerfully built, he had muscles at the age of ten and a 'bum fluff' moustache by the time he was thirteen, he was just too fast!

During quieter times, we would try to catch crickets with our bare hands, Ninja style! If we were walking through the long grass and heard the distinct, 'click, click' of a cricket, we would stop dead in our tracks and very slowly turn in the direction of the sound, staring intently at the tall blades of grass, waiting with outstretched arms, hands poised ready to try to grab it. The success rates of our 'hunts' were fairly low, but very occasionally we would actually catch one! With my hands cupped together. I would feel the little critter tickling my skin. Eager to take a look; I would ever so slightly part my hands just enough to catch a glimpse at the cricket, but not so wide that it might escape. Sometimes when I gently and ever so slowly un-cupped my hands to take a quick peek... there would be nothing there! That's the trouble with spending too much time out in the 'wilderness' ...your mind can play tricks on you!

Now, as an adult, if ever I hear the sound of a cricket in long grass it takes me straight back to those carefree days playing out the back of Molly's house. Sometimes I marvel at the innocence of it all; although it was not always so innocent. Sometimes we would stumble upon old bits of porno mags too. Disgusting I know, but you have to remember the internet had not yet been invented. We even found the 'fanny bit' from a blow-up doll once. It was actually quite disturbing. I remember we both stood for a while just staring at it from a safe distance, horrified and yet at the same time strangely intrigued ...and then Molly poked it with a stick!

They really were different times back then; if you were misbehaving an adult would not hesitate to pull you up and tell you off. In fact, most adults believed it was their right to give you a clip around the ear or a kick up the arse. Not like today, where most people are too frightened or just simply refuse to intervene.

At the edge of the woods behind Steve's house, there was an estate made up entirely of blocks of flats. A rabbit warren of passages, footpaths and alleyways. There was also an underground car park covering two levels. This too was an excellent place for a game of TAG or hide and seek. On the far side of this estate there was a brick built spiral staircase, which reminded us kids of a castle turret and which always stank of piss! At the top was a wooden bridge spanning the gap leading back to the car park side of the estate, where there was a lift servicing both the flats and car park, (which, incidentally, also stank of piss!). Molly, loved to play in the lift which had an (easy clean) stainless steel interior, pretending, when the lift doors slid open, that he was in fact stepping out of a spacecraft and into a hostile new world, complete with imaginary space weapons at the ready, ... GO, GO, GO!!

Molly and me were playing around with the lift one day when, showing off in front of my friend, I pressed the call button... and then 'spat' on said call button! It was totally out of character and to make matters worse just as I did it, a punk came walking around the corner! He must have been all of 23/24 years old, a grown man to Steve and me. He saw what I had done and didn't even hesitate as he smacked me round the head and called me, 'A dirty little cunt'!

I was just a little kid trying to impress my mate! However, it didn't frighten me that a 'grown man' had hit me, instead it embarrassed me. I felt ashamed for what I had done. I never told my parents that 'a man' had hit me, because they would have asked, 'WHY'! Then I would have got another slap. As soon as the punk was out of sight, Molly, pointing at me and sneering, said, 'Ha ha, shame'! Was the punk right?

In 1983, Return of the Jedi, hit the UK cinemas. Admission to see the latest Star Wars instalment cost £2. Molly, being a huge fan went to see Return of the Jedi 13 times; I went to see it once. Of course, Molly had all the merchandise associated with the Star Wars franchise. Millennium Falcon, X-Wing Fighter and all the poseable figures. Sometimes when his parents had gone out leaving him home alone, Molly would tie a piece of string from his bedroom window down to the washing line in the back garden. Then he would tie a small piece of cotton across the hands of some of his

Star wars figures, hook them over the line from the bedroom window to the washing line and then spray them with his 'DADS' hair lacquer (Molly's dad had an amazing quiff, a coiffure's dream!), and then set light to them and let them go down the line. Thus, recreating scenes from his favourite Star Wars moments! Steve's wanton destruction of his toys was shocking. I would have got a hiding for destroying my toys (the few bits I had were far too precious!).

I remember Steve lent me Bob Afeit, (Star Wars / bounty hunter), to take home and play with. I was really chuffed, however I didn't have a Millennium Falcon or an X-Wing Fighter to put him in, so I busied myself in the box-room at the top of our stairs and set about making a spaceship out of two toilet roll holders and an old tissue box. I had seen how to do it on Blue Peter. About 30 minutes into my 'tricky' project, I began to hear what sounded like running water on the landing outside the bedroom. Curious, I opened the bedroom door to investigate and saw my father standing on the landing, suited and booted, with one hand on the banister and the other on his old boy, casually taking a piss up against the wall! It was obviously a Wednesday.

I will never forget the look he gave me; it was a look of total disgust, as if it were my fault, as if it were 'I' who was pissing up the banister! The chances are, he was so drunk, that he never actually saw me at all. I closed the door (albeit a bit disturbed) and just carried on making my toilet roll spaceship.

I never mentioned my father's shameful behaviour, or drunken ways to my friends, I never talked to Molly about it. I was too young and lacked the confidence to discuss it without feeling like it reflected badly on me.

My mother rarely, if ever, took a drink. She always said it was because my father drank enough for the both of them. Molly's parents, Shay and Margaret however, both liked a drink; in fact, they drank quite a lot! However, as far as I was aware there was never any violence or aggression like in my house. I think for them, it was more calamity and un-manageability than anything else.

It's sad really, but Molly was left to his own devices a lot of the time, (when they went drinking). He was showered with gifts and money but was totally void of affection. A brand-new BMX, my Speedway was second hand. A brand-new Atari console, (I actually saw the same Atari, in the toy section of a local museum a short while ago! Am I that old already?), but no hugs or kisses. It's a shame because Steve's parents were good people, nice people, just perhaps not very good parents. Steve seemed to have no respect for his mum and dad; I suppose you could argue they had no respect for him either; I think he was secretly ashamed of them.

Molly never talked about his parent's neglectful ways or how that made him feel. I think due to his young age, he lacked the confidence to discuss it without feeling like it reflected badly on him.

Molly had no boundaries and could do pretty much whatever he pleased. Along with everything else, Steve loved Superheroes and comics. He hatched (to my mind) an audacious plan to visit a comic book shop, 30 miles away in London, 'Do you wanna come?', he had asked excitedly. I was 11 years old and knew the chances of my mother allowing it, were slim, but I asked anyway, 'Mum can I go to London with Molly on Saturday?' I did not get the response I was expecting, (I kid you not!), she threw a Perspex plate at my head, presumably for being 'so fucking stupid' as to ask such a ridiculous question! I took it as a NO ... but went anyway!

Me and Molly sneaked off, up to London on a bus. It was exciting, a real adventure. I had never been to the capital before. The underground, the hustle and bustle, the throngs of people. It was all very different to the council estate that was the entirety of my world. I sensed I wasn't being too smart and that I shouldn't really be in London on my own, but I was caught up in the moment and did not really care of the consequences. A characteristic of my personality that was going to get me in a lot of trouble in later years! No sat nav, no smart phones, just directions scribbled down on a scrap of paper. Unbelievably we made it to the comic book shop in Islington and once there Steve brought a naff first edition of something negligible in comic book terms. Now with our primary goal achieved and, I think both being so young, we suddenly became aware of our vulnerability and decided to make are way back home. I remember the urgency, being on the tube (a first for me), and a London bus as we made our way back to Marble Arch to catch the double decker that would take us back to the familiarity and safety of home.

What a day we had! We laughed non-stop all the way home and like the two little kids that we were, we messed around virtually alone and unchallenged on the top deck of the bus. Halfway home Molly was caught short and needed to take a 'waz', as he called it. I could not believe it when Steve brazenly took a piss upstairs at the back of the bus! Now I think about it, Molly was always pissing all over the place. If an animal did that, you might think it was in some kind of distress. I was aware that he also had a plastic sheet on his bed. I know it embarrassed him, so I never mentioned it or made a big deal of it (unless we were bickering!).

We arrived back at Steve's house late that Saturday evening, his parents didn't bat an eyelid as we walked in the door, seemingly, they had hardly noticed he had even been gone. All was calm, and then Margaret said, 'Oh by the way Pat, your mum was round looking for you earlier, she didn’t seem too happy'. FUCK!

I was battered for my bold defiance and was kept in for two weeks! When I look back on it now it was obviously a very foolish and dangerous thing to do. Two eleven-year-old boys disappearing up to London for the day and without telling their parents, although technically I had! My poor mother must have been worried sick.

****

Home video recorders had just come onto the market. The notion that you could watch a film when you wanted to! Or the fact that you could fast forward, rewind or pause a movie, or even record a television programme, was nothing short of mind blowing! Of course, Molly had one, when virtually nobody else did. Soon video rental shops were popping up all over the town. One entrepreneurial young man we nicknamed 'Purdy' (I don't know why?) went one better and started a mobile video rental business. It cost £1.50 per night to hire a film. One Saturday me and Molly took out a film called 'Jagged Edge', it was a real whodunit type of film with a massive twist at the end, a real shocker. Having watched the film and, Steve being Steve, he slipped a piece of paper under the video as he put it back in its case, before returning it to Purdy. It said... 'Jeff Bridges did it!' I still laugh about that one now.

Steve (being ginger), was also prone to what would be best described as temper tantrums, some being quite spectacular. I can remember standing open mouthed in Molly's living room as he screamed abuse at his poor dad (a lovely timid man), and then proceeded to launch his dad's country record collection across the room. Charlie Pride, 'off the wall' Don Williams, 'smashed to smithereens', (these not being album title's). 'Steven, son, will you please stop that now!', protested his dad. I then watched aghast as Molly slowly and sadistically un-sleeved Johnny Cash from its album cover. Me and Shay shot each other a disbelieving glance and stood opened mouthed as Molly defiantly and without hesitation, hurled the vinyl disc at the wall. It disintegrated into a thousand pieces!

Even I knew he had gone too far, I knew it was sacrilege, surely not the man in black? Shay's bottom lip shot out, and for a moment I thought the grown man standing in front of me was going to cry, and then I saw the change in him, I saw the anger rise up in his face, he now looked like a man who was about to kill!

I have never seen a fat ginger kid 'chip' as fast as Molly did. Steve was out the front door quicker than you can say, 'Kenny Rogers Sucks!' As I stood amongst the shattered remnants of Shay's country vinyl record collection, I suddenly felt as though I might myself be in danger. Shay looked like he was about to explode with rage, his face had turned bright red and his eyes were bulging out of their sockets. 'Erm, I think I am going to go home now.' He made me no answer as I slowly backed my way out of the living room, turned and scarpered for home.

Of course, Steve got away with it, he always did. The attention seeking behaviour of an unloved child perhaps. Or, simply the unrestrained actions of a spoilt little bastard?

MOLLY'S GONE!

Sometimes my mother would allow me to stay home from school. I don't know if this was because on these particular days, she was feeling particularly fragile or down. Perhaps keeping the 'baby' close reinforced her worth and role as a mother; however, it did nothing for my attendance record.

The school truancy officer, a Mr Weedon, who all the kids on the estate knew by sight and by car, was quite 'lax' in his approach to monitoring school attendance and tended to only follow up the worst cases! So, us kids, (and parents) knew that the odd day here and there was unlikely to ever be investigated. Still, you had to be careful, if you were walking to the shops or a friend's house during school hours; and were spotted by Mr Weedon, he would leap out of his car at the mere sight of a truant child and interrogate you on the spot and with the promise of a visit to your parents! However, that being said, for me (and Steve), school was, at times, optional.

One Sunday evening Molly and me were sitting in his bedroom taping the top 40 off the radio, 'Road to Nowhere' was playing by Talking Heads, when Steve said, 'I ain't going to school tomorrow'. '...ain't ya?' I replied. ''Na, can't be bothered'! '...Well I ain't going either then!' 'No'? '...Na... Not if you ain't, I'm not'! And that was it settled; we were both going to bunk off! We agreed I would call for him the next day.

The next day and much to my frustration, my mother kept me busy most of the morning with chores, seeing as how I wasn't really feeling up to school, but was well enough to go and call for my friend! It was midday, by the time I managed to pry myself away. Relieved to be finally free, I headed straight for Molly's house.I knocked the front door and waited, but got no reply, so I knocked again. Still no reply! Being a kid, I decided to take a look in the living room window and was surprised to see most of the furniture was gone! Baffled, I let myself in the back gate and walked around the back of the house and peered through the back windows, the place was empty.

I didn't see Molly again for six whole months, a lifetime when you're a kid. His parents had been evicted from their council house for not paying the rent. I later found out that poor Molly had known nothing of what was about to happen and had been awoken at 6am in the morning and told by his parents that they were leaving. It was unbelievable! I was there the day before and there was no hint from either of his parents that there was anything even slightly amiss. Poor old Steve was mortified; he had been belittled and shamed by his parents. We all know how cruel kids can be.

Molly and his parents were 'put up', (I don't mean to be unkind) by a very scruffy and not very well-educated family (that Molly nicknamed the Gorm's) at the far end of our estate. So poor Steve was lying low.

I think that was the beginning of the end for my good friend. He was never the same after, as a family they went from one squalid address to another, until they ended up living in an actual doss house.

I went to see them once (Steve was not very inviting by this time?) it was a house of multiple occupancy, with shared bathrooms. The place was full of down and outs and poor old Shay had a black eye, I also noticed his quiff wasn't coiffed to its former perfection. It was truly pitiful! Over time, me and Molly drifted apart, partly to do with his shame and partly to do with the fact he now lived a few miles away on the other side of town!

****

If you have never experienced it, you would be forgiven for thinking growing up on a council estate is a rough, tough and dangerous environment for a young boy... and of course, you would be right. It was! You needed to have your wits about you! However, it did have its benefits. It toughened you up for one thing and it made you fairly streetwise too. There was also a sense of community that I feel is maybe lacking in other social settings. People tended to look out for one another and help each other in times of need. Perhaps this 'social conscience' was born out of necessity. When I think of the neighbours in Tanglewood Close, mad Bridget, the Edwards, the Gentles, Percy and Reg, they were all treated like extended family and afforded the respect (that should be) bestowed on our elders. You certainly wouldn't cheek them or answer them back (well, perhaps once they were out of earshot?!).

If I were out playing in the street, older kids would watch out for me because they knew my brother and sisters. I in turn would watch out for the younger kids because I knew their families and so on. Adults would threaten to tell your mum and dad if you were being a pain in the arse or misbehaving, so you would curb your behaviour. You had to adhere to the unwritten rules! So, although, to a certain degree we were left to run wild, we were also, monitored, as it were.

That being said, you still had to watch out for bullies, and we had our share. There was a South African kid called Bruce Willis (its true!), a nasty little shit, a couple of years older than me, who didn't mind punching younger kids in the face, I managed to avoid ever being on the receiving end where he was concerned. (I wonder what he is doing now. A spot of Moonlighting perhaps!). There was Graham Callaghan, he came from a very rough family and was as thick as a whale omelette, which made him especially dangerous. And then there was my arch nemesis, Barry 'fucking' Evans! The worst of all, a horrible bully who terrorised every kid on the estate. He made everyone's life a misery. Me, and my friends were no exception. I hated that kid with a passion (I cannot stand bullys! - for obvious reasons). He was to be avoided at all costs. If you saw him coming, or even just heard him, you would be wise to change direction and try to get away as quickly as possible. However, if you were unfortunate enough to be 'caught' his first words would be, 'Chip me 10p guy'! If you did not hand it over, he would demand you empty your pockets. I have seen him do it many a time to many a poor kid. However, I am pleased to report I never gave the bullying bastard one brown penny. I always refused. It wasn't because I thought I was tough! I was just as afraid of him as everyone else, but I was 'actually' more afraid of my dad or my brother, my sisters even, finding out that I had let this kid take money of me, because then they would have battered me even more for being a 'Jesse'!

I 'got away with it' because I used humour to deflect the situation; I think it confused him. The fucking idiot! As a result, I think he was a little unsure of me, so for the most part I walked away unscathed and money (if I had any) intact.

I was not always so lucky. It was the last few days of the summer holidays before I started high school. The weather had been consistently good all summer, so I had spent the entire six weeks out playing with my friends. We had messed about over the fields and in the woods. We had walked for miles, as far afield as the old cattle tunnels that ran under the motorway past our estate and had even dared each other to go through the dark one! We had climbed walls and ran about on roof tops, we had tormented and done our very best to get a chase from Mr Hillard, the school caretaker. And, a game of Tag or hide and seek could last for days! It had been a happy, lazy, carefree summer.

On this particular day I was kicking a ball about outside my mate Chris Kearney's house. There was me, Chris, Neil Duncan, Paul McGillicuddy and Jim Sweeny. I remember it was hot, because we had all gone into Chris' house to get a cold drink.

Chris had an older brother called Billy, who was often lying on the living room floor in his pyjamas and playing with his Lego. Billy was 30yrs old and had severe learning disabilities. To a bunch of kids who had no experience or knowledge of such things, the sight of a grown man lying on the floor playing with his toys, was very odd. It's fair to say we all found it quite disturbing, except for Chris, obviously, who just excepted it for what it was. Billy was his brother, nothing more and nothing less.

Anyway, Paul had asked Chris for a drink of orange and Chris had duly gone off to the kitchen to get him one and had returned with a beaker of orange and handed it to Paul. I will never forget the look on Paul's face. The beaker had the word BILLY written across it. Paul froze and looked directly at me with wide pleading eyes, I (being eleven) immediately burst out laughing! We were just kids; we did not mean to be insensitive or cruel we simply didn't know any better. Chris wasn't too happy though. Anyway, we all had our drinks (except for Paul) and then went back outside to carry on our game with the ball.

With Paul's indiscretion soon forgotten about, we were all having a great time mucking around in the street. I know I speak for us all when I say our hearts sank and our shoulders slumped when we saw, Barry Evans and two of his henchmen bowling up the street towards us. It was sod's law that the ball had gone in their direction and Barry, had picked it up and tucked it under his arm! He stood jeering at us, as if to say, 'And what you going to do'?

Everyone just stared at the floor, shuffling their feet. Even at the age of eleven, I always felt like it was my job to stick up for my friends and not let anyone mug me / us off! I think it stemmed from what was going on at home. I have never liked violence; I have always despised bullys! I certainly did not feel tough, but I had my family honour to keep. There was a lot going on in my young head now I think about it. And, to cut a long story short I felt it was down to me to get the ball back. 'Just give us the ball back will ya', 'you can see were playing with it'!

Barry Evans just stared at me with a stupid inane look on his face. 'Give it back!' I demanded. I do not remember the whole dialogue, but I walked up to him and took it off him. As I took the ball, the fucker punched me in the face. Fight or Flight! I did neither. I was in shock; I just had not expected him to do it! It was a proper whack, and I don't mind admitting it really fucking hurt!

I was devastated. I instantly felt ashamed and gutted. I had let myself down by not retaliating. I had let my family down and I had lost face in front of my friends. At a loss, I walked away, my cheek red and my face throbbing. I walked around the back of Chris Kearney's house; then and only then did I allow the tears to come. There was no way I was going to let the horrible bastard see me cry, I suppose that's something!

My mates all came around the back of the house and to my surprise began singing my praises, for having the balls to stand up to him and for actually getting the ball back. For a bunch of eleven-year olds they were very mature with the way they dealt with my obvious shame. They kept reassuring me that I was a top bloke, saying they would not have had the nerve to stand up to him. It was kind of them, but it did not really help. I was embarrassed and I certainly did not feel like a hero, in fact, I felt like a bit of a wanker. I was annoyed with myself, in that split second when he had hit me; I hadn't done the right thing. That stung even more than the punch!

I knew it was not over between me and Barry 'fucking' Evans. I wasn't planning revenge or anything like that; after all I was just as scared of him as everyone else. I just knew it was not the end!

CHAPTER FIVE

WITH THE SUMMER HOLIDAYS OVER, I had started high school with an equal measure of excitement and uncertainty. Rotherham Avenue was where I had done all my schooling, the infants, the juniors and now the aptly named Rotherham High. A four-storey building of blue and white panelling and large single pane crittall windows. It had seemed massive in comparison to the juniors next door, I had briefly wondered how I would navigate the endless corridors without becoming hopelessly lost.

When it was built, in the 1960s it was 'probably' a state of the art hub of academic excellence, but by the time I turned up in September 1983, it was a shabby, neglected and run down shadow of its former flagship glory. It appeared tired with flaking paint on its walls and window frames. Not that I cared. I was just excited to be starting 'big school'.

Chris Kearney and me were the only two boys from our junior school who went to Rotherham that year. I remember Jim and Neil being shocked that I wasn't going to be joining them at Cardinal Newman, the Catholic school across town. 'What you're not coming to Newman with us'? They had stated in an alarmed tone! I had pretended I didn't want to go, that I preferred Rotherham (which wasn't true!), because my brother and sisters had all gone there (which was true!).

Chris Kearney was going because it was directly opposite his house, I was going because it was within walking distance, so my mother didn't have to pay for a bus pass. Also, there was no uniform requirement, so my mother didn't have to pay for one of those either and unlike the Catholic school all my friends were going to, Rotherham didn't constantly have its hand out for money my mother simply didn't have. So, the reasons were purely financial.

Starting high school had signalled a new phase. Now an adolescent, I was developing a sense of self and that of my surroundings. Just like Adam and Eve, having eaten the forbidden fruit, I was suddenly aware! I had even begun to question my place in the world. However, unlike Adam and Eve, it wasn't necessarily a sense of shame, more an awkwardness I couldn't fully comprehend!

I had heard all the stories of high jinks that my brother and sisters had got up to at high school and had felt somewhat 'obliged' to live up to their examples, even though it didn't really feel like 'me'. I think perhaps I was worried that if I didn't follow suit, I might get 'found out', although I'm sure I was not aware of these feelings at the time. I also had the family secret to keep. I was embarrassed of my drunken Irish father and also of 'my own' perception of the family's 'perceived' social standing. I think at a subconscious level, I believed we were 'lesser than', compared to other families because we never seemed to have any money (it really wasn't true, but it was how I felt). For example, I never once had a 'decent' pair of trainers. I couldn't invite friends around on a Wednesday for obvious reasons. And now I was also worried I might get into a fight and lose! I had the family reputation to think of and worse still, to live up to! I suppose what I am really trying to say is, I started high school feeling awkward, like a fraud and very much a second-class citizen. It turned out high school was not as harrowing as I had at first expected; however, I remained constantly on my guard.

Self-praise is no praise, but the truth of the matter is this, I was well liked and got on well with most. I tended to get away with things and avoided confrontation because I had learned to use humour as a method of defence. It would seem I had been blessed (an Irish blessing perhaps?) with the gift of the gab and could talk my way out of most things. In fact, people would comment on how witty and happy go lucky I was. Looking back, I now realise it was all just a front. I also 'now' know this is the case for most people.

I have always enjoyed Art, so it was a stroke of luck that my form tutor for the next five years, Ms Gabrize, also happened to be the head of the Art department. Meaning my form room also happened to be the main Art and Design studio for the whole school. It was situated on the top (4th) floor, which afforded wonderful and uninterrupted views of our estate and the motorway. I excelled at art and even had a 'piece' exhibited at the main library in the town centre. I was extremely proud of my portrayal of a soldier 'tear-arsing' (as my father would say) across a battlefield, on crêpe paper and in the medium of Poster Paint! My mother and Connor came to the exhibition, but when we got there and I saw the standard of work and the quality of the materials used by the other schools who also exhibited, I realised there and then just how 'shite' Rotherham High was.

No one is more body conscious than the young. I certainly don't concern myself with such matters as I once did. But as a young boy (I'm sure it’s worse for girls) it's important to have the 'right' look! I was a first year when it happened! I didn't think too much of it at first, it had started out as just a little spot! But by day four it had grown into a protruding rock-hard lump perched on my top lip! I could not believe my luck! A fucking wart!

There was no way to hide the unsightly appendage, it could not be disguised with cleverly applied make up (not that I would of allowed it!), nor was I mature enough to grow an 'instant' moustache, in an attempt to hide it! It was there in plain sight for the whole world to see!

I was mortified!! To make matters worse everyone at school started calling me Patrick plus! As in Patrick, plus a wart. Even my sister Evelyn's young son joined in the 'fun' when he had come toddling out of the kitchen one day with a rice crispy stuck to his lip and had tried to say 'Uncle Pat' without it falling off! That was all I needed, a 4yr old comedian! The little shit!

Naturally the whole ordeal made me extremely self-conscious. My mother eventually took me to the doctors to get something for it. Connor said the doctor would probably prescribe a hat and coat for it because it was so big! Every evening I had to smear Vaseline around the 'proboscis' like mutation and apply drops of acid with a cotton bud to the head! (it took two months to go). Even worse a girl in my school called Samantha decided one lunch time to kiss every boy in my class...... except me! And that's how I knew that she liked me (wart an all!)! All the way through school we kept 'nearly' going out with each other. She liked me; I didn't like her. I liked her; she didn't like me. And so on!

I have only ever hit a woman once in my life. I don't like men who hit women for obvious reasons, I think they are the lowest of the low. But on this occasion, when I did hit a woman, I neither regret it, nor do I feel any remorse about it! I was queuing up to go into lesson one afternoon when Samantha strolled up to me, smiled, and then without warning, slapped me straight in the balls! It was a good shot! I folded like a deck chair, lost my breath and for an instant, truly believed my testicles were going to come out of my mouth!

Samantha found this to be utterly hilarious and instantly doubled up in stitches, right before my 'very wide' eyes. So, without hesitation, I gallantly punched her straight in the back! She immediately stopped laughing and through short, sharp gasps stuttered, 'you...couldn't...... hurt... ah... fly'! Yep. No doubt about it, that girl likes me...... a lot! However, despite all the 'flirting', we never did become an item!

****

We didn't have family holidays when I was a kid. The closest thing I ever got to a holiday was when my aunty Peg or aunty Julie (my mum's sisters), would come down from Birmingham for a week or two during the school holidays. My father (having been warned), would 'hopefully' be on his best behaviour (but no guarantees). My mother would take out a Provident loan to ensure she could put on a good spread for her sisters and still have enough left over to take them for a game of bingo, (and then spend the next 12 months paying it back. But appearances had to be upheld!). She even used to paint the doorstep (red) prior to their visits! They tended to be good fun times, so although I didn't actually go anywhere, there was still a holiday feel!

So, when the school announced a day trip to France, I was understandably very keen to go. All the kids were excited about the trip and couldn't stop talking about it, mostly in a silly French accent, like in the TV show, Allo, Allo! Everyone was imagining the mischief and antics we might get up to, French girls and flick combs, how exciting! The trip cost £14, I asked my mother if I could go, but she said she wasn't sure, because she didn't really have the money. It was a tense wait to find out if I would be going, made worse by the fact it was all everyone at school was talking about. As time passed and as the deadline to submit your consent form closed in, it looked like I wouldn't be going to France. I was devastated, but I knew there was no point making a big deal out of it, if she didn't have the money then she didn't have it! However,

I had a last minute 'reprieve' when my brother and sisters, deciding that it was unfair for me not to go, scraped the money together for the trip. Unfortunately, I got the money and the consent form in too late, all the places had already been booked, so the whole year went to France without me.

I was disappointed, but most of all, I was embarrassed in front of my friends. But then I never truly believed I would be going any way. I told everyone there had been a misunderstanding with the deadline and then pretended I wasn't that bothered, just to try and save face.

As a consolation for missing the trip I was allowed to keep the £14 quid. My sister Bridie suggested we should go clothes shopping with the money (so as not to waste it) and accompanied me to a shop called, Sammy's tailors, (cheap knock off's) and then 'kitted' me out with some funky trendy garm's, (as she assured me). I recall a snazzy green jacket and a pair of funky dark green trousers, both were obliterated with zips, some of the zips opened to reveal pockets whereas others were purely aesthetic, (it was the early eighties!). So proud was I of my new togs, that I wore them to school the day after everyone got back from the trip (no uniform requirement!), but that evening when I took the trousers off, my legs were also green!

At a young age I knew if I wanted something, I was going to have to get it myself. I began working at the age of thirteen, I had the obligatory paper round, but I got sacked for dumping the papers rather than delivering them! At fourteen I helped the milkman throughout the summer holidays for £3 a morning, leaving the house at 4 30am to meet him. I don't think parents would allow it these days! I fondly remember he clipped the kerb one morning and two crates of gold top leapt off the back of his float, he didn't find it amusing or helpful when I cheerfully quipped, 'no point crying over spilt milk'! I also had a Saturday job working in a scrap yard a few miles outside of town. The old 'grunt' that owned the yard gave me the job after he had asked me how I had got there and I had said, 'I ran'! He paid me £10 per day to smash up cars. Everything was covered in oil and grease, so my hands were permanently stained black. I loved it!

One Saturday I was sitting in the little wooden hut where all the lads had their tea break, when one of the men, a brash, loud and somewhat uncouth gentleman nicknamed Pursey said, ...'Well fuck me I was in the fucking boozer last night when this old paddy, you know the fucking type, pinstriped suit, shiny shoes and Bryl-creamed hair.....', (my heart sank!) ....'well he was roaring with fucking toothache and then, you won't fucking believe this...... he fell asleep... with his head... on my fucking lap, I couldn't fucking believe it'!!! The lads all agreed it was a very funny story and joined in laughing with Pursey, ...except me that is. I was mortified and I was embarrassed, I said nothing and drank my tea, I had denied my father with my silence. Unaware, Pursey moved on to his next anecdote. The shame of it!

*****

I was 14yrs old and like most boys my age I had begun to take a keen interest in members of the opposite sex. So much so that I began to take pride in my personal hygiene and appearance. I began to bath regularly (spending a lot of time in the bathroom!) and even cleaning behind my ears! I had shed the puppy fat that had plagued my younger years and had now developed some muscles. I even remember the day my voice broke as the teacher called out the morning register. I went from a soprano to a baritone in the time it took to say, 'Yes, Ms Gabrice'! Which brought about a few giggles from my classmates. I was becoming quite the boy! It's no surprise then, that it was around about this time that I got my first ever 'proper' girlfriend.

Lisa was gorgeous and right from the off, I was totally besotted with her! She told me she had never met anyone with two different coloured eyes before, 'They're amazing', she had cooed, before we kissed for the first time! As young love always is, it was special, it was exciting, it was innocent, but above all, it was new! I just couldn't wait to get to school to see her, then once I was there, I couldn't wait to get out of school, to be with her. I really liked her! Lisa's parents had recently split up, so she was living with her Nan. I can remember getting ready to go and see her (...Lisa obviously!), and excitedly dancing around the bedroom while blasting out The Beats, 'Hands Off She's Mine', on the record player and then slapping on a bit of Old Spice or High Karate after shave, even though I hadn't had one!

It was magical and it was thrilling because I was on unfamiliar territory! Once I was at Lisa's we would sit up in her bedroom listening to 'Now that's what I call music 3', snogging and gazing into each other's eyes while declaring our undying love for one another. They were truly magical times! In fact, our love was so strong, I saved up my wages and took Lisa out on a date, it was all very grown up. We went to McDonald's and then onto the pictures to see Top Gun! We sat in the back row of course! (I 'actually' got to see the film a couple of years ago.... its rubbish!). We were inseparable. We went everywhere together, school, the park, school, the park, school, the....

At Christmas I spared no expense and bought Lisa a copy of Madonna's True Blue album on vinyl and a silver St Christopher from Ratner's the jewellers, (which gave her a rash!), the same jewellers that went bust, after the bloke who owned it, said on live TV that all their stuff was basically crap, and to be fair it was!

I was totally smitten.... even more so when I lost my cherry to Lisa one afternoon at her Nan's house (when no one was home!). 14yrs old, and already a man! So much so that I had to tell someone, the unbelievably, fantastic good news, as the weight of it was killing me! So, I told a lad from school called Ashley. However, I was disappointed when Ashley, to my dismay 'refused' point blank to believe me! 'No, you fucking didn't', he had said with a grimace as he peddled away on his racer!

Now looking back, it horrifies me, when I think of how young Lisa and I, both were. Far too young to be engaging in such adult situations. But what did we know, we were just two kids trying to be grown-ups. I went out with Lisa for an absolute eternity.... four whole months! She will always be special to me!

With all that was going on of late it was only natural that a young 'man' would wish to push himself a little and seek out some form of adventure. So, when in my third year of high school, members of the local Air Training Corp turned up, to give a talk on the merits of their organisation, me and a few of my mates decided to join. Enticed primarily by the promise of firing ranges, assault courses, 'flying' and a free uniform!

I instantly loved it and took to it like a duck to water! (Or perhaps a 'duck to the air'?). It was a million miles away from the drudgery and chaos of home. When I told my brother Connor that I had joined the Air Cadets he laughed and said, 'You'd be better off joining the space cadets'!

But I didn't care, I got to do a lot of fun stuff I never would have had the opportunity to do otherwise. On more than one occasion I got to run over a real-life army assault course (in all the camouflage gear!). I fired an array of weapons, 3.03 riffles and specially adapted self-loading riffles (SLR), it was all very macho and gung ho! And an awful lot of fun! I attended summer camp at an RAF base, and I even got to go flying! The first time was in a Venture 55 glider. It had a propeller and took off much the same as a light aircraft, but once up in the air and having reached the desired altitude, you cut the engine and glided! It was surreal, I can still remember when the noise from the engine died and was replaced by the rush of the air over the glider's wings. I couldn't stop grinning, to the point, where my face hurt!

On another occasion I went up in a DC10, on a take-off and landing training exercise, but I didn't enjoy it, up, down, up, down for about an hour until I was eventually sick (in the bag provided!). But by far the best flying experience I had in the cadets was when I was taken up in an RAF bulldog. A two-seater used to train potential fighter pilots! It was excellent! I don't think I could have been more excited, if I had at this point, 'actually', seen the film Top Gun! And If it wasn't exciting enough already, I even had to wear a parachute (knick-named – the nutcracker). Upon entering the aircraft, the parachute formed your seat and back rest. To put it on you had to sit on it, while an airman pulled all the straps into place and then did them up extremely tight (you wouldn't want it coming off). Then when you stood up to waddle out to the aircraft you found out why it was called the nutcracker! However, it was all worth it once I was up in the air. The pilot took great delight in showing off his skills and scaring the life out of me with barrel rolls and loop the loops! I don't know if you have ever seen a clip of someone trying to eat their pack lunch on a rollercoaster. But I would imagine that is how I looked!

As well as all the fun daring stuff, we also took part in parades, so it was important to look smart. I became meticulous with my uniform, pressing my shirt and trousers until they had razor sharp creases in them (I wouldn't allow my mother to touch my uniform as she wouldn't do it right!). I would also spit and polish my boots, to the point where you could literally see your face in them, I would spend hours in the kitchen with a tin of cherry blossom shoe polish and a spoon that I would heat up on the gas cooker so as to melt the polish into my boots. The result, being they were so shiny they were like glass mirrors.

Almost everyone on my estate was of the same demographic, Irish, Scottish, and white working class. Joining the cadets had broadened my horizons, it was another step away from the world I knew. In short, I began to mix with people from different walks of life. I began to make new friends. Friends of a different cultural and social background.

Ramesh, and Sanjay Sharma, were both cadets, (and as the name suggests) of Indian heritage. Their father had served in the Royal Air Force and had encouraged his boys to join up at the earliest opportunity. I got on particularly well with Sanjay, a nice kid, a good laugh, always helpful and an all-round good sport. I considered him a good friend.

As cadets we would often sell, barter, and swap bits of (army surplus) kit to one another, (camping etc.). It just so happened that I was after a pair of 'light weights', khaki green (army) trousers. Sanjay, having a spare pair, offered to sell them to me, suggesting he could bring them round to my house on the following Saturday. To which I happily agreed.

Living on the opposite side of town my friend had to catch two buses followed by a short walk to make the journey to my front door. When he arrived at mine on the following Saturday, I answered the door cheerfully and said, 'Alright Sanj, how's it going'? 'Yeah, good thanks Pat, I've got the trousers you wanted', he replied smiling as he held them up in a carrier bag. 'Ah, nice one thanks', I said, as I took the offered bag. And that's when I panicked!

There then followed an awkwardness, a long painful silence, I never invited him in! I should of, but I didn't! I knew it! He knew it! I hadn't invited Sanjay in because he was Asian. It was unforgivable! He turned to walk away, knowing full well what had just happened and as I closed the door on my 'friend', I cringed. I visibly shrunk behind the closed door. I think it crushed me as much, if not more, than it must have crushed him, I was devastated by what I had just done!

I don't think it had crossed my mind until he was standing at the door. I had momentarily panicked and had not invited Sanjay in because I was suddenly worried of what my father would say! I was worried he might say something racist or bigoted! I was worried he might embarrass my friend and in-turn embarrass me. I was 14yrs old and I had just got it catastrophically wrong!!

I had heard racist and bigoted remarks all my life, and to be fair from all sides. You only had to turn on the TV in the late 70s and early 80s to see that 'ignorance' was rife, it was part of the culture. However, I think you would have to be a truly hateful person to be an 'actual' racist. I still uphold the belief that people are fundamentally good. I just think sometimes people speak (or do!), without thinking, 'ignorance'!

The truth of the situation is this; my father was not at all a racist. My father would have welcomed Sanjay, just the same as he would have welcomed anyone else into our home, my father has never known of what took place that day on our doorstep and would, I'm sure be horrified if he did! My father (when sober), was a lovely man and wouldn't knowingly offend anyone, especially a young kid.

I have no defence for my actions that day, all I can say is I was young (I had momentarily panicked), I had misinterpreted (or perhaps even created) the situation and in an attempt to protect my friend and spare his feelings, I had inadvertently crushed them. This happened more than 30yrs ago and (rightly) it still bothers me to this day, it was unforgivable. The poor kid!

If I could turn the clock back I would, but I can't. Being kids, Sanjay and I never mentioned it, but we were never really the same after. I can't say I blame him! I wonder how many other 'awkward' situations Sanjay has experienced over the past 30 years due to his ethnicity?

Bridie said I was 'a batty boy' (homosexual!) for being in the cadets. Because it wasn't cool! You never got any encouragement or support in my family; Connor would try and scuff my boots as I passed on my way out to cadets. My father would just shake his head and tut, that is if he wasn't unconscious on the living room floor. However, despite being lambasted by the family I continued with my endeavours and became physically, super fit and decided that when I left school, I would join the RAF Regiment. I then had a change of heart and decided I might as well join the Parachute Regiment instead! I had some mad notion that I wanted to leap out of an aeroplane and into battle! The truth being I probably didn't have the courage to leap off the kitchen chair, but hay ho, the joyful exuberance of youth! But as it often is with kids, by the time I was edging my way to 15yrs old, I had left the cadets, deeming it a bit childish for a lad of my age and also full of knobs! However, I was still army barmy and had every intention of joining up, as soon as I left school.

At around about the same time as the people from the Air Cadets had shown up at my school, so had my old advisory and arch nemesis, Barry 'fucking' Evans! He had been expelled from his previous school, no doubt for being a complete cunt and had now started at Rotherham. I was gutted for I knew it was only a matter of time! I managed to avoid him for the most part, he was still terrorising kids and generally being a massive bully, but he was also still a little unsure of me and pretty much left me alone. As far as I knew, I was still the only kid who had ever stood up to him, even if it hadn't turn out to well for me. I managed to avoid confrontation for the best part of two years, which is not bad going. And then as I had expected it would, it happened.

I was in my last year of high school and would sometimes go home for lunch. As a fifth-year student I was allowed to use the front entrance of the school by the staff car park. This particular lunch time as I exited the building, I saw Barry, in the staff car park tormenting a girl from our year. As much as I would have (secretly) liked to, I could not ignore the situation as her parents were friends of my mothers. So, I had little choice but to intervene!

'Oi, Barry, leave her alone will ya' I demanded! At this point he had the poor girl in a head lock and was forcing her head towards the ground. However, upon hearing me he paused and then letting go of her, pushed her away. I instantly recognised the familiar and stupid inane grin on his ugly face, as he stood tall and said, 'and what you gonna do? You comin' cheeky'? With this he started to amble up towards me while at the same time puffing his chest out. By now, and as they tend to do in schools, a huge crowd had gathered. I was beginning to think this is all going to go horribly wrong for me here as neither of us had forgotten what had happened all those years ago outside Chris Kearney's house. I shrugged and simply said, 'Just leave her alone'. He stepped closer, so now we were almost toe to toe! 'And you gonna make me'? He sneered, while at the same time he slowly pushed his finger into the side of my face and flicked my cheek up!

That's right you've guessed it! There was no way he was going to get away with it twice, so I punched him straight in his disbelieving fucking face! I didn't stop as he staggered backwards, instead I followed up with a volley of punches to his head. As he fell to the floor, I heard the roar of the now even bigger crowd that had gathered in the car park. I jumped on him and rained down punch after punch. In his defence he fought back hard (as he had a lot at stake!), but it wasn't enough because I had already 'lost it'. At one point as I had him on the floor and I assume out of sheer desperation the dirty fucker stuck his thumb in my eye. At the same time and out of nowhere I felt a huge weight land on my back, furious and in a blind rage (no pun intended), I stood up and threw the weight off. Now an even bigger roar went up from the crowd, unbeknown to me I had just thrown Mr Richardson, the history teacher off my back and was now yet again gunning for a very confused looking Barry Evans!

I'm not sure how long our 'ruck' lasted, but I was beginning to run out of steam when (thankfully) the teachers dived in and broke it up. We were both unceremoniously hauled into the headmaster's office. He was furious and stated in no uncertain terms that he would not tolerate this kind of behaviour in his school. Me and Barry were separated by a table in the middle of the office and had both regained our composure when Barry Evans having gotten a little bit of bravery back said, 'Look at the boy crying'! He was referring to the fact that my 'left' eye, the one he had just stuck his great big dirty thumb in was, WATERY! Outraged, I didn't even hesitate as I threw the table out of the way and lunged at him, whilst also calling him a 'fucking cunt'!

He had thought he was safe in the headmaster's office! He had thought wrong! He hadn't expected me to launch the table out of the way and go for him again, it was the first time I had ever seen Barry Evans look, 'actually' frightened. So did the headmaster for that matter! Once again, we were separated by the teachers, however this time Barry 'fucking' Evans, made no comment.

The next few days were a bit testy for me to say the least, I was waiting to get jumped by Barry and his henchmen, but it never happened! There were a few dirty looks and low mutterings, but that was about it. One thing that did happen though and which took me completely by surprise was this, the day after the fight I was walking alone, along the school corridor when I bumped into Mr Temple the French teacher. He held out his arm and took my hand and shook it vigorously as he said, 'well done, Mr Delaney, I knew you would be the man to do it'! 'err... thanks Mr Temple', I said as I beamed with pride and walked on to my next lesson an absolute fucking legend!!

FIVE YEARS!

During my five years at Rotherham, I had publicly exhibited my artwork in the town centre library (my work now having been seen by tens!). I had done loop the loops in an aeroplane. I had lost my cherry! And I had restored my honour. Academically however I had achieved fuck all!

With the school's permission I was allowed to leave two months early as I had secured myself a job in a raised flooring factory. This was on the proviso that I went back to take my exams. Which I did. Nor did I do too bad considering there were no expectations at all, from either my parents or even the school. Without any revision, I achieved 5 GCSEs all grade C and above, I wonder what I could have achieved if I had actually bothered or had been encouraged to apply myself? But then school was never about academic attainment, not for the likes of me anyway. School was just about keeping you out of the way and getting you used to early starts and long boring drawn out days. The conformity needed to be ready for the workplace! If it had ever been about anything else, then all the teachers would have been sacked for being shit at their jobs!

****

Leaving school was the same as starting, it was both exhilarating and daunting all at the same time! I took the job in the raised flooring factory as a stop gap and to earn some money before I joined the Parachute Regiment. I hated it! Eager to begin my military career I went along to the Army recruitment office to join up (for twenty years). I took the entry exams and was pleased to discover I had scored quite highly! The recruiting Warrant Officer, suggested I could do better than the PARAs; The Signals or Royal Mechanical Engineers perhaps? Then he said, 'why don't you join the Irish Guards'? 'why the Irish Guards'? I asked innocently. 'So, you can be with your own lot', came the reply! A little confused (and slightly hurt), I said, 'I thought I was with my own lot'!

In the end it didn't really matter because I failed the medical! During my examination the Doctor pointed out that I had flat feet. I didn't really understand what he was getting at and remember rather childishly thinking, but not saying... so what, you've got a big nose!

My mum was openly delighted that I didn’t get in! My dreams had been dashed by my bloody feet, and she couldn't have been happier. Obviously she was worried that her 'baby' could get killed or seriously maimed (I confess as a sixteen year old I hadn't even considered these consequences and was more interested in the excitement and adventure I believed the army could offer me, (could I kill someone?). I once heard that most soldiers run into battle, firing indiscriminately, with only a small percentage of soldiers who actively select and pick of a target. I'm fairly certain I would have been of the sort who ran in kicking and screaming, spraying bullets and hoping for the best! Which, now I think about it, is pretty much how I have lived my life to date!

My mum had already asked Connor, (not my dad), to try and talk me out of joining up. So, my brother sat me down for a man to man chat. I will never forget the pearls of wisdom that flowed from his mouth as he said, 'What do you want to join the army for? I see them going up and down the motorway in the backs of lorries, they've all got moustaches and they look like cunts'. This was followed by a shrug of the shoulders and a tilt of the head!

Despite not being asked, my dad also had something to say on the matter. Typically, however, he waited until he was paralytic drunk and then cornered me in the alleyway next to our house! He looked like he wanted to kill me. His huge frame all but filled the alley as he menacingly boomed, 'Why do you want to fight 'my' people'!? What people? I was just a kid; I knew nothing about politics. I didn't have a clue as to what he was going on about. He upset me. I felt intimidated and if I am truly honest, frightened!

As my father continued to berate and goad me in the alleyway, Evelyn unexpectedly turned up at the house, saw what was going on, and totally flipped! 'Never' the shrinking violet! She let rip and began calling him every name under the sun, to make matters worse she was four months pregnant. The more insults she hurled at our father, the angrier (and so it seemed) the bigger he became! Of course, I was use to this sort of behaviour, we all were. But today was different, I was already upset, I had just had all my hopes and dreams dashed, and now this fiasco! I just wanted it to stop. But instead the opposite happened, all hell broke loose when Evelyn, went a step to far. She took hold of all of my father's drink and poured it down the kitchen sink, and snapped at him, 'How do you like that you fucking wanker'?!!

He exploded with rage and made a dive for my sister. Fearful I jumped in between them! If it hadn't been so serious it would have been comical. The scene in our kitchen resembled something like a very angry and very violent Benny Hill sketch as the three of us ended up running around the kitchen table (but without the music!).

I think it may have been sheer terror that made her do it. Evelyn snatched a butter knife up off the kitchen table and threw it directly at my father's head! It was like something from a cheap horror film, just for a fragment of a moment ...it 'stuck' in his forehead!! Everything stopped like a freeze frame in a movie. All three of us stood opened mouthed, my dad with a butter knife protruding from his head! It only lasted a split second, but it was real. Then he roared, 'well you bastard'!! That's when me and Evelyn legged it! It was my own fault, ... I should have known better than to try and join the Army on a Wednesday!

To escape the madness I went round to Neil Duncan's house. As I walked I reflected on what had just happened; if I can't handle my drunken father in the alleyway of our house then maybe leaping out of an aeroplane and onto the battlefield isn't really for me! However, this new revelation did not stop me from feeling totally devastated, by everything.

When I arrived at Neil's house his older brother James opened the front door and asked, 'Alright Pat, how did you get on with your army medical'? With a sad face and a heavy heart, I said, 'Not good James, I failed the medical... I've got flat feet'. With this a massive grin erupted across his face as he exclaimed, 'Fuck me, you should've said, I've got a foot pump out the back'!! and then he burst out laughing!

I didn't laugh and to this day I have never sported a moustache!

Chapter Six

PLAN B. I DIDN'T HAVE ONE! All I knew was I needed to work hard if I was to make something of my life. I wanted to break free from 'the shackles' that had marginalised my childhood years. I was determined to break the chain! I had no intention of ending up like my father (or mother, bless her!). I would be a good man, a decent man. When I got older, I would provide for my family, I would be a good dad and a good husband. I reasoned to achieve this I would need to earn 'big' money, I needed to get a good job!

I soon ditched the raised flooring factory, seeing it for what it was, low pay and dead end. With Connor's help I secured an apprenticeship, with a firm called Metal Fabs, as a trainee fabricator / welder. I found it interesting and enjoyable, cutting, grinding, folding and welding. Not surprising seeing as how I had just spent five years with nothing more than a piece of paper and a Berol pen!

I remember being treated differently to the other young apprentices. I think it was generally perceived that I had a bit more cop on! An advantage of my upbringing perhaps! As a result, I truly felt like one of the boys! I recall standing with all the men one day, laughing and enjoying a bit of banter and feeling much older than my 16yrs, when totally out of the blue one of the men in the group said, ...'I fucking hate the Irish'! It went suddenly quiet.

I felt embarrassed. Most of the lads were looking at the floor, most of them also knew that my parents were Irish, this bloke obviously did not! I broke the uncomfortable silence when I said, 'What , you hate my mum and dad'? 'Have you ever met my mum and dad'?

He didn't know where to look and then rather sheepishly said, 'They (the Irish), killed my next-door neighbour'. There followed another awkward silence, before I said, 'Well, my mum and dad have never killed anyone mate! They're really nice people'! And I left it at that. It was very awkward. I was 16yrs old and beginning to see the world through adult eyes, what a shame!

I didn't stay very long at Metal Fabs, not because of the 'idiot', but because the lure of the construction industry was calling with the promise of 'big' money! I liked the idea of being self-employed, it sounded quite grand. It implied possibilities that might not be available to me in a factory setting. Connor had stayed well away from construction. In fact, he stayed well away from anything that resembled the life of my father. However, it appealed to my 'ego', I had only just begun, yet I wasn't happy with my lot! I wanted more, I wanted better. A defect of my character perhaps? A flaw? Then again perhaps it is this defect of character that has propelled the human race to where it is today. Perhaps this 'flaw' is the reason we are not still living in caves! Then again perhaps 'my big ideas', were just a manifestation of my subconscious attempt to hide the fact that I felt like a second-class citizen, even though I was still too young to know it!

Apart from the pub, the only other place on my estate open on a Sunday afternoon was Charlie's petrol station. I was returning a video (not wanting to be charged for an extra night), when I saw an advert in the window, for a Dry Liner. 'what's a Dry Liner'? I had asked the bloke behind the counter. He began to explain it was the application of plasterboards to walls and ceilings, (I was still yawning), when the man who had placed the advert happened to walk in. There followed a brief exchange before I was interviewed and hired on the spot, there and then in the garage!

'Bob' told me he would pick me up at 6.30am, the following

Monday. My starting wage would be £60 per week with the promise, I could be earning as much as £300 per week within six months. Bloody hell, '£300 per week'!! Most of my mates were earning £30 quid a week on 3yr apprenticeships, so, like the 'thicko' I was, I jumped at the chance! The work was physically demanding, laborious and monotonous!

I was just a kid, making the transition into an adult world. An inbetweener, neither nor! My friends were no exception. In fact, for the first 12 months or so after leaving school we all still behaved like little kids, basically we did mad silly shit! (set fire to your mate's hair or pull his trousers down if he was talking to a girl, that sort of thing!). There was about ten of us in the early days, but then we began to split into two main groups, the students (druggies) and the workers (drinkers). I fell into the latter category. Although we all liked to do both, if that makes sense!

Me, Jim Sweeny and Paul McGillicuddy all worked in construction and couldn't wait for Friday to come around so we could get down the pub and blow our wages (like real men!). Neil Duncan on the other hand had convinced his parents that he was studying hard at 6th form, when in reality all he was doing was walking around in a daze, smoking pot, taking acid and listening to 'Curiosity Killed the Cat', on his Walkman!

Neil didn't have any money, but still liked to get pissed so he would come down the pub anyway! Neil was a bit of a loon in them days but was always an excellent laugh. Most (weekday) evenings after work I would be round at his house smoking pot on his doorstep, laughing my bollocks off and drinking pints of strawberry Nesquik, (his mum was always moaning about where all the milk had gone). Although always great fun, it was sometimes difficult to explain to my mum why my eyes were so red!

Neil's parents were good, decent people, I think sometimes it was more than they could bear with three sons in the house, it was often boisterous and chaotic, especially when they were out! Neil's older brother James was a bit of a bully (-ish, but not quite), I had to separate them on more than one occasion, having to jump on James back once when they had a full on fight in their living room, Neil wanted to listen to the Specials on the record player, but James wanted to watch The Bill on TV.

Neil's parents would often go away on walking holidays to the Lake District, which pretty much meant Neil's house was a free for all. A green light for a bunch of teenage boys to go mental and engage in silliness. Everyone would be drinking and smoking pot! On such occasions things would quickly escalate and get out of hand. Music blaring, the living room engulfed in a cloud of toxic smoke, there would be no talking just shouting like the din coming from a school playground only manic and littered with profanities and attitude! I remember Jim Sweeny, having smoked too much pot, fell asleep in Neil's dad's armchair (dangerous!). One of our number happened to have some Bangers! as you do when you're a 16yr old lad! So, we lit one and put it in an empty coke can next to Jim's ear, and then waited!

When it went off, it exploded with an almighty 'BANG'! Poor Jim, his startled face and wide eyes were a classic, he must have leapt about four foot through the air while shouting 'Ya fucking bastards'! whilst everybody else rolled about in fits of laughter! It really was a very loud bang!

It was also two in the morning! We were causing such a racket that unbeknown to us the neighbours had called the police! The first we knew of it, was when they started hammering the front door down. Startled into silence, Neil, took a fearful peek of the window, spun round and hissed, 'It's the fucking filth'!

Like a game of musical statues, everybody froze. Then, when having mustered the courage, Neil reluctantly opened the front door, the police barged past him and into the front room, demanding to know, 'What the bloody hell is going on here'!? So, we all pretended to be asleep!! I think the officers cringed with embarrassment on our behalf!

Despite our childishness, our lives were changing. My mate, Simón Pompidou, was the first of our click to get a driving licence, mainly due to the fact that his dad was a driving instructor. SOLO, that's what it said on the side of the car, Simón was allowed to use it in the evenings and at weekends. It was a brand new, 'shitty', little Peugeot, which had the added bonus of having dual pedals. So, if you didn't like Simón's driving you could slam on the brakes! We all took turns to, slam on the brakes!

Simón was also the first person I knew who owned a mobile phone! Although calling it a mobile may be stretching it a bit, it was definitely portable. Unfortunately, it was humongous and weighed about the same as a bag of cement. A large black wooden box housed the (car) battery and an old-fashioned rotary dial phone (like deal or no deal!) was fixed to the top. None of us were allowed to use it of course, because it would cost about a week's wages just to phone your mum!

Ryan Smith was the second of our click to get a driving licence and to his credit an actual car. But he wasn't 'really' one of the boys, as such and despite 'having a car' he didn't gain any Kudos or respect from us, plus I was 'fooling around' with his sister! And for some reason he didn't like it! Perhaps it was because Neil and Simón took great delight in quizzing me (always), in front of him, as to what I had got up to with his sister the night before! Obviously being a true gentleman, I never divulged, not in front of him anyway. Just for the record I was 17 she was 21 and it was a lot of fun! It did wonders for my self-esteem!

We didn't have the sense we were born with, which was great because that meant everything was an adventure and a great laugh! One Saturday night after the pub had closed, we all decided it would be a great idea to drive to Great Yarmouth (2 hours away!). In high spirits we set off, two car loads of teenage boys, Simón driving one and Ryan driving the other. We were all drinking cans, smoking weed and laughing non-stop. At one point during our journey we ended up driving side by side along a duel carriageway. We had all the windows down so we could hurl insults at each other and pass joints, all very funny when your 17yrs old.

I was in the back of Simón's car but decided it looked like more fun in Ryan's, so I jumped (or dived if you like) through the open windows and landed on top of the backseat passengers in Ryan's car! So, there I was, a moment later in the next car, drinking a can of beer and smoking a spliff! Everyone agreed it was bold, mental and extremely funny!

We never made it to Great Yarmouth that night, we took a wrong turn and ended up in Lowestoft instead. I remember sitting on the beach in the early hours, drunk and stoned and listening to the waves crash against the shore. One eye on the moon, the other on the two cars in case they decided to fuck off without me for a laugh! In that moment as I sat alone on the beach, I felt invincible, I felt invigorated, I had my whole life ahead of me. I was in my element and I loved it!

Over the years me and Simón have spoken of that night many times. I don't know exactly how fast we were going along the duel carriageway the night I did my 'jump'; a conservative estimate is 30 mph, perhaps it was only 20 mph. Either way, looking back, I shudder at the sheer stupidity of my actions. I dread to think what might have happened if something had gone wrong! When you're young, you are convinced you are going to live forever. You have no fear. I suppose that's why it's so important to live life when you're young, because, let's face it, the older you get the less chances you are going to take.

****

Now 'mobile' young adults, our circles had widened and as a result my old friend Molly was back on the scene! Although it wasn't the same. He wasn't the same. The kid who had once had 'everything' now appeared to have 'nothing'. His parent's 'mess' had clearly taken its toll, that and the fact we had both (sort of) 'grown up' and as an added consequence 'apart'! So, for me Molly's re-emergence, as pleasant as it was, was albeit brief!

Most of the lads would descend on Molly's 'latest' squalid address, his parents seemed pretty cool with everyone drinking and smoking weed in their house. In fact, they didn't seem to mind his friends turning up at all hours and treating their home like a teenage club house (guilt perhaps?)!

Late one night as we all sat smoking pot in Steve's living room a … 'mouse' ran across the floor! Half the lads shrieked, while the other half whooped in delight! Then much to everyone's surprise and joy, Neil managed to catch it under a pint glass and held it captive on the carpet in the middle of the room.

For the rest of the night we took turns in slightly lifting the glass and blowing smoke from our joints into it. We were that stoned that a couple of times, we even forgot about the little mouse! Eventually someone decided to release the beast, but when they lifted the glass, the little mouse didn't run away! Instead it just sat there on the carpet in the middle of the living room, occasionally drawing one of its tiny little paws across its whiskers (and yawning!?). The whole thing was surreal.

Of course, poor Molly was embarrassed that all his friends now knew he shared his house with rodents, even if they were the super cool, hip, 'pot smoking' variety!

The students among us (the druggies!) use to go to Molly's house every Monday night to take Acid, (fondly referred to as the Monday club). Me, Jim and McGillicuddy rarely went. To be honest it always felt a bit scummy to me, that and the fact us three all had to be up early for our work. I only ever tried Acid a couple of times (between the age of 16-18), but it was too strong for me, I didn't like it. You only had to have one wrong thought and it was game over.

I took it in the pub one night and started having a bad 'trip' and had to go home, I remember laying on my bed unable to move, like I was paralysed, when the radio started to play, 'Going Down To Rio', by Mike Nesmith, from the Monkees (the one with the woolly hat). It sounded like every musical note was slowly grinding together and there was nothing I could do about it. I couldn't even turn the radio off! It was horrific.

That's why I preferred Speed to Acid, I found it a bit more do-able. My mum came into my bedroom at 6am one Saturday morning (I found out years later, she did this regularly, to check my face!), and asked me what I was doing. 'Colouring in Bob Marley's hair, mum', came my reply! I was off my face, I still have that drawing somewhere; its actually quite good!

I liked drinking, I liked drugs (I liked drawing!), I had good friends and I was enjoying myself. My job paid well, and I was starting to live life. I was changing into a young man. I was also starting to fall in the door late at night, extremely drunk, which didn't go down too well with my mum. My parents, being old fashioned, knew nothing of my recreational drug use. My father said I was, 'At the fools age'! My mother said I was just like my father! Before adding, as long as I had a shilling in my pocket, I would be in the pub. I found her comments hurtful! But …true!

Such is the boom and bust culture of the construction industry that Jim Sweeny briefly found himself out of work. His mum (like all Irish mums), had no intention of allowing her son to sit around idle, so she insisted he did a few shifts behind the bar in his uncle's (Irish) pub. Jim reluctantly agreed!

It wasn't just for the novelty factor that I had nipped into see him; I actually fancied a pint! It was early doors on a Saturday morning so there were just a few regulars (and me) sitting around the bar. Me and Jim were chatting away when he made a witty remark, and everybody laughed! I came back with an even wittier reply, but only me and Jim laughed? It was noticeable!

Jim's mum worked in the pub, so everyone knew 'his' parents were Irish. It was clear, 'they' did not consider me the same as Jim, it was obvious that 'I' was 'not' considered one of 'them'! Sitting amongst them at the bar, I actually felt offended. I could see my good friend Jim was embarrassed on my behalf! However, I was not about to say, 'Oh it's okay everybody, my parents are Irish too, ...weh'!!

Instead, I suppressed my contempt and just thought, 'Fuck the lot of em'! The reason I mention this is because throughout my adult life I have come to notice that Irish people tell me I am English and English people tell me I am Irish! In short, I am denied by both sides. It's insulting! I can assure you I'm not trying to be either. I'm just me! I'm just Pat, as a result I don't consider myself Irish or English, I consider myself British!

I am not into football, (apparently, I'm 1/1000!) but even so, I have never worn an Ireland shirt, nor have I ever worn an England shirt, I can't! because I would feel like a fraud either way! All my life I have heard racist comments, from both camps! It doesn't really bother me; I recognise it for what it is.... ignorance! I love my country of birth and I am proud of my ancestral heritage. I am also glad that as a consequence of geography, I am spared all the bullshit! '...Why do you want to fight 'my' people'! No wonder I didn't have a clue as to what he was talking about?!

****

Jim was sick of drinking coke and eating peanuts and couldn't wait to get out of the pub and back on site, so when his mum told him she had got him a couple of shifts working with a few of the 'paddy's' (ha ha!), from the pub, he was over the moon! She told him he had to be outside the pub at 6am Monday morning to meet the lads! Jim, turned up as promised and found some men gathered outside the pub. 'You waiting for a white transit van lads'? enquired Jim. 'We are', came the reply. At 6am on the dot the van pulled up and everyone piled in the back, Jim 'picked' a 'shovel' and sat down before the van sped off heading for the motorway. A few minutes later the driver turned in his seat and looking back into the van did a double take when he saw Jim!

'Who are you'?!! demanded the startled and confused looking driver. 'Oh, I'm Jim mate, I'm starting today'. 'yeah, and who told you that'?!! barked the driver! 'erm...'? Jim hadn't bothered to ask his mum 'who' he was starting work for and as he didn't know, the driver had stopped the van and kicked him out! Jim had a half hour walk back home in the cold, clutching his sandwiches!

I also used to get picked up in a white van for work. My boss Bob lived just around the corner from me and most mornings I would get in the van 'fucked', this was because I had usually been up all night smoking pot or 'fooling around' with Ryan Smith's sister (or with any luck both!). 'Youth' being the one and only reason I could make it through the day!

One evening Bob was dropping me off at the bottom of my Close, when he said, with some alarm, 'There's a police car outside your house'? With a knowing shrug off my shoulders I said, 'yeah, it's alright Bob, that'll just be my dad'! Bob looked a little perplexed and somewhat concerned as I got out of the van and waved him off.

As I walked through the back door into the kitchen, I could see someone had spilled coffee and sugar granules all over the work top as they had attempted to make a coffee! I could hear voices coming from the living room. As I entered the room, I saw that my dad was demanding that a fresh faced, 'yet acne-covered' copper (there were two policemen), shake his hand!

'Shake'! (it was a pathetic macho display of strength; it still makes me cringe to even think of it). My dad had a habit of squeezing your fingers until they felt like they were going to break. He had been doing it to me since I was a little kid. I really didn't want him doing it to the cooper! I could see the young policeman was becoming annoyed (and embarrassed) because my dad was starting to 'boy' him off! 'What's going on'? I asked, as I stood in the open doorway. The older of the two policemen, gently explained that they had found my dad slumped on the pavement in the town centre and had picked him up, to make sure he got home safely! I could see they were growing tired of my dad, as he was now starting to become offensive. Not wanting the situation to escalate, I quickly jumped in and thanked them both and said I would take over from here. They knew exactly what the score was! They could see that I was embarrassed, so much so, that as they got up to leave, they gave me a look as if to say, 'unlucky mate, what a shit dad'!

I was annoyed, he had shamed me in front of two police officers and my boss! But I wasn't shocked or surprised, it was normal. He (my dad) was even brought home by a fire engine once, not so much stuck up a tree, as stuck up the fucking pub! He had gotten so drunk he had collapsed on the flyover in the middle of the town centre. God knows how many people must have driven past (around!) him. What a total disgrace! The local fire brigade happened to be coming past, stopped, picked him up and dropped him home. Thanks lads!

Chapter Seven

(Christmas 89)

It was my first (proper) Christmas out on the town with my friends. The previous year we were all still pretty wary as to whether or not we would get served. But by now we were regular (confident) and well-established faces around the town. Christmas Eve was as I had hoped, brilliant! The whole town was decked out with festive lights and music played out of speakers erected high up on the lamp posts (out of reach!).

Every year the local council put up a huge Christmas tree outside the town hall, and every year groups of drunken louts would do their best to climb it, before getting dragged back down by the local constabulary. The annoyance of the local coppers being off-set by gaggles of drunken girls draping their arms around the smiling officers and cheekily asking for Christmas kisses! All the pubs were full to the brim with drunken revellers and blasted out everybody's favourite Christmas songs. High on good cheer every one of us was 'busy' getting drunk and trying to snog as many pretty girls as possible. It was truly a magical atmosphere!

However, being young lads, we still knew that we had to watch ourselves, we all knew we had to keep an eye out for the older blokes. The ones who are now settled and don't get out as much as they use to! The 30 something's, who go into town Xmas Eve to buy the missus a present and end up on the piss all day because its Xmas (gift purchased, or not!). The lone wolf! Or worse the whole pack, practically guaranteed to start on us younger lads. There was always some element of danger, but that just made it all the more exciting, all the more electric! I felt alive! I didn't want it to end!!

By contrast, Christmas day always was and always has been a massive let down in our house as my dad 'always' ruined it. By the time dinner was ready he would be so drunk that he would be sitting at the table slobbering all over his dinner. My mum would be in a foul mood before he had even had a drink, because experience had taught her and us what to expect. I don't recall one single happy Christmas from my childhood. Year after year it was always the same, everyone would be on edge. A fact made worse by the knowledge that every other household in the land was having a great time! (I know that's not really true, lots of people had it worse than we did, but it didn't make it any easier to bear!). In the end we all just accepted, that was how it was. My sister Bridie tried to make it 'Christmassy', bless her, I remember she brought my dad a lovely watch and presented it to him. I also remember how embarrassed he looked, because he hadn't brought her (any of us) anything! Christmas day in our house was like the longest, most boring, drawn out Sunday imaginable! Unless there was a fight!

Boxing day, oh the excess! Oh the boredom! Oh get me the fuck … …out of here! I still had some money left and was itching to get down the pub to meet my mates. It was still the old style Sunday opening hours in them days, my dad had already been out to the local pub and had come home at closing time to change into a different suit, so he would be ready for the evening shift (my dad was always impeccably dressed when he left the house, not so much on his return!). Excited to be going out, I had made the flurry of phone calls from our hallway (like a military operation!), to all the lads and had then rang the taxi! Then just before I left, I poked my head in the front room. My dad was sitting in his chair by the fire. Fresh suit on and as usual hair Bryl-creamed to perfection! 'You going out', he said as he turned in the chair to look at me. 'I am', I smiled. He gave me one of those knowing dad looks and said... 'And when will I be seeing you again'? To which I cheerfully replied, 'later, ...a lot, lot... later'! And then I scarped out the front door to join my friends.

I came home that night, my dad didn't. Which was strange because my mum has always said, he was like a homing pigeon, no matter 'how' drunk he got, the 'fucker' always managed to make his way home whether that be by ambulance, squad car or fire engine!

My dad was pronounced dead at 4 30 am on the 27th Dec 1989. He was 58yrs old. The hospital had phoned. Some poor unfortunate nurse had been given the unenviable task of phoning our house at 5am two days after Christmas to inform my poor mother that her husband was dead.

My dad had gone back up to the pub the evening before, had got drunk as usual and then, unusually, had gone to an old friend's house for another drink. Apparently, he had fallen asleep on the settee and his friend had gone to bed leaving my dad to sleep it off! But he never woke up! There was talk at the time that he had been sick and had, in fact chocked on his own vomit, but at the coroner's report the verdict was recorded as death by alcohol poisoning.

My mum told me to tell my friends that he had died of a heart attack, because of the shame it would bring on the family if people knew that he had died an alcoholic death! I resented having to lie to my friends. I had been lying about his drinking all my life, which I suppose is why I had spent most of it feeling like a fraud. I felt uncomfortable in front of my mates and remember looking at the floor when I explained his 'heart attack'! But I said nothing about how I felt, as this was what my mother had asked, and I didn't want to upset her!

Being only 17, I had the option of not going to the morgue to see my dad. But I was his son and I felt it was my duty to pay my last respects. Plus, I didn't like the idea of him lying in the morgue on his own, without his family around him. I can still see him lying peacefully in the coffin, it had a red silk lining. He was wearing his best suit and as usual his hair was Bryl-creamed to absolute perfection, he looked serene. I kissed his forehead and remember it was cold. Even though I was just a boy, I knew that my father was long gone and all that remained was the carriage that was once his body. After the visit to the funeral parlour it was hard for me to accept that I would never see him again.

Me and Connor were the front pallbearers. There was a huge crowd gathered outside the church, I can remember lifting my head and looking at the sea of faces, all staring back at us. I was pleased he had such a good turn out, I hadn't realise how well liked he was and how many friends he had. I think it was the first time I considered that he had had a life before me.

At the age of seventeen and with the whole community looking on, I paid my father the final and ultimate honour of carrying his coffin into the church. I will never forget the weight of his coffin on my young shoulder, nor will I forget the haunting sound of my mother's sobs as she followed behind the casket. And as quick as that, he was gone out of our life's forever!

A few days after the funeral, I overheard my mother saying, 'At least now I will get a few years peace'. The sad truth is, she meant it! The poor woman was heartbroken. I was there when she took the call, I saw the look on her face and I heard the tremble in her voice as she cried, 'No, no, please God no'! I saw the shock and disbelief in her eyes when she told me my father was dead. Despite everything she had loved him and so did we.

She had always said he was a bastard, she told him frequently that she hated him and wished him dead. I have lost count of the number of times I heard my mother say that when he died, she would bury the 'cunt' at the bottom of the garden. She blamed him for making her life a misery and for all that was wrong in the world. Yet she was distraught. Why? Because she loved him.

Feelings and emotions run deep, despite all the pain, the physical and verbal abuse. The misery. Deep down she knew he couldn't help it; good people do bad things. When he was alive, she never showed him that she loved him, there were no open displays of affection. But she had loved him. She did love him. I think in some ways she had always pitied him, and I think that she was hurt that in death he had abandoned her. Is it possible to love and hate someone at the same time, I think it probably is!

I don't know who it was, but my dad's possessions were returned to my mother (the hospital perhaps?) He had on his person the watch my sister had given him two days earlier, £2 in money, a comb and a tin of golden Virginia tobacco and that was the entirety of his wealth. 58yrs and that's all he had to show for it.

We weren't allowed to have the television on for 6 weeks. My mother said it was disrespectful, she was in mourning. She wore black for months. We live in modern times, but it amazes me how we snap back to old fashioned traditions and customs when it's called for.

For a long while after his funeral, I kept seeing his face when I closed my eyes and I heard his voice. But as the months turned into years they began to fade. I can still see his face, partly because I have pictures, but his voice, well... I haven't heard that in 30 yrs!

My father's death had been a shock! I had my resentments and I also had little respect for the man who had been my father, but I loved him, nonetheless. Growing up it had often felt like there had been a death in the family and now there had. We were all walking on eggshells and doing our best to comfort and console our mother.

It's fair to say my behaviour had been somewhat 'wild' of late. So out of respect, I curbed my drinking and stopped staying out late with friends. How could I stand in the pub, laughing and joking with friends in light of what had just happened, nor did I want to! However, I am ashamed to admit, that secretly I felt 'hard done by'. I had just started to enjoy 'my' life and now I felt as though I was being dragged back into my parent's (mother's) melancholy. I had been having fun. For the first time in my life I was an equal, I was one of the boys! I had stopped feeling like a fraud, like I had something to hide, something to be ashamed of. That's why I had resented having to lie to my friends about the cause of my father's death! I didn't want it anymore!

The 'mourning' period, as heartless as it may sound, reminded me of when I was a little kid, out playing in the street with my friends and one of my sisters or my brother would come and get me and say, 'You have to come home, dad's drunk'! (as my mother would want us all together!). So, I would have to leave my friends while they all had fun and I would have to return home to bedlam, oppression and misery. Forgive me if it sounds callous but it's the truth! I am not a heartless man. Of course I was as devastated as everyone else in my family; I too was heartbroken. But I silently vowed that there was no way I was going to allow my parents (dad), to prevent me from enjoying my youth. After all, I now knew what I had to look forward to. It had been shown to me that life is shit.... and then you die!

So, like the dutiful son, I behaved myself for a while and then as time passed, I resumed my previous antics.

****

As if she hadn't put up with enough over the years! One Saturday morning my mother came down the stairs and walking into the kitchen found me passed out, laying naked on the kitchen floor and in a pool of my own piss! I was 19yrs old!

It's hard for me to describe the magnitude of shame and remorse I felt that morning as I took the biggest bollocking of my life (whilst naked)! I remembered nothing of the night before! I was mortified! I could barely meet her eye as she told me I was a fucking disgrace and that she was disgusted with me! 'You're no fucking good, you're just like your cunt of a father'! She had screamed it at me! I was so full of shame, I kept saying, I'm sorry, I'm sorry. I begged her not to tell the family (I don't think she did?). A day or two of frostiness, ...and it was all but forgotten!!

Being young I dismissed the 'incident' and put it down to youthful exuberance! However, a strange thing had happened in more ways than one. Growing up it had always been 'us' against 'him'. Now he was dead. Now it felt like it was 'them' against 'me'! It hurt, I was distraught by this realisation, but most of all I was confused.... because I am nothing like him!

CHAPTER EIGHT

FAMILIES DON'T STAY THE SAME. They shift and change shape, they expand, they shrink, they branch off in new directions creating 'new' family units. The dynamics alter. Over time the 'old' family nucleus collapses and fades away into obscurity. My family was no exception! When Kathleen had left all those years ago, she had quickly married the local baker's son (a bun in the oven perhaps?). My parents had not been invited. Not only were they not invited, they didn't even know the marriage had taken place. My poor mother only found out about the union, when a friend congratulated her up at the local shops! It must have cut like a knife (through a cake perhaps!)!

I never found out why. Perhaps Kathleen was worried my father would get drunk and embarrass her? Perhaps her new husband was controlling? Or maybe she was ashamed of her roots? The truth is I simply don't know. What I do know is... regardless of the reasons, she should have told my mother. It was cruel! And it was uncalled for! How painful it must be, your first-born child and you're not welcome, you're not invited!

Kathleen remained a stranger and went on to have three children. (some years later she walked out on her husband and children, and as far as my mother was concerned it was unforgivable; it was the ultimate sin!).

You would think it would have been the complete opposite, but Evelyn, appeared to love a bastard, (I can't imagine where she got that from!). In fact, she married two on the trot! I don't know all the details but there was violence in both marriages. Although I strongly suspect she always gave as good as she got. Evelyn also had three children, the first being the little git with the rice crispy!?

Connor was much more conventional, a good man with traditional values, he married his childhood sweetheart and bought a house before he, too, had three children.

Bridie - well she wasn't prepared to take any shit at all! No man was going to rule her! She had been loved up alright. She had even, upon discovering she was pregnant set up home with the father of her unborn son. But as some men do, upon recognising her newfound vulnerability, he became bullish, controlling and possessive. So, she told him to do one! and moved back home to my mother's house with her baby boy.

Me, well I had my mates, I had my weekends. I had no intention of settling down. I was barely 20yrs old, I had all the time in the world! I did not want to be restricted in anyway, nor did I want to shoulder any responsibilities, I was enjoying myself to much. As far as I was concerned my friends were family enough! I was out, all, and every weekend and then during the week (when the money had gone!), I would be round at Neil's house smoking pot on his doorstep. I loved getting stoned at Neil's, the only drawback was walking home late at night on my own in the dark, whilst really, really stoned! Being young I never admitted it to Neil, but most nights as I walked home, I would be shitting myself at every noise, shadow or passing car! I recall walking past a garden late one night and something snarled and nipped at my ankle! I think it might have been a little dog, but I can't be certain, because I didn't bother to stop and look! It frightened me that much, that I didn't miss a step as I bolted for the safety of home!!

Life was once again good. It wasn't the same, but it had returned to some level of normality. I was (as promised) earning good money, in fact the job was going well.... and then it was gone! I had a disagreement with Bob and that was that!

I wasn't too concerned. Like with most things in my life I took it all in my stride. As luck would have it one of our neighbours in the close, a man called Bill, got me a job working with him in a powder-coat shop on the outskirts of town. I hated it! It felt like a huge fall from grace. But not working was not an option. You needed money if you wanted to be one of the boys! It was really boring work, monotonous and unskilled. The money wasn't very good either. In fact, I really hated it!

It was around about this time that I briefly dated a girl called Carla. She was stunning and I was quite taken with her! I even went as far as meeting her parents and did my best to impress them. But being so young I don't think I fully appreciated just how beautiful Carla was. We had been seeing each other for a couple of months (so it was serious!), when a college friend of hers invited us both to his 21st birthday party, at his parent's house.

They were not my type of people, and I found the party to be very dull, so I got drunk and ended up upsetting the host! He (rather selfishly) decided at 1am in the morning to turn all the music off and 'make' everyone sit down and watch a film that he had made at college.

Having had a 'few', I thought it might be 'fun' to do a running commentary to his film début. Unimpressed, he threw a tantrum and asked me to leave. Now embarrassed and as a way of deflection, I called him all the names I could think of, until Carla (quietly) burst into tears. At which point I told the bloke 'he was fucking dead ...the next time I saw him' and then we left. I told my mates about what had happened, and they all agreed I shouldn't let this knob get away with embarrassing 'me' and upsetting 'my' girlfriend?!

I explained how he would have got a dig there and then, but he had all his mates with him, and I was on my own, but the next time I saw him .... he was going to get it! Defo! Of course, it was all bravado! I was clearly at fault; I knew I had done wrong, but I was a young man and I wasn't about to admit it.

It was almost forgotten about, when a few weeks later I walked into a pub in the town centre called, The Old Cock Inn, (yeah, I know!). As I walked in, I saw a friend of mine called, Cormac, sitting at a table in the corner with a scruffy looking old bloke who had a massive, grey scraggly beard. I nodded in Cormac's direction and he came over to the bar. 'Alright Cormac, who's the old tramp', I enquired? Looking terribly offended, Cormac said, 'That's my dad'! I couldn't stop myself and burst out laughing, I had no idea!

It wasn't long before all my mates had piled in, Neil and Paul were bickering at the bar about who was better, The Stone Roses or Oasis! I then heard them both agree that MC Hammer, was shit! Sweeny was done up to the nines and clearly on the 'pull' but was in hysterics when I mentioned my earlier 'faux pas' concerning Cormac's dad. The drinks were flowing, and everyone was on good form, ...when the door to the pub opened and in walked the lad who had told me to get out of his party! The one whom, as I had told everyone had ' ...made my girlfriend cry'!!

Being the boisterous bunch that they were, my mates all started egging me on saying things like , 'He wouldn't get away with it if he made my girlfriend cry', and, 'You should give the surly cunt a slap'!

The truth was I really wasn't that bothered, I wasn't really a fighter, I never did like violence. (plus, I secretly knew I had been in the wrong!). But I didn't want to look like a mug in front of my friends either, so I am ashamed to say I bowed to peer pressure! It wasn't one of my finest moments when I punched him in the gob! Inwardly I instantly regretted it. My only defence (?), he truly was a surly, snooty-nosed git. But still he didn't deserve a dig! I didn't let on to my mates, instead I went along with the charade that he had got what he deserved. The fucking 'weasel' reported me to the police!!!!

He didn't know where I lived so he gave the police Carla's home phone number! I really liked Carla. When I had met her parents, I had made the effort to be polite and courteous I had remembered my manners, please and thank you! Because first impressions count! However, they didn't 'count' for very much after the police had phoned their house looking for me!

Poor Carla wasn't a ruffian like me, she wasn't used to the sort of thing I was. She was actually quite worried about it all. So much so that she came to see me and explained rather apologetically that her parents had given the police my address and that she 'thought' they might come to question me. In other words, I was going to get nicked!

I have always found it useful to maintain a sense of humour in times of stress. As Carla was telling me all about the police phoning her house, I happened to be standing at the dining table, with my back to her. I was flicking through a newspaper, when out of the corner of my eye I noticed a children's 'paper shop' disguise lying on the table. Black plastic glasses with a false nose, moustache and eyebrows all attached! I could hear the genuine concern in Carla's voice, when she said, 'What are you going to do if the police turn up'? With this, I spun round wearing the disguise and said, 'I will just say Patrick ......whooooo????!!!

Carla did an almighty belly laugh. It was pure comedy genius! Once we had both managed to stop laughing, I reassured her that there was no need to worry, as it was hardly the crime of the century.

At 6 30am the next morning I answered a knock at my front door to find two policemen standing on the doorstep, 'Patrick Delaney' said a rather miffed looking cooper! (No, I wasn't wearing it!). I was promptly arrested and taken to the local station. There had been a third policeman at the back door of my house, presumably in case I had tried to do a runner! The policeman had looked miffed when I had answered the door because the little 'weasel' had described his assailant as a fucking giant 'brute' of a man (perhaps with a shock of red hair for good measure!)! Obviously, I wasn't what they were expecting! At the station the arresting officer said, 'So what happened then, did you give him a dig because he was acting like a dick'? I decided to go with it and simply said, 'Er, well yeah'! To which he quietly mumbled to himself, 'not surprised, the surly little shit'! I received a caution, a fry up, and a day of work! Me and Carla didn't last long after that, I think her parents might have 'steered her clear'!

Over the years whenever I have regaled anyone with this story, I tell them that I was arrested at half past six in the morning by three policemen for hitting a bloke in the cock!!

Despite what you might think, neither myself nor my friends were fighters and we certainly were not bullys. We were more about having a laugh and a good time than causing trouble. It was all fairly innocent stuff really. But we were young men, full of testosterone and usually alcohol. Sometimes you just couldn't avoid trouble.

****

The opening of a new bar in town was something to get excited about. 'Chicago's' opened its doors under a huge amount of hype and fanfare, and was for a long time thereafter, the 'in place' to go.

It was the Bees Knees, none of us had ever seen anything like it. It was pretty cool stuff! The actual bar was situated in the middle of the pub and had a Harley Davison suspended above it! It reminded me of the American TV show, CHEERS! At the weekends you had to queue up to get in, because it was always rammed! We didn't mind queueing though because it was always full of women too! For about 18 months all you ever got out of any of my friends was, 'you going to Chicago's'? 'Meet you in Chicago's'? '...Did you see that bird in Chicago's'!?

One Saturday night 'I just happened' to be in 'the' pub! I was chatting to a lad called Paul Collins, a real decent sort of bloke who wouldn't say boo to a goose. I suppose you would describe him as a nice boy from a nice family. As me and Paul were chatting, a couple beside us at the bar began bickering and then totally out of the blue and for no apparent reason at all, the lad punched the girl straight in the face.

It was sickening! Paul Collins didn't even hesitate and punched the bloke straight in 'his' face. I was impressed as it was so unlike Collins to do this. Paul was outraged by what he had just seen. And so were the large group of thugs that just happened to be with the lad that Paul had just 'rightly' smacked!

It was as if someone had thrown a switch! Within seconds the whole place erupted, fights were braking out all around us, with me and Paul in the thick of it! I don't think either of us even gave it a thought. I think we felt validated and justified by what had just happened, so we both just got stuck in! It was like something out of a film, as the two unlikely heroes fought side by side. The booming music had now stopped, and all the lights were back on. Bouncers were diving in and dragging people out of the fray left right and centre. Girls were screaming and glasses were getting smashed as tables went over.

The chaos, violence and mayhem spilled out of the pub and onto the street, where more fighting ensued. The bouncers were struggling to restore order when we heard the first siren! And with that everyone scattered. Pumped up on adrenalin and high on excitement, me and Paul legged it down the street, jumped in a taxi and fled the scene. Only then did I notice that during the tumult I had lost a front tooth! But at that precise moment I really didn't care because it was all too terribly exciting. It was my first ever proper Bar Brawl!

The next morning (Sunday) sporting a fat lip and missing a nasher, I nipped into the petrol station near town, where my mate Eugene had a part time job. As I walked in I saw him standing behind the counter serving customers; he had a perfect Nike trainer foot print on the side of his face! I started laughing and said, 'Were you in Chicago's last night'!? He just looked at me and grinned!

None of us took anything seriously back then, we just lived for the weekends, nothing mattered, we had our whole lives ahead of us! It cost me £250 quid for a false tooth, after I had spent 3 weeks unable to say anything beginning with 'F'. Now you can't say, 'thwera thwan thwat'!

The job at the powder coating shop wasn't going to well. I hated it, or 'thwuking' hated it to be exact. Remarkably, despite not liking my job, I had been promoted to charge hand, which meant I earned a (whopping) extra 25p an hour, ...but everyone on the shop floor hated me!

It really was a god-awful job and very much like being in school! However, I did get on very well with Keith, the main boss. Keith had a little port-a-cabin which served as his office situated just outside the work-shop. As charge hand I would sometimes have to go to the port-a-cabin to discuss matters regarding the shop floor.

Being a polite and courteous young man (?), I would always knock the door before entering!

'Pat, there's nothing that goes on in here that you shouldn't know about', Keith would say. 'There's no need to knock the door', he would continue. Each time I knocked before entering the little office we would have the same conversation. I couldn't help it, I felt uncomfortable just opening the door without knocking, it just didn't seem right!

One morning I had to discuss a matter with Keith regarding the quality of some of the work. I approached the door to his office, hesitated and then without knocking opened it and walked straight in! I immediately burst out laughing, in fact I was in hysterics!

There was Keith, my boss, standing there in a little pair or red bikini briefs with the most gutted look I have ever seen on a grown man's face! He was getting changed to go and play golf (so he reckons?). You're supposed to fear your boss, its healthy! I will never forget the look on his little face, ...bless him!

There was a girl that worked on the shop floor. When I had first began working at the powder coat shop, I genuinely wasn't sure if she was a man or a woman, so I didn't know if it was okay to fart in front of her or not. It turned out she was a woman, so it was okay! My God, but she was a hard woman to look at! She was also as horrid a human being as your ever likely to meet. She possessed no people skills whatsoever; she was constantly rude and lacked the most basic of manners. Perhaps it wasn't her fault, perhaps she did not know any better? Nonetheless it made it extremely difficult to interact with her at any level!

I like to think I am not a horrible person; I like to think I have a certain level of decency about me. I certainly wouldn't go out of my way to be unkind to someone or intentionally hurt their feelings. But then again, I am only human!

She had it in for me! She had clearly taken umbrage of the fact that I had been promoted. Nor did she make any attempt to hide it. In fact, at every opportunity she undermined and pooh-poohed every suggestion or request that I made. I was painfully aware that the shop floor was very much like the school playground, so after being promoted I was mindful not to be perceived as 'now' acting like a dick! I never once, told or ordered anyone to do anything (nor would I), instead I always politely requested or asked. It made no difference, she waged her hate campaign against me with a vengeance, it was plain and simple, nasty and unjustified. I ignored it! I put up with it! I made allowances for it! But a man can only take so much!!

I was on the shop floor one day when she was directing one of her vile tantrums at me, (she used to blame it on her time of the month! Urghh!). I had finally had enough when I snapped, and then roared at her...... 'Why don't you fuck off, you fucking fat lesbian looking cunt'! Everyone stopped dead in their tracks and turned in our direction in complete disbelieve at what they had just heard. I can assure you I am not homophobic in anyway shape or form I had just simply had enough! She then burst into tears and ran off, 'now' the victim! I angrily took off my overalls and threw them on the floor before marching out of the factory. I headed to the Café which was just around the corner on the same industrial estate. A little while later the foreman (my neighbour Bill) came and found me. 'Keith wants a word with you Pat', he said, with a look that implied, 'What have you done'!

Out of courtesy to Keith, plus the fact I had to wait for Bill to finish his shift to get a lift home, I went to the port-a-cabin and 'knocked' sheepishly before I entered. He really wasn't very pleased. 'Pat mate', 'Why did you call her a fucking fat prostitute?' 'I never', I replied. He shot me a, 'Are you taking the fucking piss', look and said, 'Everyone fucking heard ya Pat'! To which I replied, 'No – you mis-understand, Keith', 'I never called her a fucking fat prostitute'. 'I called her, a fucking fat 'lesbian'. She has told you I said 'prostitute', because she is embarrassed about the 'lesbian' bit because she knows I'm right'! He was gutted, then with a total look of exasperation he looked at me pleadingly and said, ...'Just apologise to her and you can have your job back'! He had a sense of finalisation in his eyes, like he had sorted it all out. I truly felt for him, when I said, 'I don't want my job back, thanks'!

The poor bloke, his shoulders slumped, his head lowered and then he let out a defeated sigh! Keith had a lot of time for me, he knew I wasn't a mug and despite the shit storm I had unwittingly created, I think he was secretly chuffed with my gall!

Believe it or not, I actually kept my job (that I didn't want!) I think I had a few days off, as a cooling off period. I don't recall apologising to the girl, but I imagine I would have made some gesture of an apology, (once I had calmed down). I do remember she was actually okay with me after that, she was no longer the horrid she-devil she had previously been and actually we managed to get along. My mate Jim has always said, 'It does you good to rare up now and again, keeps people on their toes'!

****

Two Christmases had come and gone since my father had passed. And true to form they were both shit! My dad had always ruined Christmas with his presence (not gifts) and now he was ruining them with his absence. My mother refused to allow anyone to enjoy themselves believing it was disrespectful to my father's memory. Thus, Christmas Day was a solemn affair.

Where my father had sat at the table slobbering all over his dinner, my mother now sat with a long sullen face staring at her plate and forking her meal. Alcohol was not allowed, because it had killed our father and, 'Hadn't she had enough of it in her lifetime'!

I don't think I was aware of just how selfish she was being. As a 19yr old, you don't question your mother! (or at least I didn't!). So, our Christmas Day was as per usual very sombre and like the most boring Sunday imaginable. Of course, it was made worse by the knowledge that every other household in the land was having a great time.

Another boring Christmas over with and I was back at work in the job I loathed! I stayed on only because over the festivities me and my mates had decided that this year, we would have our first lads' holiday abroad, to Shagaluf! So, I needed to stay steady and keep a wage coming in, plus I wanted to have driving lessons and at £7 a pop they were a bit steep!

Like all good drivers I passed my test on my second attempt, the first attempt was a disaster as ten minutes in, the very grumpy old bastard of an instructor grabbed the steering wheel from me as I careered across the dual carriageway and into oncoming traffic. Realising it was definitely a fail, (and having immediately lost all interest in gaining my licence) I couldn't wait to get it over with and get down the pub to meet my mates.

I got very drunk that day, pulled some girl and ended up having blatant and unashamed 'relations' with her behind some secluded bushes in a nearby park that afternoon, (classy!!).

Rather chuffed with myself, I had arrived home to my mother's house early that evening and as I staggered in the door smiling (with grass stains on my knees!), my mum took one look at the huge grin on my face and shrieked, 'Oh you passed'! Swaying from side to side and grinning from ear to ear I said, '.... No... I did not'! I re-sat the test a few months later, the instructor was a very nice lady who had no need to grab the steering wheel! I passed with flying colours and like a good boy I went straight home, sober! All I had to do now was save up for a car! Things were starting to pick up, I had stuff to look forward too, I was optimistic, and I was happy.

Chapter Nine

I was busy at work in the powder-coat shop and singing along to the radio one afternoon, when Bill came up and said, 'Pat there's a phone call for you'. A phone call for me? I didn't need to be Einstein to know it wasn't going to be anything good. Why would someone be ringing me at work?

I stopped what I was doing and made my way to the phone and picked up the receiver, 'Hello, who's that'? It was Connor's wife, Jean. She said, 'Pat you have to come home'! 'Why what's up'? There followed a long pause before she said... 'Kathleen's dead'!

Kathleen died on the 20th June 1992, her 'now' boyfriend Sean had woken to find my sister dead in the bed beside him. She was 32yrs old. The coroner's report said she had died of alcohol poisoning. There was no need to lie to my friends about the cause of my sister's death. The story was so tragic it made the local papers. The headline read, 32yr old mother of three, found dead from alcohol poisoning.

My mother was heartbroken, she was inconsolable. She never said, but as well as being overcome and wrought with grief, I knew there was also a level of shame because the whole community knew it was an alcoholic death. My whole family was in total shock, we were devastated. It was totally unexpected. There one minute gone the next. Three small children deprived of a mother.

I had the option of not going to the morgue. But I was her baby brother, I felt it was my duty to pay my respects, plus I didn't like the idea of her lying in the morgue without her family around her.

Me and Connor were the front pall bearers. We paid our dear sister the final and ultimate honour of carrying her coffin into the same church we had carried our father into just over two years earlier. Only this time it wasn't the weight of the coffin on my shoulder that has remained firm in my memory, instead it was the heart-breaking guttural sounds of my mother's wails and sobs as she was helped and steadied along behind Kathleen's casket. It is the most bone chilling, haunting sound I have ever heard. Up until that moment I would not have thought it possible that a human being could produce such a pitiful, heart wrenching, cry. I pray I never hear such a sound again. It filled my ears and was all I could hear as I walked slowly towards the church, placing one foot in front of the other with Kathleen's coffin on my shoulder. I kept my eyes firmly fixed to the ground as I heard and imagined the scene behind me.

I wanted to stop! I wanted to go to my mother. I wanted to console, I wanted to comfort her. I wanted to take away the pain, but in that moment I was powerless. There was nothing I, or anybody else could do to help her.

Unlike when my father died, I never shed a tear for my poor sister. It saddens me to say it, but to me it was as if a distant aunty had died, rather than my big sister. I didn't say this to anyone, I didn't disclose how I was feeling because I felt ashamed. I also felt tremendously guilty. She's my sister and yet I feel sort of void of emotion towards her death. Perhaps I was stunned or in shock. Perhaps it was some kind of coping mechanism which I didn't fully understand; nevertheless I was uncomfortable with my apparent lack of feeling. Of course, I was devastated! Obviously, I was upset, but still I never shed a single tear! As well as grief I also felt guilt.

When Kathleen died something within my mother died too, she was not the same woman she had once been, a fire had gone out inside of her. She was so heartbroken over our sister that no one in the family dared speak Kathleen's name in case we upset her. I suspect my poor old mum was simply too grief-stricken to bring herself to talk about our sister. So, for a long, long time after her passing it was almost like she had never existed at all.

Blame plays a part in the process of being bereft. My family were no exception. We all attended the Coroner's hearing at the local courthouse shortly after Kathleen's, death, to hear the coroner record a verdict of death by alcohol poisoning. Kathleen's boyfriend Sean also attended. Outside the hearing Evelyn, who unlike me had been very close to Kathleen and of a similar age, attacked Sean and told him it was 'his' fault that our sister was dead and that it should have been him who had died and not her. Clearly it wasn't Sean's fault, it wasn't anybody's fault. The poor boy (just 31yrs old), had woken up one morning and had found his girlfriend lying dead beside him, what an horrific ordeal for anyone to have to endure. I cannot begin to imagine the sheer state of terror and panic, that young man must have gone through. He didn't deserve to be so poorly treated by my family, and without a thought for his grief or feelings. I can remember him bursting into tears as Connor and I pulled Evelyn away from him.

That day outside the Coroner's court was the last time I ever saw Sean. I have no idea what became of him or where he is now. I wonder what effect it has had on the rest of his life; I don't even know whether he is dead or alive, it has been such a long time now. But if I ever got the chance I would apologise, I would tell him how sorry I am for his loss! And for the terrible treatment he received by my heartbroken and grieving family. He was looking for and needed our support, but he never got it. My mother was never the same again!

Out of respect for my mother, I once again curbed my drinking.

Also, out of respect for Kathleen I cancelled my lads' holiday to Magaluf, so all the lads went without me. How could I jet off to the sun, how could I stand in a bar laughing and joking with my friends after my sister had just died (nor did I want to). It had taken a long time to get over my father's death and now Kathleen. I am ashamed to admit that, secretly, I felt hard done by. I apologise if it sounds callous, but it reminded me of when I was a little kid out playing with friends and my sisters or brother would come and get me and say, 'You have to come home dad's drunk'!

Yes, you have read this before! History has a habit of repeating itself and lightning does strike twice! It took a long while, but as time passed things did begin to level out and returned to something like normality. But it was never the same.

****

Although I hated it, I continued working at the powder coat shop, but only until I had enough money to buy a second-hand car and then I left. I went back on site (on my own), as a self-employed dry liner. The money was good, and I also felt as though I had clawed back some level of status; masculinity perhaps. However along with the good money and the kudos, came the excessive drinking and drug taking. Much to my mother's dismay I was yet again falling in the door drunk!

CHAPTER TEN

PAT, DO YOU WANNA GO TO AMERICA'? Asked Jim excitedly. 'Yeah alright, when'? '...Err duno, in a couple of weeks'?! And that was it, decided!

I had never even considered going to America before Jim had mentioned it. I suppose I had always thought it to be a dangerous place what with having heard all about the Bloods and the Cripps, and I had seen enough episodes of 'Murder She Wrote' to know there was a good chance I might get 'bumped off'! However, it was simply too exciting an opportunity to miss. There was no way I was 'not' going. Jim had instantly piqued my interest. As I suspect he know he would.

Jim said we should head for Los Angeles, because it had been in all the newspapers that there had been a wildfire in a place called Malibu (on the outskirts of LA). The fire had apparently destroyed a lot of homes belonging to the rich and famous and as a result they were 'crying out' for British builders! I agreed with Jim, that 'Yes', it was indeed, an excellent idea! We couldn't wait to get going.

Neither Jim or I, actually knew anyone who had ever been to the United States. People round our way didn't holiday in places like America (they didn't holiday full stop!), so we were big news on the estate. Even our friends were excited for us, 'Have you heard the news? Pat and Jim are going to get robbed and shot in LA'!!

We booked our flights with British Airways and departed for Los Angeles, two weeks before Xmas, 1993. We had £600 and a rucksack, each. It was all terribly exciting for two 21yr old lads, who had hardly ever left the town they had been born in!

The day before we left, the news broke in the papers that it was all a hoax! There had indeed been a wildfire, which had burned down a lot of homes, but no one was looking for, or hiring British workers as the papers had wrongly reported! Unbelievably it was thought that the fire had been started by two (off duty), part time fire fighters trying to earn extra money, but it had quickly got out of hand and had spread in the arid Californian landscape. Hundreds of Brits had headed out (there was a recession on at the time), looking for work that didn't exist, had ran out of money and had then become stranded on the west coast of America. Even more unbelievable was that Richard Branson, laid on a Virgin Atlantic aeroplane and flew all the stranded Brits home for free! Despite this new and shocking revelation, Me and Jim still went! 'Fuck it, we might as well', was our response.

A Trans-Atlantic flight was a first for me, I had never before been on an aircraft that had an actual destination (other than where it had just taken off from!). So just getting to the States, was an adventure in itself.

I can remember our excitement as the plane banked to begin its decent into LAX airport. As we came into land, we could see airport workers shunting their trucks about on the tarmac below. 'Look Pat, Americans', said Jim unable to hide his excitement. We were both grinning from ear to ear!

Once through customs and having passed under a huge picture of a (for now) smiling Bill Clinton, welcoming us to the united states, we finally stepped out into the Californian sunshine and onto American soil! We had arrived!

When we had booked our flights, we had been promised 'free car hire', which never actually transpired mainly due to our naivety and also the fact that the car hire firm wanted the entirety of our cash as a deposit. So, with little option we took the bus! I was disappointed it wasn't one of those silver, greyhound thingys you see on the telly and that it was in fact just a fairly normal looking bus heading for the downtown district of Los Angeles.

It was by now starting to get dark and we still had to find somewhere to stay. Me and Jim were still excited, but truth beknown we were both beginning to get a bit jittery, a matter made worse by the forebodings of an old black lady on the bus who told us down town was a dangerous place for two white boys 'clearly' a long way from home (we both had rucksacks on our backs! We might as well have both been holding maps, whilst wearing cameras around our necks!). Of course, there is every possibility that she was a lunatic. Either way her kindly concern didn't really help!

I can tell you that the main bus station in downtown LA, is a dodgy looking place, full to the brim with even dodgier looking people, that look a whole lot dodgier in the dark! We had been told that Santa Monica and Venice beach were the places to head for if we wanted to find digs and eventually work. So as soon as we were off the bus, we wasted no time and hailed a yellow taxi. To our surprise the driver was a British Pakistani with the added bonus of a cockney accent! Drawing comfort from the familiarity of this unexpected encounter we immediately relaxed! We explained our predicament, that we needed to find a cheap motel for the night. 'not a problem', said John, 'I know just the place'!

It was a strange, yet wonderful sensation as Jim and me sat in the back of John's cab being driven through the dark streets of Los Angeles. We stopped off at a store and brought supplies of American (kahuna!) burgers, Mountain Dew and American cigarettes (how cool!), before John, dropped us off at a motel (with assurances), which to me looked very much like a Mexican villa complete with arches and palm trees. Still grinning, we checked into our room and then drew the curtains as a safety measure before turning on the most mentalist TV I have ever seen. A Billy Graham type character was shouting at us through the television screen. Personally, I didn't like the look of the room, so my first night in America, I slept fully dressed and on top of the bed covers. By the time I went to sleep that first night I had spent about a quarter of my money!

The next morning, I woke up early and found I was feeling slightly subdued and a bit groggy from the flight. I sat on the edge of the bed and lit a Marlborough cigarette; I was concerned about what lay in store for Jim and me. Reality had hit home!

As I smoked, I noticed daylight spilling through the little window at the back of our room, I got up from the bed and walked over to the window and drew back the curtains, a huge grin erupted across my face! It was beautiful. Bright sunshine, blue skies, palm trees and a mountain towering in the background. I noticed the pavement and the road seemed very wide compared to back home. Directly opposite our room hung a set of traffic lights suspended on a cable above the road, beneath which sat a black American sports car revving its engine waiting for the lights to turn green. With sheer delight I shrieked, 'Quick Jim, ...look'!

I felt instantly happier. I had a renewed vigour in mine and Jim's endeavour. Its true, things do look better in the cold (hot) light of day. So good in fact we couldn't pack our things away quick enough. We heaved our rucksacks on to our backs and hurried out the door and made our way down the street heading in the general direction of the coast.

As we walked, we marvelled at all we saw. We seemed to pass lots of groups of Mexicans (mostly men) who appeared to be just hanging around on the street corners. Obviously, this was all very new and strange to me and Jim, I don't think either of us had ever seen real live Mexicans before. I wouldn't wish to offend any Mexican who may read this but in my slightly excited and nervous state they all looked a bit sly, dangerous even. I now know that, how they looked, was desperate!

I didn't know it then, but they were in fact the American equivalent of the Irish men who could be found standing on the street corners in Cricklewood in north London hoping to be picked for a day's work! However, despite my uncertainty and being British, I still said good morning to each and every one of them as I scurried past!

Without actually knowing where we were going, we continued walking for about half an hour, before we turned a corner and stumbled upon the world-famous Santa Monica pier and the breathtakingly beautiful Pacific Ocean. And then like the two big kids that we were, me and Jim raced each other to the end of the pier with our rucksacks still on our backs. Laughing and in high spirits, we rested a while still not quite believing we were actually there!

The day was starting to warm up, the ocean glinted and shimmered in the morning sun and as we looked back along the coast line we could see a mile or so off into the distance that it appeared a little more built up and a little more busy, so we reasoned that it must be Venice beach.

It was shrouded in an early morning haze which gave it a mirage effect. We heaved our rucksacks up on our backs and took a stroll along the boardwalk heading towards the throng!

It was a lot for our young minds to take in. People were jogging and whizzing by on roller skates and generally looking (beach) good. Street artists entertained. Some were break dancing to little boom boxes, some were singing, one man was juggling moving chainsaws, while another wearing a turban was roller skating whilst playing an electric guitar, although I don't believe he was a Sikh! And towering above us on the side of a building was a huge mural of the late Jim Morrison.

It was a heady atmosphere which immediately sucked us in! We could see the iconic lifeguard towers situated on the beach with the yellow lifeguard trucks parked next to them. In amongst all this wonder, I also saw a lot of homeless people! I had seen Baywatch on the TV and it was nothing like this! There was an old black man pushing a shopping trolley full of tin cans. He didn't look like he was in any hurry or going anywhere in particular. I watched a homeless woman who looked like she had once been very glamorous, as she rooted through a bin and to my amazement pulled out a paper plate with some discarded and half eaten pizza and chips on it. She then sat down at a table next to the bin and composed herself with real poise and dignity, before commencing to eat her meal. She was just about to tuck in when out of nowhere a seagull swooped and cleared the plate! I didn't know whether to laugh or cry! I remember thinking it would be very easy to slip up in a place like this!

Me and Jim 'hurried' along past Muscle Beach, before eventually coming to a stop outside the Venice Beach Youth Hostel! It was a large four storey building which had a concourse of raised arches surrounding the ground floor which was in keeping with the architectural norm of the area. The entrance opened onto a large staircase that directed us up to the first floor and the front desk. I remember noticing that the place was sparsely furnished, but the walls were adorned with posters of exotic locations such as London, Manchester and Edinburgh, (I smiled when I saw that Edinburgh was actually spelt as 'Edinborough'!).

Me and Jim presented ourselves to the reception desk and were greeted by a Geordie who introduced himself as Martin. I didn't know it then but me and the Geordie were to become good friends. He later told me that the first time he saw us, he thought we were a right pair of mean hardy-looking bastards! Which was laughable and came as a bit of a surprise to me and Jim. We were no mugs, but we weren't nasty fuckers either. Still it didn't hurt if that's what people thought.

It cost $9 a night for a bunk bed in a dormitory that slept twelve. However, the hostel was fairly empty (for its size), because apparently, they were carrying out earthquake reinforcement works (I recall raising an eyebrow upon hearing this and quietly thinking to myself, bloody silly Americans!). So, we had our pick of the rooms. We chose one with a balcony overlooking Venice beach and the Pacific Ocean! The only other person in our dorm was a Chinese bloke, who was lying on his bunk, he was huge! He must have been at least 6′ 6″ and was built like a brick shit house (yes, it is quite unusual!). He was also extremely ripped and was wearing a muscle beach T-shirt. I nodded a quick hello as I went passed his bunk. But he didn’t acknowledge me! I couldn't help being reminded of the big Indian 'Chief', in One Flew Over the Cuckoo’s Nest!

The international residents of the Venice beach youth hostel were a motley crew to say the least. There were two Dutch blokes and two Dutch girls (that's double Dutch to me!). There were two French geezers, but the Geordie threw one out for thieving! The massive Chinese fellah, a Kiwi, an Argentinian, a little prancing Puerto Rican gay hairdresser (who Jim allowed to cut his hair!), who would dance around the hostel to classical music! A Hispanic guy called Mar-tin'e, but whom I insisted on calling Martin, a German, and a boss-eyed American with a ponytail (why would he be staying in a youth hostel?), and a rake of Brits! The place was ours! We all but stuck a flag in it!

Meeting this lot in the communal living room was a bit like the scene in the film 'The Beach', when Leonardo DiCaprio and the French couple finally discover the small community living on the secret island (but without the dark underbelly!). Sorry I am assuming you have seen the film. Me and Jim quickly ingratiated ourselves into the group. Within a matter of hours, it felt as though we had always been there. Our first night in the hostel we got some beers in and the Geordie put us in touch with some Dude who sold us some marijuana. And so, we sat in the communal living room drinking beer, smoking weed and watching COPS on the TV with our feet up!! The boss-eyed American walked in and said, 'Hey, you guys having a pardy'!

Within two days of arriving in America both me and Jim were working, it wasn't the 'clamorous' construction work we had hoped for, but we were in (poorly paid) employment, nonetheless. Jim had found work in an ice-cream parlour on the beach, (one scoop or two!), and I was helping the boss-eyed American and the Hispanic guy Mar-tin'e, with the earthquake repairs! Basically, I was covering the new steel work with plasterboard.

'Hey, Pat, can you do, A loom-men-um strip'? Enquired the boss eyed American. I didn't know what he was talking about, so said, 'Err no mate I don't think I can, sorry', I thought it strange that he looked a little disappointed in me. It later transpired that he was asking if I could put on the metal corner beads prior to the plastering (aluminium!).

Me and Jim weren't earning very much, but it helped us eke out the small bit of cash that we did have, we actually did okay in the end. Whilst working on the hostel I was telling Mart-in'e, the Hispanic guy, how Jim and I had come to be in Los Angeles, how it had been in the papers back home about the fire in Malibu. That's when he told me he was going to Malibu the next day and if

I wanted to, I could come along for the ride. 'Yeah that would be great, I would love to, I said, before adding, 'How comes you have to go to Malibu'?

Mart-in'e told me how his girlfriend had gone into hospital to give birth to their daughter, the hospital had routinely tested his girlfriend for drugs, and she had tested positive for cocaine! So, they had both got 'busted' and had to attend a rehabilitation programme and court hearings, or risk having the child removed from their care! 'Shit' that's serious', I said. I then felt a little silly for stating the obvious! I then asked Mart-in'e if he had done a lot of coke to which he replied in his American drawl, 'Man I did a line of coke all the way from here to fucking England man'!

I liked Mart-in'e, I could tell he was a nice guy, perhaps not the best candidate for parenthood, but he obviously loved his girlfriend and daughter very much and was clearly doing his best to keep hold of them both, so he was a good man in my book.

The next morning, I sat at a bus stop across the street from the youth hostel waiting, as instructed, for the Hispanic guy to pick me up. I could have happily sat there all day watching the ordinary Americans going about their business. But as promised I didn't have to wait long. I smiled when an iconic beige coloured 1970s Dodge Van pulled up alongside the bus stop and a chirpy looking Mart-in'e leaned out of the driver's window and hollered, 'Hey Pat, yo wanna go to Malibu'?!

Grinning, I jumped in and the two of us headed off along the pacific coast highway up towards Malibu. The road hugged and snaked its way along and around the Californian coastline a hundred foot above the waves. As we motored along, Mart-in'e began telling me of his life growing up in California, as he talked and as interested as I was, my mind momentarily drifted as I gazed out across the ocean far below the cliffs and rocks. I marvelled at its beauty. I thought of the contrast between what I was seeing and the drab greyness of my existence back home. Then without warning something truly incredible happened. About two miles out, a huge tail rose up high out of the water, it seemed to hang in the air for all of a second, maybe two, before it fell back and slapped the surface of the water hard and then it was gone as quickly as it had appeared. Despite its distance the tail looked like it was the size of a bus! I couldn't believe my luck! I had just seen a blue whale breach the surface of the water, the largest animal that has ever existed on our planet, and I have just seen it from the front of Mart-in'e,s van!! There are people who spend their whole life's and entire fortunes travelling the world's oceans trying to catch a glimpse of such a magnificent spectacle (and don't!). and I had just seen it by chance whilst sitting next to a massive coke head in the front of his van on our way to the courthouse!!! Life is truly a wonderful thing!

We stopped at the courthouse and Mart-in'e went in to attend to his business. I didn't pry as to the details, instead I sat outside on the steps soaking up the sunshine. I was in awe of everything, the buildings, the people, the cars, even the rare discarded bit of rubbish blowing by held my attention. When Mart-in'e returned from his appointment we drove on and eventually arrived at a place called, Topanga Canyon, which as far as I could tell was actually a mountain!

This was where the infamous fire had started. Mart-in'e, like most Americans I had met was very polite and asked if I wouldn't mind if he stopped off to say hello to an old friend. Of course, I didn't, if anything I would be delighted to meet them!

An old friend indeed! We pulled off the main road and onto a dirt track and a few moments later were confronted by a wizened looking old lady with long grey hair tied in a ponytail which went all the way down her back. The woman looked as weather beaten as the wooden shack she had just stepped out of. Hildi was 90yrs old, but despite her age, she had a spark of youth about her, like as if she had just got back from the summer of love! She welcomed Mart-in'e with open arms and a huge smile.

She had an aura about her that you could almost touch and an air of authority that was almost regal yet at that same time soft and compassionate. Mart-in'e introduced me and I received the same warm welcome of a hug. Hildi invited us to take a seat on the front porch amongst the wind chimes and dream catchers, I could feel myself involuntarily relaxing just by being in her company. She made us coffee and as she handed me my cup, asked where I was from. She seemed disinterested when I explained 'my' council estate near London! (I got the impression it was messing with her 'good' vibe!), so I changed the subject and told her how I had just seen the tail of a blue whale!

Her face instantly lit up, 'Oh you met my friends, yep they come on by here every year, right 'bout' this time to say hallo', she said with a smile. Then Hildi, told us of the night of the fire! How she could see the flames, up on the top of the mountain and how she could feel the heat of the fire as it grew ever closer. She told me she had never prayed so hard in all her life, that her home would be spared, which clearly it had been.

We stayed talking and sipping coffee on the front porch for over an hour and then it was time to go. I thanked Hildi for her hospitality, 'You're welcome honey' she cooed, before standing and hugging us both. As we left, I remember feeling very privileged and honoured to have had the opportunity to meet and talk to this old hippie lady who had spent her entire life on the side of a mountain. (I don't suppose she felt the same?). As we drove away and began to drive further up the mountain it dawned on me just how close the fire had got to Hildi's shack. Not 5 minutes after leaving her home and the trees began to blacken and the land began to look scorched. 10 minutes and the mountain had turned from pristine woodland, to something I would liken as from a disaster movie. The higher we went up the mountain the more grand the homes became, and the higher we went still, the more devastation that unfolded in front of my eyes, until eventually we reached the top and there was only the charred outline remains of once grand residences. On the crest of the mountain top we drove along a precarious dirt track until we came upon a set of electric gates. Mart-in'e got out of the van and pressed the intercom. A little while later a man appeared who Mart-in'e knew, he opened the gates and let us in. He worked for the family who had owned the property that had been destroyed by the fire. All that was now left was a couple of stone walls and a pile of ash! It was a very sombre and dark mood up on that mountain. The man was sieving through some ash that I noticed was blacker than the ash surrounding it. He explained that this was where he believed the bed side cabinet had stood and he was looking to see if any jewellery had survived. It was awkward. Almost voyeuristic on my part. Although the man didn't say as much, I felt like I was intruding. So, I was mindful not to out-stay my welcome. Coming back down the mountain was very different from going up. Watching that man sifting through the remains of somebody's home had been very emotive. The story that had gotten me and Jim so excited with possibilities back home, now had a very real human element to it with a real human cost. Half the mountain had been burnt to a crisp. You could see how far the fire had travelled because there was a clear black line running around the mountain, I remember seeing half a burnt tree! One side black one side green. When Mart-in'e dropped me back at the hostel, I thanked him for bringing me along. It had been an amazing day for lots of different reasons!

There was a buzz all around the hostel, everyone was in

party mode and that was because Christmas was only a couple of days away! Martin the Geordie had a girlfriend, called Diane, a Liverpudlian, who was a big girl with an even bigger heart! She suggested that if everyone chipped in 3 dollars towards a Christmas dinner, then she would 'coo...k' it. So, everyone did! Gregg, the (Jewish/American) man who actually owned the youth hostel heard about this and generously brought us a large turkey. And then as if caught up in the 'Christmas' atmosphere and spirit of the occasion also put up (to everyone's joy) a huge Xmas tree in the communal living room. The tree was about 7ft tall and must have been at least (at its widest point) 12ft in diameter. The tree was situated in a large square glass bay window which jutted out above the street and was bathed in glorious sun light. The tree had no lights or decorations and being so big looked extremely bare and actually a little sad.

The beer of choice of the back-packing community in the hostel at that time was Miller-Light which came in black and gold cans! I don't know who did it first, but somebody had finished their can of beer, scrunched up the can and had then stuck it on the end of one of the branches! The idea caught the imagination of everyone in the hostel. The tree quickly began to fill up with scrunched up beer cans and what's more, it worked, the black, gold and green worked. The tin sparkled and shimmered in the sunlight and at night-time it glistened from the streetlights below. Everyone smiled when they saw the Xmas tree!

Christmas Day 1993

Outside it was warm and sunny! Inside a space was cleared in the communal living room and some tables were put end to end to accommodate the seating arrangements. Diane covered the tables in white paper cloth and the two Dutch girls helped her set the table. Diane did herself proud and cooked a very impressive meal. At 2 o'clock on Christmas day, the international 'motley' crew of the Venice beach youth hostel all sat down together and shared, in my opinion, the best Christmas meal I have ever had. It was bizarre, but excellent to be seated with this unlikely ensemble. The massive (now smiling) Chinese bloke to my left, the good-humoured Argentinian to my right and the ecstatic little gay Puerto Rican fellah opposite. The atmosphere around the table was brilliant, everyone was jovial and in high spirits. There was no one sat staring at their plate with a long sullen face, no one so drunk that they were slobbering all over their Christmas dinner. It was a wonderful and enchanting experience, to share Christmas with people from all over the world.

After we had finished our meal, we each, in turn, went around the table raising a glass and toasting one another, (all except the Chinese bloke who just smiled), we wished each other good health, good fortune and good luck in all our endeavours. That Christmas I hadn't brought any gifts, nor had I received any gifts (me and Jim didn't buy each other anything because we were blokes and wouldn't do anything so gay!). I was 6 thousand miles away from home. I didn't have any of my family with me. I was 21yrs old and it was the nicest and best Christmas I had ever had.

After dinner, as we sat drinking beer, smoking weed and watching the Christmas special edition of COPS on TV. Diane told me and Jim about the wealthy American woman she cleaned for in the exclusive Burbank area of LA. Diane's boss was having a posh new year's eve party at her house and needed two men to 'supervise' the door for the evening. 'I hope you don't mind', she said apologetically. 'but I mentioned you and Jim, are you interested'? Diane obviously had the same opinion as the Geordie, and believed we were quite tough, (so it was all good!). I think she may have had a bit of a soft spot for Jim, which didn't hurt, although I think it frightened him a little! I told him he had to sleep with her to make sure we got the job. Obviously, I was joking (sort of!). Diane said we would be picked up and dropped off and we would get $50 bucks each. Not having any plans for new year and recognising that $100 dollars would help, me and Jim agreed, in fact we said yes immediately!

On New Year's Eve, a very smart looking Jim, Diane and myself were picked up in a brand-new Cadillac and chauffeur driven to Diane's boss's house. It was a very large, very grand house with a long sweeping driveway, full of very expensive-looking sports cars. By the time we arrived, it was dark, however the whole house was illuminated with festive lights and decorations which added a touch of magic to the place! There was even a life size Santa Claus complete with sleigh and reindeer lit up on the roof of the house. It was such an impressive residence it was almost intimidating.

As we stepped through the oversized front door and into the vast hallway, it was all I could do not to gasp. Two flawless staircases swept effortlessly up each side of the hall to an open balcony, underneath which sat a white piano on a deep plush white carpet. Just inside the large front doors of the house was a pool with a cascading water feature which was home to a bale of snapping terrapins. Next to this stood a fairly large tree! The very grand front doors of the house, had above them a half moon of glass. The branches of the tree inside the hall came (grew) over the top of the doors and out through the half-moon of glass, the glass being (seamlessly) cut around the individual branches and finished with lead. I had never seen anything like it!

We were then introduced to the lady of the house (Diane's boss). She was respectfully pleasant, but it was clear from the off, that we were just 'the help'! She informed us of what was expected, before handing both Jim and me a torch each. She explained (having noted the expressions on our faces), this was so we could patrol the grounds and the illuminated hedgerows to prevent gate crashers.

We were also required to flank two seated and very attractive young women at the front of house as they relieved the arriving (young) guests of their car keys (sensible) and a $15-dollar, (I assume?) surcharge! I found it a bit odd that they were charging guests, I have never charged anyone coming to my house for a party!! I did however thing it rather sensible that they were taking the car keys!

Talking of sensible! Me and Jim had lied through our eye teeth when we assured Diane's boss that security would not be a problem, as we were both ex forces! Although I don't think the Air Cadets really counts! Me and Jim were both aware that gun crime was a very real issue in the United States, so rather sensibly and when out of ear-shot of everybody else, we quietly and secretively made a pact, we even shook hands on it. Any trouble and we're off!!

We were only 21yrs old and we were the door men for a party in LA. Our heckles were well and truly up! Nervously and for the first (and only) time we began to patrol the sweeping driveway and hedgerows for potential threats! And that's when I spotted it out of the corner of my eye. However, I remained silent... waiting, biding my time, for the right moment. When that moment came, I spun round with a shriek and shone my torch in an alarmed manner as I yelped in a frightened and disbelieving tone, '…Jesus, Mary and Joseph'!!

Jim, immediately fearing the worst, spun round and with real fear in his voice, stammered, 'What...what'! And there it was, ……nestled in the hedge, ...the most beautiful nativity scene! All lit up with fairy lights and emanating a warm rosy glow around Mary and Joseph and their little infant baby Jesus, fast asleep in his crib. Ah! Jim couldn't contain himself and burst out laughing (probably from relief!), before calling me a 'Fucking cunt'! for scaring him half to death. It was very funny!

The humour of the situation had alleviated the tension and had lightened the mood to such an extent that since the first time we had arrived we both began to relax and actually enjoy ourselves.

We returned to the front of house where the two girls were seated and once all the guests were inside, we began to flirt outrageously. Jim, ever the babe magnet, ended up snogging the prettiest of the two, while I ended up being the shoulder to cry on for the other one, who did a good job of boring me to death about her uncaring, but nonetheless, love of her life, boyfriend! Obviously, I persevered, but alas to no avail! However, the evening wasn't a total loss as Diane continuously slipped me cups of Brandy disguised as coffee when no one was looking! which obviously went down a treat (it was new year after all!). In fact, me and Jim were having a great night 'bull-shiting' the two girls with our stories of heroism and greatness. The evening was going well, (we were getting away with it!) with no issues at all, when all of a sudden and out of nowhere two carloads of blokes pulled up at the end of the driveway! They were rowdy and had clearly been drinking and obviously were not invited to the shindig. I could see that the two girls were now looking very worried, I looked over at Jim. 'Go and sort it out then Pat', said Jim matter of factly!

I couldn't believe my ears, 'You ...fucking ...cunt'! I thought, but I didn't say it in front of the girls. However Jim read my mind and just smiled at me. The two girls now looked at me pleadingly and expectantly with doleful eyes. 'No problem', I stated with a false confidence, but I directed it straight at my friend!

I walked up the drive towards the two car loads of blokes, fearing the worst. Then with true conviction, I stated, 'You're not coming in here lads'. The driver of the first car, upon hearing my accent leant out of the window and said, 'Hey where you from dude'? I was not about to start explaining the intricacies of where I hailed from to some American thug, so I simply replied, 'London'! The driver smiled and said, 'Yeah, my pal's from London'. With this he called into the back of the car.... 'Oi, ...Rizz'! A moment later a cheeky little cockney pocked his head out of the rear side window and said, 'alright mate how's it going'? Now grinning I shock his extended hand and then me and the boy from Bow (turns out he was an actual cockney!) enjoyed a bit of light-hearted banter much to the amusement and delight of his American friends! (ha ha fuck you Jim!).

With the pleasantries over I explained it was a rather posh event, so they would all stick out like sore thumbs, so there was no point in even trying! They all agreed before adding 'You shouldn't let these rich fuckers exploit you man, come and party with us'! My God it was tempting! They actually seemed like a good bunch of lads! I won't lie, I would have loved to have jumped in the car with them, however I graciously declined. I couldn't tell them I needed the money! We all shook hands, I told them to have a great night and to take care, I said goodbye to (my new mate), Rizz, and waved them off as they drove away, smiling, tooting, and waving back. I could not believe my fucking luck!

I walked (perhaps sauntered!) back down the long sweeping drive-way to Jim and the two girls and smugly said, 'It's alright don't worry, ...I've sorted it'! The girls were impressed (that's right Jim!). And then I just stood there, like a fucking hero!

The rest of that night is a bit vague, probably (definitely), because by now the brandies had begun to kick in and I confess I got a little bit tipsy! The night was again going well, however the 10yr old son of Diane's boss had started to hang around by the front door, like a bad smell. He was beginning to irritate both Jim and me. Mainly due to the fact he was an arrogant little shit, complete with the standard blonde mullet (think Hanson, think Um Bop! Yep you got it!). He just would not fuck off! At one point the boy looked at me with a cocky assuredness and said, 'Go get me a coke'! Jim guffawed in disbelieve as my face turned to thunder and I told the boy in no uncertain terms, 'Go get it yourself, you cheeky little fucker'! The boys bottom lip trembled, chided, he did an abrupt about turn and annoyed us no more. Jim found it all very amusing!

As the night drew to a close, me and Jim were called to the rear of the house, due to a disturbance by the swimming pool. A young lad had drunk a bit too much and was now making a nuisance of himself and upsetting the rest of the party goers! I was trying to reason with the young man to leave quietly and of his own accord when, without warning, Jim grabbed him in a head lock and dragged him unceremoniously through the party, through the house and 'ejected' him straight out of the front door, while at the same time I smiled and gestured politely with my hands at all the gob smacked party guests! I was impressed. Good cop, bad cop, It worked! It was now Jim's turn to play the hero!

I think it's fair to say we had been a great success, we had started the night feeling a bit dubious, thinking we might be a little out of our depth, but had ended up having a great time. We also had an extra $100 dollars! I remember little of the drive back to the hostel. The late night, the excitement of the evening and the brandys, had all taken their toll. (I hope I didn't snore!). A new year to remember! Just for the record Jim and I wouldn't dare be 'bouncers' in England, because quite frankly we would get battered!

The next day I was surprised to find I was nursing a bit of a hang-over and I was even more surprised to find mine and Jim's antics were the talk of the hostel, Diane had been singing our praises to anyone who would listen!

****

The hostel was a great place to be, because there was always something going on. Ralph the Kiwi, was convinced he was going to make it as a big movie star someday. He was going around the hostel asking everyone and anyone if they wanted to be extras in an up and coming new movie which was about to start filming. Ralph said he knew of a production company in Hollywood that was auditioning and was anyone interested?

I have never had any inclination for the big screen, well no more than anybody else! I'm sure we have all at some point in our lives fantasised about being a famous Hollywood actor with all the trappings of success, but for most that's all it is, just a fantasy. The Kiwi said he and a friend (another wannabe), could accommodate 10 people between them in their two cars. So that's how many went to the audition. I was one of the ten!

Hollywood is not all glitz and glamour (as I had wrongly imagined!). In fact, apart from Hollywood boulevard most of it is a shit hole! We pulled off the main strip into a side street and Ralph brought his car to a stop outside an unassuming office block. As we all clambered out of the cars I noticed a 'crack-head' hurrying towards us, (they always seem to be in a hurry!). He had wild hair and hardly no teeth. As he got closer I could see that he had pissed himself! As he scurried past, he mumbled something nonsensical, to no one in particular. I looked straight at Ralph and said, 'Hooray for Hollywood'!

Ralph, led us all up to an office on the sixth floor where we were greeted by a small, sweaty, nervous looking Jewish bloke who never stopped talking or fidgeting with his spectacles. He was sat behind a large oak desk which had upon it two phones and an overflowing ashtray. There were some posters (not framed pictures), of big-name movies stuck to the walls all around his office. To the left side of the desk stood a well built, serious looking man in a cheap grey suit who never spoke a single word the whole time we were there.

The little Jewish bloke began telling us about the disaster movie that was to begin being filmed the following week. They needed extras for the mass evacuation scenes due to be filmed at a high school in the valleys (an area just outside of the city). He started to direct comments at us, saying things like, you would be good at this and you would be good at that. At one point he told me, I looked like a lead man! I don't think Ralph liked that! All was going well, then the little Jewish fellah said, 'Have you all got equity cards'? (Of course, we didn't!). He was saying that's a real shame, but not to worry because he could sort them out for us for just $30 dollars each! That's when I knew!

He continued that $30 bucks was cheap, and he was doing us a massive favour, because we would get $150 for the day's filming, plus we could then use the equity cards to get more film work. I quickly said I didn't have any cash on me! The little Jewish bloke knew I knew! So did the big bloke in the cheap grey suit, who still hadn't said a word! To be honest it was a bit intimidating, so I wasn't going to say anything either.

Over half the ten paid up, Ralph the Kiwi was given a phone number to ring the day before filming, to confirm times, etc. Obviously, the filming never started, and no one ever answered Ralph's phone call. Everyone that had paid, lost their money. Poor Ralph was really disappointed, he had really wanted it. It didn't help that every time he walked in the room back at the hostel, I started singing,

'They're gonna put me in the movies;
they're gonna make a big star outa me,
...gonna make a film bout a man that's sad and lonely'!
and all I gota do is... act-natur -a – leeeee!
Well I bet you, ...I'm gonna be, ...a big star'!!

Poor Ralph! I wonder if he ever did make it, (I've never seen him in anything!)?

The next day was unusually quiet around the hostel as it was a lovely day outside, in fact it was a scorcher, so most people had gone out. Jim decided he was going to go for a walk along the beach, thus leaving me alone just poodling about in the communal living room. After a short while I decided I needed to use the bathroom, so I headed upstairs to use the one in our dormitory. The big Chinese fellah was lying on his bunk bed; I nodded as I hurried past him to the bathroom at the end of the room. Once there I closed the door behind me and cheerfully went about my business. When I had completed my important paperwork! I stood up, turned towards the cistern and pulled the handle to flush the toilet, as I did this the 'whole' bathroom began to shake violently. My first thought was that I had broken the toilet! My next thought was that the Chinese bloke was having some sort of steroid rage and was outside the door, shaking the whole bathroom! At a loss, and as my mind furiously scrambled to try and make sense of what was happening, I gingerly opened the bathroom door to see a very wide eyed, confused looking Chinese bloke on his feet and swaying from side to side. And then ...the violent shaking stopped.

We both just stared at each other. Then as my mind tried to apply reason to what had just occurred, I thought, 'Oh my God a plane has hit the building'! I ran down the stairs and out into the street, there were people everywhere and sirens were going off all over the place, then I heard someone say it was an 'earthquake'!

It later transpired that it was in fact an earthquake 'tremor' measuring, 3.6 on the Richter scale and was generally perceived to be a warning for the actual earthquake which was sure to hit! How exciting! Despite the fact that I was carrying out earthquake reinforcement works on the hostel, it never actually occurred to me that one might actually hit!

Jim told me he had been walking along the beach when it had

struck, he said it was totally surreal, to feel the actual beach shake! And even more surreal to watch the waves as they slapped hard against the shore (like sloshing water in a washing up bowl!). I was actually envious of Jim's experience and would have much preferred to be taking a stroll, rather than a shit, went it happened!

Our American adventure was drawing to a close, our plane was due to leave in a few days' time. As amazing as it had all been, things had not exactly gone to plan; we had not secured the high paying jobs we had hoped for. I was chatting to the Geordie lad about it, when he said rather matter of factly, 'Fuck it, just stay! You'll survive. You've done alright so far'! After all I had experienced in such a short time it was very tempting! So, I put it to Jim, 'What you reckon'? Jim didn't even hesitate as he said, 'Do what you want Pat, but I'm going home'! The truth was I didn't really have the bottle to stay on my own, so I decided I was going home too.

The day before we were due to leave, Gregg, the owner of the hostel, called me in to his office. He said he was sorry to hear I was leaving and thanked me for all the work I had done on the building! I was flattered and surprised! He also said I was the only one who hadn't hassled him for money when his father had died (he had died the week after me and Jim had arrived) and that he respected me for that.

It was suddenly awkward. I felt a little embarrassed because I was only doing just enough work to cover my rent, so he didn't really owe me very much! However, standing alone with him in his office I decided to go with it! I said, I knew what he was going through, because 'I', too, had also lost my dad, Gregg, slowly nodded his understanding. He then made me cringe by presenting me with a large bottle of Sierra Tequila and said, 'I want you to have this; take it back to England with you and whenever you think of America, have a drink on me'!

I was stunned and I was touched, I instantly regretted not getting to know this man better, what a genuinely nice thing to do! I can be a bit of a 'softie' at times and don't mind admitting it actually brought a lump to my throat. I thanked Gregg and shook his hand and told him how much the gesture meant to me and that I would indeed take it home and whenever I thought of this great land, I would have a drink on him! I was chuffed!

I'm ashamed to say that bottle of Tequila never made it back to England; it didn't even make it out of the youth hostel. As soon as Gregg's back was turned I, (under a certain amount of peer pressure) cracked it open! Cries of, 'Don't be a wanker' 'Tight cunt' and 'Just fucking open it' proved too much! So, me, Jim and the Geordie all got stuck in!

It was our last night, our farewell drink! So, having already finished off the Tequila, me, Jim and the Geordie brought a rake of beer and weed and decided to sit upstairs in one of the dormitories and get completely wasted! The word quickly got round about the 'party' on the 3rd floor and soon we were joined by Diane, Kiwi Ralph, the Dutch girls, the little gay dancing Puerto Rican bloke and practically everyone else who happened to be staying at the Venice beach youth hostel! Even Gregg's wife (who I had never met) put in an appearance! It was brilliant; there was great banter, everyone was laughing and having a good time, then we heard what sounded like shouting from the street below. Instinctively, and I suppose like school kids on a coach, we all ran over to the windows to see what the commotion was! Outside, in the street below a group of drunk homeless people were having a huge row!

Laughing with excitement and turning back to everyone in the dormitory I flung the window open while 'shushing' them all and saying, 'Listen, watch, they all know it'! Then leaning out, I shouted down to the group of homeless people. 'Oi lads'! They momentarily stopped their fighting and looked up as I said, 'Do you know... ‘Yesterday’ ...by the Beatles? I could hear sniggering from behind me as the biggest and most aggressive of the homeless group, looked up and then flung his arms wide open and bellowed...’ Yesterday, ...all my troubles seemed so far away' (bit of a pause!) 'Suddenly'!! And with that a chorus went up as they all joined in. They had forgotten about their spat! And were now singing their hearts out! We were all in fits, I was laughing so hard I had to hold onto the window! Then having composed myself a little, I again 'shushed' the room saying, 'Listen, watch'! I then lent back out the window and shouted, 'Oi mate, do you know, “Shut up and fuck off I'm trying to get the kids to sleep”?! And that's when they switched on to me! They started going ballistic! 'You fucking bastard'! 'Come down here man, I'll rip yo fucking head off and shove it up your ass'!! So, I shut the window!

You might think I was out of order for tormenting these poor unfortunates (which I was!), but you have to remember I was only 21yrs old (3 floors up!) and out of my face on weed, beer and Tequila! The rest of that night remains a bit of a blur, my last recollection being leaning over the side of my bunk bed and being violently sick on Jim's rucksack, which I failed to mention to him the next day! (I only got away with it, because it wasn't (and I apologise!) a chunky soup-like consistency, instead just pure liquid, as in beer!). I felt bad for drinking Gregg’s kind gesture - on 'two' counts!!

I felt sad leaving the Venice beach youth hostel and I was going to miss this motley crew. There were hugs and kisses and firm handshakes all round. Me and the Geordie, swapped phone numbers and promised to stay in touch (although neither one believed we really would) and even the big Chinese fellah made a point of waving us off (I never once heard him speak). I kept looking back hoping he might shout something out as we left, but he never did.

Hoff, one of the Dutch lads agreed to give me and Jim a lift to the airport in his battered up old brown Lincoln continental, for five dollars! (American cars are great).

****

Me and Jim made our way through the airport with our rucksacks on our backs, every now and again Jim would stop, spin left, spin right and then scrunching up his nose state that he kept getting a strange smell. I grinned every time he wasn't looking (Tequila 'n' puke!). We boarded our British Airways fight to Heathrow and took our seats. What an excellent adventure. My eyes had been opened to new possibilities; a new world far different from anything I had ever been used to. A seed had been sown.

Once home, Jim and I enjoyed a brief celebrity status amongst our families and friends, everyone was keen to hear what it was like in Los Angeles. Me and Jim were quick to impress and regale our friends with our exciting tales! A week after our return it was all over the news that a huge earthquake measuring 6.7 on the Richter scale had hit L.A. The Santa Monica freeway had collapsed, hundreds of buildings had been destroyed, thousands had been injured and 57 people had died. It said on the news that it was the costliest natural disaster in US history!

We had missed it by one week! I was genuinely concerned about everyone at the hostel, so I phoned the Geordie. He assured me everyone was safe, and the building was still in one piece! He said he had never experienced anything like the sheer violence and total devastation of the quake. Adding, 'You could feel the tension building in the air just before it hit'! I wasn't sure if I was glad, I had missed it, ...or not!

Chapter Eleven

BACK HOME, LIFE SEEMED TAME IN COMPARISON. Everything felt stale and flat, it certainly wasn't hip and happening like in LA. It was quiet at my mum's, because now it was just the two of us. It may sound silly, but I found it hard to re-adjust. I had just had the best four weeks of my life and now I was back home, skint and sitting in with my mum! I couldn't get America out of my head, I dreamed of going back!

I knew if I was to make this a reality, then I needed to earn some serious money. So I threw myself into my work. I worked harder than I had ever done before and as a result I started earning really good money! The intention being I would save every penny and head back to the states with plenty of 'dosh'!

More money than...cents unfortunately! I found it virtually impossible to stay in at the weekends, whilst knowing all my friends were out on the town, drinking and having a great time, without me. I was young and the temptation was just too much.

Week after week, I worked hard, but as soon as I got paid, I was out on the town and blowing all my wages. My weekends only seemed to last five minutes! Friday I would get paid, my pockets would be bulging with cash, 'blink', and then It would be Monday morning again and I would be totally skint. And the whole cycle would start over again! It wasn't long before America seemed like a distant memory.

My mum wasn't happy about my drinking (for obvious reasons) and let me know about it at every opportunity. She could be quite brutal when she wanted to! It wasn't my fault she had had a bad marriage; it wasn't my fault she had had a shit life. I didn't see why I should 'not' enjoy my youth. I didn't see why I should live the same miserable existence as 'her' or 'him'! So, I ignored her protests and her predictions. The trouble was, I was having too much fun to consider listening to the voice of reason!

****

I was of an age where women were plentiful, and I confess I did okay! Having a friend like Jim Sweeny didn't hurt either, because women simply adored him. Drawn like moths to a light bulb. It was an amazing thing to watch, Jim would stand in the pub and 'they' would just gravitate towards him, which was great because I usually got her mate!

There were lots of girlfriends in those days, but never anything too serious, never anything that might get in the way or prevent me from having my fun! There was one girl, called Tanya, who I quite liked, but who I believed was a bit out of my league. However, I surprised myself one night by asking her out on a date, ...she then surprised me ...by agreeing!

The night of our date I can remember being 'rather' pleased with myself, as I walked in the pub with Tanya on my arm. My mates were already at the bar and upon seeing us, started giving me the old nudge, nudge, wink, wink routine behind her back. Being well chuffed, I just smiled smugly and gave them 'the' knowing nod!

Me and Tanya really hit off, we had a great time, non-stop chat and laughter as we made our way from pub to pub. Not only was she petite and very good looking, but she could also drink like a fish! I was starting to wonder where she was putting it, because quite frankly I was beginning to struggle. To cut a long story short the girl drank me under the table!

We were the last ones out of the pub! We were also the last ones out of the night club too (I remember the lights coming on!). Not satisfied, we then went on to, 'Jimmy's', an infamous kebab shop that sold special (whiskey) coffees, and we were the last ones out of there as well.

Needless to say, I was delighted when Tanya suggested we go back to hers, I thought this is looking promising. She then however reminded me that she still lived with her parents. At this point I had a vague recollection of hearing that her dad was a complete lunatic, who was liable to give me a proper hiding if he were to catch me sneaking into his house in the early hours of the morning with his daughter! However due to the amount of alcohol I had consumed, I just didn't care! That and the fact, that the little head was now ruling the big head!

When we fell out of the taxi at Tanya's house, she realised she had forgotten her keys and knocking on the door wasn't an option, so we climbed through the kitchen window! Whilst trying to be as quiet as possible, well, as quiet as two drunk twenty somethings can be, climbing through a kitchen window at 4.30 am. I was hoping and praying that her dad wouldn't hear us and as luck would have it, he didn't. Eventually I reached the sanctuary of her bedroom (bingo), I stripped off and dived into the bed with her. However, I'm sorry to report that there were no shenanigans! I pretty much passed out as soon as my head hit the pillow.

When I woke up the next morning, my head really hurt and I was slightly confused as to where I was, and to make matters worse, I was also soaking wet!!! Oh, the shame of it! I was totally mortified; I could not fucking believe it!

Tanya was gorgeous, I had risked life and limb sneaking into her bedroom, and I hadn't even shagged her, instead I had just pissed the bed! I had never felt so ashamed, nor had I ever pissed the bed before. Try as I might I just couldn't make eye contact with her, nor could I stop apologising.

She was really quite good about it and told me not to worry. Right there and then I made her promise me that she wouldn't tell her mates, as I quickly got dressed, and 'then' found my pants! I stuffed them in my pocket, like a cheap whore, before I scarpered out the front door without looking back. Disgraced, I headed straight for the pub.

When I walked in the pub, McGillicuddy was already at the bar, he took one look at me and with a massive grin said, 'What have you done'! It must have been written all over my face! I don't know why, but I confessed everything, he cracked up laughing, then turned to the only other person at the bar, pointed at me, and said, 'He pissed the bed last night'! ...thanks Paul!

Neither her or her friends ever mentioned the 'incident' and I was regretting ever having mentioned it to Paul; it was beginning to seem like the girl had kept her word and had not told her friends. However, needless to say, me and Tanya never went out again.

A year or so passed and I had almost forgotten all about it, when I saw a group of Tanya's friends in a pub one night. That's when I overheard them talking about her. Apparently, she was notorious for 'wetting the bed' when she had had too much to drink. As far as I could gather from their conversation, she had been doing it for years! No wonder she had been so good about it all, so understanding. No wonder she hadn't told her friends. The cheeky bastard!

****

I was living a very blokey existence! I was losing my boyishness.

I was doing well at work and had developed a good reputation as someone who was not only good at their job, but also someone who could knock out a lot of work in a day. As a result, I was consistently earning good money, although being so young, I didn't always fully appreciate the fact (plus it continuously burnt a hole in my pocket!).

The construction industry has always been a testosterone-fuelled, male-dominated environment and, as a result, I developed a rather bullish, somewhat aggressive workplace persona. I didn't ask for things, I demanded them, and if I wasn't happy about something, I let it be known. I usually got my way.

I was 21yrs old, well-built and with a muscular physic, I had quite a stern face and a shaved head. As McGillicuddy, once said, I would be the last bloke you would start on in the pub. The truth of the matter was this, I was just a big softy, it was all a front! I was just playing a workplace game and what's more I was wining! If this next bit sounds contradictory to what you have already read, then I apologise, however it is the truth. I have never liked violence and I have always despised bullies.

The thought of hitting someone, of hurting their feelings and embarrassing them was, and has always been, totally abhorrent to me. I just wanted to like everyone and more importantly I wanted them to like me too. But most of all I just wanted to have fun! And that was what the weekends were for. I was burning the candle at both ends, but I didn't care, because life was good and I knew that one day I would achieve greatness, I had time on my side! But for now, I was busy, enjoying one hysterical piss-up after another!

It was a typical Friday night out with the lads. As usual we were all fairly drunk and in a boisterous, but good-humoured mood. As we made our way through the town centre going from pub to pub, we passed the local (and extremely busy) Pizza Hut restaurant. Always up for a laugh I decided it would be great fun to pull a moony! So, I did! I ran up to the large front plate window and dropped my trousers, bent over and pressed my bare arse up against the cold glass pane! While all the lads cheered! I then made my right hand into a fist and banged as hard as I could on the window to ensure everyone would look up from their plates and in my direction! It was extremely funny and as I ran away laughing and pulling up my trousers, I am sure I caught a glimpse of some very amused dinners.

Of course, in today's culture, I would have been arrested and placed on the sex-offenders register for life having exposed myself in the middle of the town centre! But in those days, I think most people took it to be what it was - high jinks and just a bit of fun, albeit very 'cheeky'!!!

The next weekend I was again out with the lads, once more we were making are way from pub to pub, drunk, boisterous and as usual on good form. When yet again we passed the local Pizza Hut restaurant. This was when Neil Duncan in a show of drunken bravado decided that he, too, would do a moony against the glass! Neil ran over to the window and dropped his trousers, again there was cheers from the lads! However, as he bent over, he realised all too late, his terrible mistake, ...he was to 'close' to the window! Poor Neil only succeed in knocking himself over!

His trousers and pants went down around his ankles and his shirt rode up his back as he lay flaying about on the pavement, all but naked in the town centre, much to the delight of a gaggle of passing drunk girls who were all shrieking, whooping and pointing in delight at Neil's naked misfortune!

Not all of my friends were drunkards! Jim (ever the ladies' man) preferred to take it easy on a night out, while Simón (who hardly drank) preferred recreational drugs and a night in! Simón had gone and got married to his childhood sweetheart at the grand old age of nineteen! Secretly we all thought he was mental! But I am glad to report that 30 happy years later he (they) proved us all wrong! I for one am glad, it's reassuring to know the sanctity of marriage is real and still exists!

Simón and his new wife were living in a flat just a stone's throw from the town centre. Its close proximity to all the pubs and clubs dictated that more often than not we would all descend on Simón's gaff at closing time. It was not unusual (or now I think about it, fair!) for a load of us to be hammering his door down and shouting through his letterbox at 3am until he let us in! Simón has always been a top bloke and a good friend. He never once turned us away even though he would have been well within his rights to do so!

One night after the pubs had shut, Neil, Paul and myself were drunkenly making are way through the town centre to Simón's flat, when we passed a charity shop doorway, and noticed that some good Samaritan had left a box of clothes in front of the door. 'Naturally', having been drinking we opened the box and wasted no time in dressing up in the most ridiculous forms of attire. I had on a pair of sensible corduroy slacks complimented by a cream woollen knitted cardigan with the biggest chocolate brown buttons you have ever seen. Paul was wearing a pair of 1980s, red shorts, a silk shirt and a tank top!

Paul 'literally' pissed himself laughing when he turned to see what Neil was wearing. Neil had discovered the most beautiful pink dress!! which I can only describe as something you might see Snow white wearing in a sickly-sweet Disney film. It was frilly around the sleeves and boob area, flat and figure hugging around the midriff and then fanned out like a Tu-tu for the skirt bit. I have to say it went exceedingly well with Neil's aggressive drunken snarl, 18-hole Doc Martins and shaved head! Unfortunately, no one had camera phones in them days!

Neil was determined to leave it on until we got to Simón's (perhaps he liked the feel of it?), but as we made are way through the town centre we spotted a group of equally as drunk and raucous blokes making their way towards us, so Neil ripped 'his' dress off, just in case (and there was every chance) that they were a bunch of hoodlums like us! We didn't want a reason for a fight and let's face it, one of them was going to say something to a bloke in a pink dress at 2am (alright darling?). We just wanted to get to Simón's, relatively in one piece and smoke some pot.

It was always a great laugh and more often than not, even better than the actual night out! Invariably we would sit about listening to music, telling funny stories and trying to invent new ways of smoking hashish! Bong, hot tongs, blow backs, a plastic bucket and a straw perhaps? Someone always over-did it and passed out (usually me!), and unwittingly invited the others to draw, paint and generally interfere with the unconscious 'blank canvas'! There was never a dull moment, it was always wild, messy and fun (unless you happened to be the neighbours)!

****

Most people, ordinary people tend to have hobbies or interests. They may spend their weekends playing some form of sport (golf perhaps), or they might belong to a volunteer group or charity organisation of some kind. Not me, I had no interests at all. I just loved Saturdays. I would be in the pub with all the lads from the moment it opened until they called last orders! The pubs were always packed back then, full of excitable young men all championing the heroics of the previous night's events. The mass hysteria of all-day drinking. The underlying excitement of what 'might' happen. The supercharged atmosphere akin to the camaraderie of men commencing to go into battle, convinced victory is just a matter of course! Theirs for the taking!

I loved it and as a consequence I found myself getting into some awful drunken states. Again, I put it down to the fact I was young, I had no responsibilities, what else was I to do at the weekends? Sit at home with my mum and watch 'Telly Addicts'?

I can remember seeing young people my own age, coming into the pub on Saturday afternoons laden down with bags of new clothes, which they had brought themselves for that coming night. One, maybe two drinks and they were gone again! I would be fairly drunk and sitting in the same spot when they returned that evening all dressed up in their new clobber ready for a night out! It never occurred to me that perhaps I should be doing the same!

All of my friends were descent young lads from descent, salt of the earth, families. There wasn't one bit of badness in any of us. Rambunctious is probably a fairly accurate description. Most of us had by now (I certainly had!), spent the odd night in the police cells. Never anything serious of course, just the usual silliness and devilment of a night out. Which usually resulted in a slap on the wrist the next morning when you had sobered up enough to be told to...'off you fuck'! It was normal...ish!

However regardless of whether you were a troublemaker or not, if you drank in the town centre long enough, then trouble would surely find you! You can't say, 'thwera thwan thwat'! I lost another tooth, only this time I didn't find it exciting or exhilarating, I just found it bloody annoying!

I was leaving a night club in the early hours of the morning. As I walked down the street away from the club, I saw some bloke giving a young girl a hard time. He was being very abusive and banging his hand on the side of her head! Me being me, I couldn't just walk past and ignore it, so I told him to leave her alone. A few insults were exchanged between us before the lad jumped into a passing black cab.

And that would have been the end of it, had the lad not lent out of the cab as it drove away and called me a 'baldie headed bastard'! I was livid, I was furious! So, without thinking, I chased the taxi up the street. And then to my horror it stopped, and the lad jumped out with no shirt on! It turned out he was from the Irish travelling community, bless him (one of my lot, perhaps?)!

Needless to say, we went at it 'hammer and tongs' in the middle of the road. I keep saying it, but I really don't like fighting, but then I don't like being treated like a mug either. For all the young man's gesticulating, chest expanding and proclamations of what he was going to do to me.... he took an awful hiding! In my rage I ended up knocking him to the floor and rained down punch after punch.

While all this was going on, I could hear Neil Duncan shouting in my ear, that the lad on the floor was in fact Jim Sweeny's cousin! As I came to my senses, I slowed down and taking on board what Neil was shouting I let the lad up, as I called him a few choice names and then walked away. I was halfway down the street when I heard footsteps behind me, a tap on the shoulder, I turned, and got sucker-punched straight in the gob! It knocked 'my other' front tooth out! Angry, doesn't quite cut it, I was raging, 'with myself' for being so foolish. Right there and then I learnt a very valuable lesson, if they're down, don't fucking let em up! Regardless!

Obviously, the fight re-ignited but it quickly got broken up again by my mates and his. I later found out that Neil.... had been mistaken! You live and learn! It cost me £500 to get my 'Hampstead's' sorted!

As well as doing a lot of heavy drinking, I was also taking a lot of what you might describe as recreational drugs (speed and ecstasy), I worked in a male-dominated environment and I lived for the weekends and my mates. Something was definitely missing! I wanted the comfort of female company. I don't mean 'just' sex, but more, pleasant companionship. Nicer, quieter times. Romantic meals perhaps and dare I say it, cosy nights in!

I noticed her across the pub because she stood out from the crowd. She had gorgeous long black hair and the most amazing luscious red lips I had ever seen. Having had a few pints of bravery I decided to 'chance my arm' by going over and introducing myself. She told me her name was Emma and that she worked as a beautician.

My mates were all keeping a keen eye on me from across the bar. Emma asked me if I worked in construction (I was wearing a check shirt, jeans and boots, I have to admit I looked every bit the builder!), but I replied, 'No, I'm a 'gliding' instructor'! Emma smiled suggesting she was impressed, before I added, 'I'm actually very lucky I could have ended up working dead end jobs in construction (I tilted my head in the general direction of the lads!) like my mates, if it were not for my love of aviation'! I then went on to explain how I had 'nearly' died in a particularly rough and dangerous landing at a nearby airfield. Emma's friend became quite excited and started enquiring about cheap gliding lessons! 'Sure, not a problem', I said, in an off-hand way.

Then Emma gave me a double take and said, 'Oh my god... you've got two different coloured eyes'! Emma was lovely! We started dating and I received the comfort I had been longing for!

Being with 'M', allowed me to explore the more sensitive side of my personality. I don't mean 'A' feminine side, because obviously being so manly I haven't got one. What I refer to is the more gentle, timid, loving (secret I suppose?) side of my personality. The side my friends did not know existed. I could go out with M to a restaurant and enjoy a pleasant meal and a pleasant evening without the calamity and chaos associated with being with my mates.

Like most girls I had dated, M hadn't experienced the same rough and tumble upbringing that I had. As a result, she tended to gravitate towards the finer, nicer things in life. Which was a breath of fresh air to me. She enjoyed the classics, she also enjoyed art (as did I!). Emma was a very bright, loving and thoughtful person. She would visit stately homes and drag me along to soak up and enjoy the grandeur of a bygone era. I used to pretend that I found it boring, because I was so blokey! But in actual fact, I really enjoyed it too, plus more often than not M would drive, so I would be able to sneak in a few pints here and there so as to stave off my alleged boredom!

One Sunday we drove to Oxford and visited Blenheim Palace, the childhood home of Mr Churchill. I had never been anywhere so ...palatial! It was, to state the obvious very impressive! As we walked around the Palace, Emma began telling me all about the young Winston Churchill and how his mother, was (on the quiet), a bit of a 'wanton hussy'! M informed me that Winston Churchill was buried in the nearby village of Woodstock, so on our way home we stopped off and visited his grave. I was struck by how ordinary looking his head stone was. Death, the great leveller!

There was nothing to suggest the significance of his contribution to the world, nothing that lent towards the greatness of the man, at a quick glance you wouldn't have thought it was anyone of any importance who was buried there.

****

Emma liked to pamper me! It's true! When her dad was out, I would go around to hers (we both lived with our respective 'parent', her mum having left some years earlier) and sometimes she would give me a massage using essential oils! Being a trained beautician, she knew what she was doing with her hands, and of course, it always turned sexual! They were very happy times indeed. In fact, I use to fondly refer to 'it', as the happy half hour (on a good day maybe even longer!). It was nice being spoiled, I had never been spoiled before, soiled yes, but spoiled no! In all things were pretty good. However, there was a slight problem. I was not being entirely honest with Emma.

I loved her, I truly did, ... but I wasn't 'in' love with her. And as we all know the two are very different. Secretly my friends were always more important to me than she was. I was never horrible or cruel towards her, I never went out of my way to hurt her feelings or upset her. I was just, at times, a bit indifferent towards her. Perhaps to a woman that's worse than being horrible or cruel. As I write this, I can now see how immature I was back then. That said, me and M, enjoyed each other's company and we had a lot of fun times. Life wasn't too serious, we were both young, there were no kids involved and we had plenty of time to worry about the future.

Another issue was that I still longed to go back to America one day. Every time I had a drink, I would bang on about my intended trip. I was also increasingly aware that if I didn't do it soon then I would probably never do it. I would inevitably get bogged down with responsibilities and become rooted in my hometown. I didn't want to grow old and regret never taking the opportunity to live out my dream.

As I found it virtually impossible to stay in at weekends and save money, I began to wonder how I could achieve my goal. As a self-employed, sub-contractor I received a yearly tax rebate, the sum of which depended on my annual turnover against my yearly expenditure. So far, any tax rebates I had previously received had just meant a few good weeks on the piss around town with the lads.

The truth of the matter was, that I was beginning to feel like M and me were getting a bit 'too' settled, a bit 'too' serious. if I'm honest, I suppose it scared me! I certainly was not aware of these feelings at the time. Maybe my inability to commit to Emma had, at a subconscious level something to do with my own parents' disastrous marriage? Then again, perhaps I was just a dreamer with ideas above my station! The grass is always greener!

Either way my trip to America began to take on a level of urgency. I began to formulate a plan. It wasn't much of a plan, but it was better than no plan. If I could just save enough out of my wages each week for my flight. Then I could use my tax rebate to partially fund the rest of the trip. I estimated I could get as much as £1400 pounds.

I waited until I was extremely drunk before I explained my 'genius' plan and my intentions to M. 'Brilliant, that's a fantastic plan' she said sarcastically as she rolled her eyes at me. She didn't believe a single drunken word of it and why would she, I had been spouting the same ol' shit every time I was drunk since we had first met. I think Emma believed it was nothing more than a pipe dream and that may well have been the case had I not received the phone call!

I had come home from Neil's house one night with two eyes like piss holes in the snow! I was very, very stoned. My mum still didn't know that I smoked pot, I think she just though Neil Duncan must be an awful piss head if every time I went around there, I ended up drinking!!! Anyway, my mum told me there had been a phone call for me (no mobiles!) and it was someone called Martin, they had said that they would call back the next evening at about seven o'clock.

Through my fog-fuddled brain, I tried to figure out who it could be. I didn't know anyone called Martin. I was beginning to think my mum (being old, mumsy and Irish!), had made a mistake. But as my pot-induced stupor began to subdue it suddenly dawned on me that the only Martin, I knew was the Geordie, from Los Angeles!

The next evening, I sat in the hallway glued to the phone waiting for it to ring. I didn't know it then, but that phone call was to be life-changing, in fact I didn't find out how life-changing for years to come. At seven o'clock the phone rang!

It had been two years since the Geordie and I had promised to stay in touch. So, when I answered the phone and realised it was him, there followed an excited exchange. Not only was it good to hear from him but I was also pleasantly surprised that he even remembered me. Martin explained how he had stayed in LA and had been kept fairly busy due to the amount of re-building work going on after the earthquake.

He said things were going well for him, but then he had received news that his father had died, so he had come back home to attend the funeral. He said he had been visiting friends in London and had passed a sign for my place on the motorway, so had decided to give me a ring to see how I was doing. I invited him to come and stay on his return from London, but he declined, as he needed to get back up north. Instead he invited me up to his place just outside Durham.

It turned out Martin was as much of a Geordie as I was a cockney, not that it made a difference, I have still always referred to him as the Geordie. One month later me and Emma took a train heading north; M, to Darlington to visit her cousin and me on to the next stop, Durham.

The Geordie meet me at the station and took me to his mother's house in a little coal mining town a few miles away. Like me, they too lived in a council house, it was very much a home from home, except for the beautiful rolling hills in the background! Martin's family made a huge fuss of me and I was made to feel very welcome.

They were good, genuine, working-class people, who oozed northern hospitality. Me and Martin wasted no time in hitting the pubs and working men's clubs, I remember being quite taken aback when one of the clubs had a men-only bar, women were not permitted, I thought how my sisters might have reacted to this rule! I even wondered if it was actually legal! This train of thought soon slipped my mind as me and the Geordie had a great time reminiscing about our time in LA and getting drunk on pints of Caffrey's which was a popular drink at the time, a kind of mix between lager and ale and very potent!

As the drinks flowed, I told Martin all about M. We both laughed when I told him how I had said I was a 'gliding instructor' and agreed it was more original than 'dolphin trainer'! I told him how I had been longing to get back to the states. I informed him of my genius plan and how I wanted to work my way up the west coast through California, Oregon, Washington state and then cut across into Canada before eventually reaching Alaska.

I have always had a fascination with the wilderness, I liked the 'idea' of being a mountain man! I think it stems from watching 'Grizzly Adams' on the telly on Sunday afternoons when I was a kid!

Martin nodded in agreement and told me how he, too, was definitely going back. He said this place was too small for him now, there was nothing left here for him anymore, he had outgrown it. As the drinks flowed, we decided we would go back, and we would travel together!

CHAPTER TWELVE

IN THE FEBRUARY OF 1996 THE GEORDIE AND I HAD BOTH BOOKED our flights to LAX international airport USA. Although I had no intention of coming back any time soon, I still booked a return flight; this was so as not to arouse any suspicion with the US immigration officials. I was going to the states on a standard holiday visa, which I had every intention of violating and in fact staying in the US as an illegal immigrant! Martin had overstayed by four years and upon leaving the states had been given no real grief. Immigration didn't care if you were leaving the country, it was entering that was the problem. (although I am sure it's very different these days!). Martin had as a precaution renewed his passport, hoping his new passport would allow him entry with no problems. I was aware I was taking a big risk. If at any point on my adventure I became ill, I would be fucked. If at any point I got hurt, I would be fucked. If I got arrested for any reason, I would be fucked. If I got caught working illegally, I was fucked! Basically, if I wasn't careful, I was going to end up really fucked.

But I was blinded by the excitement of it all, I was 23yrs old and I just didn't give a fuck! It's funny but it never crossed my mind to try for a work visa through the proper channels! My thinking, if indeed there was any thinking, was just go, just do it! At 23 you tend not to worry about consequences, or at least I didn't.

I got my anticipated tax rebate! I was delighted to receive £1800 pounds which equated to $2700 dollars. Game on! I told Emma I was going. She was shocked, but I think she understood. I explained it wasn't personal, I was not going away because I wanted to sow my wild oats or because I no longer cared about her, it was just something that I had to do. Poor M was upset. I also think she was embarrassed that her boyfriend was leaving her and going off gallivanting 6000 miles away. Actions speak louder than words, or so they say. I am ashamed to admit I never once considered how awkward or embarrassing it must have been for her in front of her friends; we all know how bitchy young women can be. I didn't mean to put her in such a position, I didn't want to hurt her feelings. I just had to go.

My mother was also upset, she didn't want her 'baby' leaving and moving to the other side of the world, as she saw it. I think she thought it was like in her day when young men would leave Ireland never to return or to be heard from again.

Perhaps it reminded her of when she had left at the age of 19, in the years following she had only managed to get 'home' to see her own mother a few times before her eventual death in 1981. I think my leaving brought back painful memories of a time lost. The morning I left for the airport my mum was at the kitchen sink doing the dishes; she had kept her back to me and had barely said goodbye. I think she didn't want me to see how hurt she was that I was leaving her.

Despite all her criticisms and her harsh words, I knew she loved me, and I loved her too. I remember feeling that her reaction was a very old-fashioned way of carrying on. I had no real intention of never coming back, it was a possibility, yes, but all I was really doing was going off on a young man's adventure. It never crossed my mind that I was leaving her all alone in the house (she could have her pick of the bedrooms now). She had lost her husband; she had lost her daughter and now in her eyes she was losing her youngest child too. Obviously, the facts didn't change a thing and I still went.

****

Me and the Geordie had arranged to meet by the departure gates for our flight. Me being me and the fact that I couldn't wait to get going (as it had been a long time coming!), I had arrived at the airport considerably early, a good few hour early in fact. I was so excited I could barely contain myself. Perhaps it was because I had been hanging around the airport on my own for so long, that I got pulled in by the airport security officers. Alarmingly they confiscated my passport and began to ask me lots of probing questions. I began to panic a bit, as you do if you get pulled in and questioned. As my mind began to race, I started to think that somehow, they 'knew' I was planning to overstay my visa and live and work in the US illegally. It may sound stupid, but why else would they have pulled me in. Some time passed and a lot of questions were asked, before one of the officers asked if I had ever lived in the Manchester area, to which I gruffly replied, 'No'! I was beginning to lose my cool, I became flustered and was aware that I probably looked guilty regardless, so I demanded an explanation, 'Look, what's all this about'? That's when one of the security officers began to explain that a man, going by the same name as me, was wanted for murder! And as a result, all the airports were being monitored, my name had flagged up on their system when I had arrived and that was why I had been pulled in for questioning!

To this day I don't know whether the two security officers were serious or whether they were just bored and on a bit of a wind up. Either way it was a relief when they finally handed me back my passport and told me I was free to go. I headed back to the departure lounge, not only feeling, but also looking incredibly guilty for no 'real' reason at all!

Had I given it any thought, I might have considered it a bad omen! It was another half hour before a very happy and excited looking Geordie arrived and greeted me with a firm handshake and a huge grin, with the pleasantries out of the way we wasted no time in heading towards the bar! There was a lot of exited talk about what we could expect in the coming weeks and months. So much so that we only managed to get a couple of pints in before our flight was called. Not that we minded, obviously we were both keen to get going, but it was also free beer on the plane! Cruising at 30,000 feet, doing 700 miles an hour and drinking free cans of Stella Artois, it's not a bad life is it!

8 hours into our flight and I was gagging for a fag, (if you're a smoker you will understand!) so I sneaked off to the loo and had two quick puffs before returning to my seat. A few moments later an air stewardess passed by and I asked for more drinks! Her smile immediately changed to a grimace, 'astounded' she barked, 'have you been smoking'!!

I didn't get a chance to deny the accusation, as I instantly turned bright red and looked straight at the floor, like a little boy! She gave me a proper telling off in front of all the other passengers and explained that she could have me arrested when we landed. Thankfully she didn't grass me up (probably because I looked like I was going to cry!), but we didn't get any more beer for the rest of the flight either! I spent the next three hours, glued to my seat, cringing, and getting dirty looks from all the other passengers and all the stewards every time they passed. I couldn't wait to get off the fucking plane!

CHAPTER THIRTEEN

WHEN IT CAME TO BEING AN ILLEGAL IMMIGRANT, Martin knew the score. He knew what to do, where to go and more importantly he knew what to say (and what not to say!). It was very reassuring having the Geordie with me, I was more than happy to follow his lead. When we arrived in Los Angeles, we headed straight for the HOSTEL CALIFORNIA, which was situated on Lincoln boulevard and only five blocks up from the Venice beach youth hostel where me and Jim had previously stayed. When we arrived at reception, Martin asked the bloke behind the counter if Klaus was around, Klaus was the owner and he and Martin were good friends. As the bloke went off to find Klaus, I took in my surroundings, I could see a large communal living room bathed in glorious sunlight which emanated from two large skylights above. Big comfortable couches, armchairs and games tables (foosball, space invaders etc) were scattered around the place. And on the far back wall (which was of double storey height) there was a very impressive picture of the Challenger space shuttle orbiting the earth. I instantly liked the place; it had a good vibe! When I looked down at the counter in front of me, I smiled when I saw some yellow flyers which read 'Welcome to the Hostel California', 'You can check out'. 'But you can never leave'!

When Klaus, eventually appeared at reception he was clearly delighted to see Martin and bellowed, 'Ahh Martin, you fucking drunken English bastard', as he grabbed the Geordie and gave him a massive bear hug. They shook hands and the German said how great it was to have the Geordie back. Martin then introduced me to Klaus, but all I got was a grunt and a bare acknowledgement, obviously it would take a while for the German to accept me.

My first impressions of Klaus were not very good. He was scruffy, 6ft tall, anaemic looking and there wasn't a pick on him! His clothes (all black) were hanging off him and he had long white hair which went all the way down his back, to where his arse should have been! He also had white eyebrows, which made him look almost albino. In fact, Klaus looked like the worlds shittest wizard! And a bit of a tramp! But he clearly loved Martin, so it was all good.

Me and Martin rented a double room as opposed to a dormitory, as this place was busy compared to the last hostel, so it was good to have some level of privacy. Our room didn't overlook the Pacific Ocean like the Venice beach hostel, instead in overlooked a McDonald's and a car wash.

When I was a kid, if I ever contemplated an American car wash, I would think of loads of 1980s looking American black blokes all working away singing Rose Royce songs! You know 'Huggy bear' type characters (what's the word on the street!), but this car wash was nothing like that. Instead it was worked by Mexicans, Guatemalans and Puerto Ricans, they nearly all wore bandannas and I didn't have a clue what they were singing about. I used to watch them from the window in my room, I would see a wealthy white woman or man, standing there, while the lower classes subserviently and hurriedly washed their expensive cars, I remember thinking just how shit 'real' life actually is! That was one of the things that struck me about LA, at street level I didn't actually meet that many bona fide Americans, I met more back packers, illegal immigrants, drug addicts, prostitutes and Mexicans more than anything else! You know, salt of the earth type people. The type of people who would probably help you out if you were in trouble, as opposed to the wealthy people with the nice cars, who probably wouldn't!

After me and Martin had settled in (dumped our stuff!), we headed down the road to find a liquor store! We bought what I can only describe as a four-gallon plastic drum of Evan Williams (a cheap version of Jack Daniels) for the princely sum of $14 dollars! Martin had rightly pointed out that this was a great deal and good value for money and would last us weeks!

It was now dark outside as we sat down at a table in the hostel and poured ourselves a drink. Soon we were joined by a welsh bloke called 'Tewy', he was good company and the banter flowed as the three of us began a half-hearted game of Trivial Pursuit. I was having a great time, nor could I believe I was actually back! It was a tremendous buzz just being in L.A. There was a brief lull in the 'back'n'forth', so I announced I was going to ring my mum to let her know I had arrived safely, which immediately evoked a Welsh and Geordie chorus of 'pussy' to which I replied, 'bothered' and went and made the call!

Having carried out my obligation to my poor old mum, I returned to the table and resumed our game of Trivial Pursuit. A history question! Which 16th century monarch beheaded his second wife? I was asked, 'I ain't got a clue and what's more I couldn't give two fucks', I chortled as I poured myself another large glass of Evan Williams.

I woke up with my head on the table, there were small pieces of 'pie' scattered about the board and one stuck to my forehead. In front of me there was a small pool of dribble! I sat up and saw there was no one around. I looked up, the clock on the wall said it was 6.30am. I glanced at the four-gallon drum of Evan Williams and smiled, there was a tiny drop left, barely covering the base of the plastic container. In my head I heard the Geordie in the liquor store the night before, saying, 'it will last for weeks'! I squinted at the daylight coming through the window and thought to myself .... 'Did I win'!

****

I grew to love the coffee in America, for the most part it was always bitter tasting and strong. I soon learned that a couple of large cups was great for curing a hangover!

It was midday before the Geordie, or the Welsh bloke appeared. And after they had obligingly filed in all the gaps of the previous night's drinking, we all decided to go out for some 'breakfast' and headed for a diner called the 'Café 50s'! It was exactly like you would imagine, the waitresses were all dressed in 1950s attire and each booth had a little jukebox situated on the end of the table, which accepted five cents to play a record. I must admit it was pretty cool stuff. Everything on the menu had a 1950s theme, I remember ordering a Labamba omelette! The reason I bother to mention this, is because the Mexican waitress that took our order was quite possibly the most beautiful looking women I had ever seen. I was totally mesmerised by her. The Geordie even told me off for staring, but I couldn't help it. She was lovely! I had an urge to ask her for her number, but I wasn't really brave enough, plus I felt a bit silly, having just ordered a Richie fucking Valance themed breakfast.

Once we had finished our food, she returned to the table to clear away our plates, as she leaned across us with an outstretched arm, we all saw it! Our eyes darted between one another in quick succession. Jet black coarse hairs as thick as rope, 'creeping' all the way up her arm! It was actually very disconcerting; I immediately had a change of heart (the poor girl). As she walked away clutching our plates and when I was sure she was out of earshot, I lent in close towards Tewy and Martin. Following my lead, they also leaned in close, as I whispered in a very hushed but serious tone, 'I would love to ...'pluck' her'!

Being a level headed and sensible trio and having just enjoyed a rather nostalgic culinary trip back in time, we all agreed the only viable option for three single and not so skint British blokes in the centre of down town Los Angeles to do , was to head to the nearest bar and get completely and utterly shit faced! So, we did!

I think all of us can look back and recall a particularly memorable day out on the piss with friends! Well this was one of those occasions. I can remember daytime becoming night. I have a vague recollection of flying about the city in the back of yellow taxi cabs. I remember we grew louder and more raucous with each bar we were asked to leave, sometimes politely, sometimes not! As the night progressed, we became drunker and wilder as we travelled all over the city. I saw sights and characters I had not seen on my first visit to LA. At some point we found ourselves in an Irish theme bar chatting to some American bloke who had taken it upon himself to join our company. It had started off pleasant enough, but I suppose looking back he was what you might describe as a bit of an 'ejit'!

As the drinks flowed our conversation turned to how 'lame' an Irish theme bar it was, all agreeing that sticking a neon shamrock in the window, charging 6 dollars for a Guinness and repeatedly saying the word 'begorra', didn't make it Ireland, (plus Tom Jones was the most Irish thing on the jukebox)!! As we joked about the worst Irish theme bars we had ever been to (I mentioned a particularly bad one in France but was trumped by Tewy's recount of one in Chile!), our new American friend told us about a more authentic Irish bar that he knew of, on the other side of town and invited us along. We happily agreed and someone suggested calling a cab. But the American said, 'No need! The Jeep’s out front'!

The American was just as drunk as we were as the four of us piled into his open top Jeep and raced off through the dark L.A. Streets. Blasting out thrash metal from the Jeeps stereo he drove like a lunatic, screeching round corners and flooring it on the straights between blocks. And as if that wasn't 'fun' enough, as an added bonus he also had a massive bag of very strong-smelling weed! It's hard to roll a joint in an open top vehicle doing sixty miles an hour, but I managed it anyway! Exhilarated, drunk (and a little stoned) we arrived at the Irish pub, laughing and still all in one piece! And to the Americans credit! It was truly excellent!

Once through the door you would have been forgiven for thinking that you were actually in the Emerald Isle. The Guinness was as good as any I had ever had, and the traditional live band were exceptional. The place was heaving, the atmosphere was brilliant, and everyone was having the 'Craic'!

High on laughter, holding onto the bar and slapping each other on the back it was turning out to be a great night of good humour and camaraderie. And that's when our host, the hapless American stunned us all into shocked silence when 'smiling' he said, 'Man, I fucking hate the British, because they are all 'Wankers', aren't they!?' My heart sank!

I think being extremely drunk and due to his current surroundings, the poor bloke 'thought' it was the right thing to say! He had obviously, wrongly interpreted the Geordie and Tewy's accents to be some form of Irish brogue and with me having a particularly Irish sounding name, well that had just sealed the deal as far as he was concerned. It was at this point that I actually began to feel sorry for him. The Geordie went first! And called him a 'stupid looking fucking American cunt' and 'a racist fucking prick'! Tewy went next, telling him he was lucky 'we' didn't take him outside and give him a 'right good fucking hiding'!

Suddenly I felt like I was struggling to hold back two barking, snarling Alsatians (or perhaps bulldogs!), a leash in each hand! They looked like they were going to rip him to pieces! The poor American looked totally gob-smacked (and very nearly was). I saw his eyes darting about in his head, as his alcohol fuddled brain was franticly trying to figure out his catastrophic mistake. He really didn't know what he had just done wrong!

Fearing the worst, I quickly intervened and tried to calm the situation, I pointed out, that he was just an idiot and being an American he didn't have a clue as to what he was talking about and perhaps we should just 'ease' up on him a bit. He clearly didn't realise how insulting he had just been, (having Irish parents, I had heard it all before anyway!).

Martin and Tewy, reluctantly agreed, although it was clear they were far from happy about it. Naturally the atmosphere had now 'soured' and the poor American spent the next couple of hours getting terrorised and repeatedly sent to the bar 'out of turn', until eventually (and unbelievably) we ditched 'him'!! But not before I had helped myself to a handful of his weed! Well I did save him from getting a slap! 'Yankless', we made our way to another bar. Much smaller and quieter than the Irish bar we had just left. It was dimly lit with a much more mellow vibe. It was at about this point that Tewy began to flag, so the Geordie and I thought it best, to put him in a cab and send him back to the hostel. Obviously, we didn't go with him!

Now it was just the two of us sitting at the bar sipping our large Jack 'D's and cokes, whilst pretending to be less pissed than we actually were! It was then that I noticed two American girls sitting at a table in the corner of the pub. 'Bingo'! That will do me, I thought as I nudged the Geordie and nodded in their direction. With no encouragement needed, Me and the Geordie picked up our drinks and waddled across the bar room and plonked ourselves down at their table. 'My one', was much better looking than 'His one'!

She was a very attractive brunette with a lovely curvaceous body!

She told me her name was Becky, and that she worked as a voice over artist for one of the major film studios in LA. I told her I was a property developer, which wasn't a total lie, as I had in fact been decorating the box room at my mum's just before I had left! As she gasped and whooped at my tales of adventure and woe, and giggled at all my hilarious jokes, we began to cosy up, we also began to get very touchy feely! So, I whispered into her ear and a few moments later we sneaked off into the gents! No sooner as we were in there, than we began to eat the face of each other! I have a vague and I have to say wonderful recollection of lifting her top up and exposing her breasts before I commenced to 'motorboat' the hell out of them!

I don't like to be crude, but I have to say they were exceptional! Needless to say (being the old romantic that I am) I had the intention of leading her into one of the cubicles and going the whole hog! However, it was at this point that I experienced a rare moment of clarity, I can remember thinking, 'fuck, I bet AIDS is rife in L.A.', and I don't have any condoms! However, despite this realisation and the combination of being a hot blooded 23yr old bloke who was currently cupping a pair of very warm, very welcoming and adorable looking brown nosed puppies, I think I probably would have (had to!) still gone for it! That is to say that, if at that precise moment my 'misty' beer googles hadn't decided to slip halfway down my face.

And thus, It was, with tremendous difficulty that I prised my eyes away from her award winning 'Nellie's', looking up I all but let out a shriek when I saw her face! I take it you have heard of Susan Boyle!

With that the bathroom door flew open and a rather annoyed and I have to say, repulsed looking barman burst in and shouted, 'hey, for fucks sake, you can't be doing that in here man, …Jesus fucking Christ'!!!

Like a true gentleman I bolted out of the still open door, too ashamed to look the barman in the eye and leaving the '*I dreamed a dream*' singing sensation to rearrange her clothes and tuck herself back in! (Who says chivalry is dead!).

Just like a sobering punch to the face, the shock of the barman bursting in had momentarily snapped me to my senses. As I flew into the bar, I could now see for the first time just how empty the place was! I looked over to the table where we had been sitting and all I could see was the back of the Geordie's head moving in a slight circular motion as he clearly had 'His one' pinned to the wall and was obviously eating the face off her! 'Fuck me but that American bloke's weed must be strong', I thought to myself as I ran over and rescued my friend and got us both the fuck out of there!

I know we went to more bars that night and I am pretty sure we ended up in a night club too, but that's all I remember. When I woke up the next morning back at the hostel, I was fully dressed and on top of the bed. As I sat up, I pulled a business card out of my back pocket, it read;

Becky Sloane,
Voice-over artist
Universal Studios
Burbank CA
04 03 3575649

on the reverse it said, 'call me', I chucked it in the bin and went downstairs and made myself a strong bitter tasting cup of coffee!

****

We had been in the states for just over a week and had been partying hard and having a fairly wild time. Today was Sunday and Klaus, the world's shittest wizard, had invited Martin and me to join him for a drink down on the board walk at around two that afternoon. I agreed because firstly he owned the hostel, he was our host, and secondly because he and Martin were good friends. The truth of the matter, I had taken an instant dislike to the scruffy German, which was unusual for me, generally speaking I liked everyone but there was just something about him.

Us being us! We had started early in a bar under the pier in Santa Monica called 'The Bar under the Pier'!! It cost five dollars for a ridiculously 'large' can of foster's lager (you needed both hands to pick it up!), so being the greedy type, I started on them. The exterior walls of the bar were virtually all glass which offered spectacular panoramic views of the Pacific Ocean, and also the huge wooden pillars that supported the Santa Monica pier above us. You have probably seen this view before, as it has been in countless movies and pop videos. Big wooden pillars going out into the sea with the waves crashing in around them and onto the shoreline? I'm pretty sure 'Rocky' trained there in his grey sweatpants and I think Lionel Richie might have smouldered while belting out Endless Love!

As I sat taking in the stunning scenery and slurping my huge beer, I began to very subtlety (or at least I thought I was being subtle!) flirt with the very attractive Californian barmaid. Being young and brimming with confidence I sauntered over to the jukebox and thought I would select some cool tunes in an attempt to try and impress with my excellent and super cool taste in music! I opted for the Beatles, so as to confirm my status as both British and very cool!! Having made my selection's, I swaggered back to the long wooden bar just as the first few notes of 'Helter-Skelter' came blasting out from the jukebox.

With this the barmaid spun round with a look of complete horror on her face, as she stated in an alarmed manner, 'oh man, I totally hate this fucking song, it gives me the fucking creeps, it reminds me of that freak Charles Manson, you know who murdered that actress Sharon Tate, up there in Hollywood.... urghhh! Sorry dude I gotta turn it off'! She then looked at me like 'I' had killed Sharon Tate!

The Geordie looked at me, smiled and just said, 'Unlucky son'! Disappointed by her rebuke and now wanting to leave, I hurriedly set about draining my supersized can of lager (which took some doing), as I finished I gave the Geordie a sly cheeky wink and then directed a final satisfactory 'burp' across the bar at the back of the unsuspecting barmaids head which made the Geordie laugh! 'Stank you'! I mumbled as we left the bar and headed off down the board walk towards the hustle and bustle of Venice beach.

As we ambled along past the street entertainers and bars, I heard, to my surprise a familiar, but foreign sounding voice exclaiming, 'Hey, its Pat'! I turned in the direction of the voice and discovered it was Hoff, the Dutch bloke who two years previously had taken me and Jim to the airport! It was a pleasant surprise! 'Fucking hell, ...Hoff'! 'How you doing mate'?! I asked as we shook hands and exchanged man hugs! 'I can't believe your still here Hoff, so, what you been up to? how are ya'?!

Of course, me and Martin joined him at his table and got the beers in, it really was excellent to see him. He explained that he had saved his money and now owned a boat down in the marina and earned a living taking tourists out on boat trips. He told me he lived on the boat with Anna (a beautiful black Dutch girl who also use to stay at the Venice beach hostel). I was pleased for him; I was pleased he was living his dream.

As I listened to Hoff speak, there was a part of me that was thinking how comes nothing like that ever happens to me. I started thinking perhaps Hoff had a better start in life, perhaps he had parents who actively encouraged him to do well. Maybe Hoff came from money or maybe, just maybe, he was in fact just a better man than me!

It wasn't 'sour grapes', It wasn't jealousy, I liked Hoff and I certainly didn't begrudge him his success. I was just aware that sort of thing was unlikely to ever happen for me. Still, I was happy for him. Hoff had two maybe three beers and then said he had to go as he had things to do. Me and Martin didn't budge from our seats and just ordered more drinks!

At 2 'o'clock we headed off to meet Klaus in the sidewalk café. We walked into a great atmosphere as a life band belted out music from the stage at the back of the venue. I instantly liked what I heard as they reminded me of a cross between the Red Hot Chilli Peppers and Crosby Stills and Nash. The lead singer, clearly a head case, was running around the bar playing a mouth organ while the band carried on playing on stage. At one point the lead singer (while still mic'd up!) ran out onto the board-walk and commandeered a guy's bicycle! The bemused cyclist just stood open mouthed as the lead singer rode his bike through and around the bar whilst 'still' playing the mouth organ! It was excellent!

Everyone was having a good time and the beer was flowing fast, when for no reason at all, Klaus looked at me and said, 'Just because you are drinking with Klaus, does not mean, you can take, now, the piss!' (that's how he said it!). I hadn't said or done anything, in fact I had hardly spoken to him at all since we had arrived, I was too busy enjoying the band. However, I didn't like his tone, it immediately got my back up. I straightened up in my chair and lent forward across the table and said, 'You have obviously mistaken me for some sort of mug Klaus, if you think I am the kind of man who needs to 'try' and take liberties. I wouldn't take the piss out of anyone; I was brought up better than that and 'I' know how to conduct myself. But I am glad you have brought the subject up, because I wouldn't want you thinking that just because I am staying in your youth hostel that 'you' can take the piss and try and lord it over 'me' in a pub! Perhaps I have misread the situation Klaus, but I thought we were just two men having a drink ...on a Sunday afternoon ...as equals?!

For the first time since I had meet Klaus, he smiled at me and raised his glass, proffering it to me, we chinked glasses and he said, 'cheers'! I noticed the Geordie visibly relax in his seat!

The tall, skinny, scruffy looking German wizard was absolutely sound with me after that. Perhaps I had read him wrong, perhaps he needed (wanted) to know where 'he' stood as opposed to the other way around. In fact, after that incident in the bar I couldn't put a foot wrong as far as Klaus was concerned! I had been accepted. And fuck me, but did I take (now) the piss!!!

There were only two rules at the Hostel California. Number one, the smoking of marijuana was not under any circumstances permitted inside the hostel. The reason being, Klaus had once had a friend who had fallen down some stairs whilst stoned, had broken his neck and had died. So, the German was dead against it, no pun intended! Adhering to this rule was not a problem, firstly because I rarely had any weed and secondly the LA evenings were warm and long, so it was no hardship to simply sit outside and chuff away to my heart's content.

Rule number two: at eleven o'clock each night the main doors were locked, so if you needed to get in after this time you had to ring the buzzer and then wait for whoever was working on reception to come down and open the door. They would half open the door, ask for your name and room number and then close the door and go and check that you were indeed a paying resident before entry would be allowed.

One morning at about 2 am, me and Martin arrived at the front door of the hostel California so drunk that we could barely stand up, in fact we just about managed between us, to ring the buzzer! A few moments later a young black lad arrived, half opened the door and politely asked our names. Martin barged him out of the way and called him a 'stupid looking cunt' as I followed suit. The poor lad got in a bit of a tizz and started shouting, 'Hey you can't do that', to which he received a chorus of, 'Fuck off you mug' and 'Shut up you fucking job's worth'! 'Go fuck yourself', and lots of giggles as me and the Geordie negotiated our way up the stairs to our room. The lad didn't know what to do, so he ran off heading in the direction of Klaus's room shouting 'Klaus, Klaus, two men have just barged their way in and told me to fuck off!'

Me and the Geordie burst into fits of laughter when we heard Klaus bellow out, 'are they English and drunk'? To which the bloke replied in a frightened voice, 'Yes Klaus, they are'! I nearly fell over when I heard Klaus roar, 'That's just Pat and Martin you stupid fucking bastard! Wake me up again... and your fucking sacked'! I actually felt sorry for the poor bloke.

****

As I previously stated when I booked my flight to the US, I had also booked a return flight so as not to arouse any suspicion with the immigration officials. After three weeks of heavy partying in Los Angeles the day had come when my plane would be leaving ...without me!

It was a strange feeling! I was aware that it was now a shit or bust move, up until this point I had, had the option of jumping on the plane and going home, after today I was in it for the long haul. Me and the Geordie decided that as it was such a momentous day for me that we should definitely get pissed. I remember sitting in a bar on Venice beach drinking jugs of Margaritas as I watched the clock on the wall. Two hours until my plane takes off! More Margaritas, one hour until my plane takes off! Even more Margaritas and then at 1500 hours the Virgin Atlantic 747 took off heading for Heathrow airport with at least one empty seat on it!

'Well it looks like I'm fucking staying!' I cheerfully announced to the Geordie. 'You've nothing to worry about Pat, honestly you'll be sound' he assured me. It was at this precise moment that my American adventure truly began! We stayed rooted to the bar getting very drunk and singing Jimmy Buffet's, 'Wasted away again in Margaritaville'! I was halfway through another rendition when I fell off the barstool and cracked my head on the bar on the way down, like a true Brit, I came up smiling. However, the barman was not. 'Okay buddy, you're done. That's it, no more', he announced as he waved his arms like a boxing ref declaring the fight over! 'It's alright mate I'm English', I said hopefully, but he was not going to be moved on his decision. I was extremely drunk, but I was also aware that I was extremely drunk, so as I entered the next bar along the board walk, I pretended with all my might, to be as sober as a judge! It took a lot of doing, I had to concentrate really hard, but I think I could have won an Oscar for my portrayal of a sober man. What's more I was aware that I was getting away with it, right up until the point when I reached the bar and attempted to order a drink, but couldn't, because I had lost the power of speech! I needed a lot of coffee the next morning!

A few days later me and Martin were sitting chatting in the communal living room on a couch under the huge picture of the challenger space shuttle, when Klaus came walking past. 'How are you two today?' he asked. 'Yeah were good thanks Klaus' we replied almost in unison. He paused and looked at us quizzically; he was no fool. 'You have been partying hard for weeks now, Yes?', a squint in the eye and another pause. 'You must be getting low on 'the' money'? 'I won't feed you.... I won't give you money'!

'but you can both stay here, you will have a roof over your heads, you pair of cunts'! And then shuffled off without saying another word.

I was momentarily taken aback; I was also impressed! I had clearly been wrong about Klaus; I had misinterpreted his German ways. He had gone up in my estimations, I thought it was very good of him to offer. Not that either the Geordie or myself had any intention of ever taking him up on it, but still it was nice to know all the same (and just in case).

He was right we had been hitting it hard! We had been spending a lot of money (I loved spending American dollars! It felt good as opposed to English pounds), neither of us had really considered knuckling down and working yet, as we were too busy having the times of our lives! But it 'was' time to get down to business! So naturally we discussed it over a few drinks!

Martin knew the score and this was what he advised, 'First things first, we need to buy a car, before we run out of money'. 'You, also need to put in for a driving test', he said 'because you can use your licence as ID for getting work. I don't need to because I have already got one!' He then explained, 'We need to get hold of some fake IDs, green cards and social security cards to be exact'! 'And then we both need to open a bank account for wages and stuff to be paid into'. Martin took a big swig of his beer and said, 'And then finally, you need to 'not' get fucking caught, because if you do you will end up in a deportation prison with loads of fucking Guatemalans, ...which will make 'you' exotic!, before they kick you out of the states'. 'And ...that's it really', he said rather matter of factly, as he opened another beer!

'Hmm, well that all sounds quite straight forward'!! I said sarcastically as I drained my can of beer!

We bought a car! In fact, we bought the best car in the world, without doubt the best car I have ever owned. I wish I still had it! It was a 1980s dark blue, Country Squire, Ford station wagon which had wood panelling down both sides and on the rear tail gate. It had a 4.9ltr V8 engine with a column change shift next to the steering wheel (gear stick to you and me). The interior had a plush lined light blue carpet with real leather front and back bench seats (for a total of 6 passengers), and in what 'we' might refer to as the estate bit at the rear of the car there were two fold-up doors in the floor, which when you pulled them open, became the back rests for more seats in a sunken foot-well, which in turn could accommodate four more passengers! Unbelievably the car was 17ft 11 inches long! If it were possible to marry a car (you probably can in some states!), then that would have been the car I would marry. I loved it!

We bought the station wagon from three Kiwi lads, who had themselves bought it for $1000 dollars from a family in Colorado (it still had the Colorado tag on the front, where 'we' would have our registration plate!) and had driven the car all the way down to Los Angeles. They were reluctantly selling 'HER' as their trip around the states had come to an end and they were due to fly back to New Zealand the next day. It was plain to see that the three lads were decent, clean living, and I suppose what you would call nice boys! I am sure their American experience was completely different to the one I was currently embarking on. They kept referring to the car as 'her' and 'she', which me and the Geordie found mildly amusing! We agreed on a price of $400 dollars, which was an absolute bargain as the car was in mint condition; there wasn't even so much as a scratch on it. The lads pointed out we clearly had the deal of the century, but as they couldn't put it on the plane and take it home with them it was ours! They then asked if we wouldn't mind posing for some photographs with them and their beloved station wagon. Obviously to complete their photographic journal of their epic American adventure. I remember leaning across the vast 'Hood' of our newly purchased vehicle and smiling for the camera, as I shook hands with one of the lads. We gave them the $400 dollars and assured them we would take good care of .... 'HER'!

As they walked away, they kept looking back longingly over their shoulders, like they were leaving a much loved but impossible to care for child in the care of strangers!

I was a bit nervous driving 'her' at first, she was after all nearly 18ft long and I was also on the 'wrong' side of the road, but I soon found a couple of beers steadied my nerves! The first night we had her we decided to take her for a spin around the city. Inevitably as we drove around from pub to pub, we began to get drunk! In fact, we got completely shit faced! The last place I can remember being was in Santa Monica. I am quite proud of the fact that we rather sensibly decided that due to our current condition we would leave the car where 'she' was and take a cab back to the hostel.

The next morning neither the Geordie nor myself could remember where we had left the car. To make matters worse neither of us knew the registration and our combined efforts to recall the description of the car were poor to say the least. We knew it was long, we knew it was blue and we thought (or rather hoped) it might be somewhere in the Santa Monica area of Los Angeles!

So, with sore heads and for the next three hours we tramped the streets of Santa Monica, desperately trying to retrace our steps from the night before. The longer we looked the more certain we became that the car had been towed away! We couldn't believe it $400 fucking dollars and no car! We were just about to call it a day and give up, when in the distance I glimpsed what appeared to be the top of a station wagon glinting in the hot Californian sun, my heart skipped a beat as I realised 'she' had returned to us! It had been a close call. We both agreed we would never make the same stupid mistake again, in future, no matter how drunk we got, the car was coming home with us!

Obviously owning a car made a huge difference, it meant we could now go further afield, which was good, because by now I was itching to get out of the city and see a bit more of the states. My first chance to get a small way out of the city at least, came when an old friend of the Geordie's, a truck driver from Hull, named Mikey invited us to a strip club in nearby Pasadena, just a few miles south of LA. My first thought was, 'I ain't taking my clothes off for no one'! My second, 'Mikey might be a bit of a dirty old man', (he was probably in his mid-forties, ancient to me!).

I had never been to a strip club before. When I look back now, I realise just how young I actually was, as green as grass. I definitely was not as worldly wise as perhaps I 'thought' I was. But I was 23, so off we went. It was dark as we pulled off the interstate and on to the gravelled parking lot outside 'the' club. A huge neon sign read 'The World's Most Beautiful Women'! It was quite a bold statement, one which I instantly dismissed as I thought to myself, I will be the judge of that! (isn't it wonderful being British and aloof)!

I entered the club with a certain amount of trepidation. It was dimly lit inside, not quite dark but almost. There was a long-crowded bar down the right-hand side of the venue and across the room to the centre left was a brightly lit stage. A naked and extremely attractive lady was writhing around a pole as groups of raucous men, easily identifiable as construction workers, postal workers and office workers (you know how the Americans love to don a uniform), were loudly cheering, drinking and throwing dollar bills onto the stage, as the lady contorted and cavorted for their entertainment. I could see topless waitresses serving trays of drinks to groups of men who were stuffing dollar bills into the waitress's thongs and then slapping them on the arse as they turned away to serve other gentlemen! Somewhere a PA system blasted out tunes like, 'you can leave your hat on' and 'American woman'. It was an electrically charged atmosphere which blew my young mind. I thought I had died and gone to heaven! I didn't see a single woman who wasn't a perfect 10! We (or rather I) made sure we got a table right at the front of the stage, so as not to miss anything! I was like a kid in a sweet shop!!

As the very attractive naked women on the stage came to the end of her 'dance' routine, the lighting went up a notch and the music stopped, she then dropped to her knees and began scurrying around scooping up the dollar bills that had been thrown upon the stage. At that 'exact' point I began to feel very uncomfortable and the whole thing took on an element of sleaze I had not been expecting. It all seemed rather a bit shit! It's a very unfair thing to say, but in a matter of seconds the lady had gone from being a smoking hot sex siren, into a pitiful looking back street whore! That is not what 'I thought' of the woman! That's just how it looked, and I felt awkward and uncomfortable being a part of it.

As me, Martin and Mikey sat at our table, an attractive topless waitress arrived to take our order, she was all smiles and tits! 'And what can I get you guys tonight' she beamed. 'I will have a beer please' I said as I tried to remain eye contact and not look directly at her exposed breasts (which is easier said than done!). 'Gee, that's a lovely accent you have there honey. Where you from? Australia?'! I smiled politely, 'No, I am from England'. 'England, oh wow, I love the British', and with that she turned and left to go and get our drinks (but not before I shot a quick glance at her bare arse!).

A few moments later the lights dimmed, the music started up again, and the most beautiful girl I have 'ever' seen appeared from behind a sequinned doorway and stepped out onto the stage. I was instantly mesmerised, like Mowgli from the Jungle Book, his eyes spinning as he stands trance-like in front of the snake Kaa!

The girl was of average height with shoulder length black hair and was so good looking, she would probably stop traffic! I was quite proud of myself when I also noticed she had the most beautiful piercing brown eyes! She practically smouldered as she began to gyrate and slowly peel away her layers of clothing. I don't think I could have looked away even if I had wanted to!

Her body was pure perfection, pert breasts and an arse than I can only describe as a perfect, country fair, prize winning peach, that I would have gladly sold my soul to have taken a bite out of! I was transfixed as she danced and writhed on the raised stage no more than three feet in front of where I was sitting. At one point she spun herself seductively around the pole in the centre of the stage, looked me directly in the eyes and held my gaze! I instantly felt myself blush. She was clearly very good at her job! She continued to hold me under her spell as she turned herself upside down and slid her gorgeous body down the pole, then, bringing herself to a stop, she slowly and very seductively parted her legs!

My god, I could barely believe my eyes! I instantly felt a stirring in my loins as I gazed upon ...the holy grail, the incredulous, the very reason for being! I kid you not it was fucking incredible, like gazing into the eyes of an angel! I'm sure I felt my lips involuntarily 'purse' as if I was going to have some remote chance of kissing it!! I swear that girl winked at me (with her eyes!). I began to feel embarrassed at being so turned on and had to remind myself that I was in fact sitting at a table with two drunken northerners!

As the music stopped and as her 'dance' routine came to an end, I finally looked away, but this was only because I didn't want to sully her memory by watching her scooping up the dollar bills from the stage floor. I simply cannot put into words how utterly fucking amazing she was! I turned towards Martin and Mikey and with a dropped jaw simply said, 'a fuck ...a-me'!

Grinning they both nodded in agreement and then Mikey said something which completely blew my mind! 'She will be out in a minute; you can get a lap dance for $10 dollars'!! Jesus Christ could this night get any fucking better. Well yes actually it could.

I saw her as she emerged from behind the stage, now partially dressed she began to make her way through the club. She was wearing a pair of white strapped high heels and a white satin see through negligé. Underneath which I could see the warm white glow of her skimpy bra which barely contained her pert breasts. In the low lighting of the club the whiteness of her underwear glowed against her soft golden-brown skin. I didn't hesitate as I brazenly approached her and in my best clipped English accent (I was also good at my job!) said, 'excuse me for interrupting, but I just wanted to say how much I enjoyed your performance, you were sensational and if it's okay with you I would very much like to have a lap dance'!

'Well thank you' she gushed. My god, even her voice was sexy! She then gave me the most beautiful smile and said 'Awh, what an adorable accent you have, where is that from'? 'Oh, I am from England' I said rather bashfully! 'Well of course you can have a dance honey', she then took me by the hand and led me over to a chair in a slightly more secluded part of the club and to my surprise and joy, sat on my lap! I think I may have jumped the gun a bit because at this point there was still no music playing (can't give a lap dance without music!).

She looked at me quizzically and asked, 'How old are you honey'? 'I'm 23', I said as I felt myself blush again. 'Awh, you're just a baby, don't worry I'm going to take 'real' good care of you' she giggled. As we waited for the music to start (I was hoping they might play bohemian rhapsody, ...because it goes on for fucking ever!), she told me her name was Sophia and she was from Brazil. She told me she danced part time because she was studying (hmm).

I am not a fool; I know she was just doing her job. But she was definitely flirting with me, a little anyway! I was by far the youngest bloke in the club that night. I was fairly fresh faced. I was very polite. And I was British. I was probably a breath of fresh air compared to her usual clientele! I remember (probably foolishly) thinking, if I had just arrived in the states and still had a lot of cash, I would have chanced my arm and asked her for her number. Now you are probably correctly thinking stop being a mug mate, but I am telling you, she liked me! I know she was very good at her job!! Of course, she was playing me, and I am sure she would have rinsed me for every penny or cent! But still, you know when you know! And anyway, It might have actually been worth it!

As the first opening bars of a song began to play (sadly not Bohemian Rhapsody!), she smiled and said, 'You ready for this baby' I just nodded that I was.

Sophi'a stood in front of me and slowly removed her negligée before gently throwing it around my neck. She then slowly but firmly, drew it back across my skin before discarding it on the seat next to me. She then began to swivel her hips seductively and gently gyrated her swaying body in front of me as she ran her hands up and down her soft brown perfectly formed figure. Then she turned away from me and bending forward placed her hands behind her and onto my knees and then raised her gorgeous peach of an arse and slowly circulated it in front of me before she slammed it down hard into my lap! She then proceeded to bounce up and down, hard and quickly whilst she turned her head in my direction and gave me a really hot sultry look. Bringing herself to a stop, she stood up slowly and turned around to face me and gave me another gorgeous smile, before she began to arch her back as she lent into me and rolled her near naked body over me until her breasts were almost touching my face.

It was absolute heaven! It was so intoxicating I had almost forgotten about the other two hundred blokes in the club! She then surprised me by straddling me and placing her arms on my shoulders as she clasped her hands together behind my neck and then furiously began bouncing up and down on my lap like she was in a lap fucking contest and I had the last one on the planet.

As she slowed to a gentle rhythm and slowly drew her arms away from around my neck, she let out a little whimper and slowly, really slowly, gyrated herself up and down and around on my lap! She then did something I will remember for the rest of my life. She looked me straight in the eyes and gave me a very serious 'I'm soooo..., going to fuck you, long and hard', look! With this, she then dug the tips of her fingernails into my bare arms and slowly and very sensually dragged them, scratching my naked skin, up the whole length of my arms sending shivers through my entire body! As she did so, she lent into me, pressing her whole-body weight against me, I felt the warmth of her breath as she exhaled on to my lips. She then let out a tiny little sigh and seductively brushed her soft check against my lips as she pushed past the side of my face and took the small of my earlobe into her warm wet mouth and gave it a long, 'hard' wet suck, before gently biting down with her teeth. Then slowly she pulled away, letting my earlobe slip from her mouth! I knew it, she knew it! I had the hardest boner I have ever had in my life!

The thought did occur to me that I might at that very moment explode in my pants, and also, if at that precise moment 'my' Sophia had asked me to kill someone for her, I fucking would have! Sadly, the song had come to an end, the lights had brightened. The 'dance' was over! She really was an amazing woman; we had a brief chat before she left and moved on to her 'next' mug! I however couldn't go anywhere! I had to stay put for a while and think about the time 'Tibby' died, before I could risk going back to join the Geordie and Mikey at our table. Thank the lord for Ford station wagons and strip clubs!

So now we had a car, the next thing we needed to do, was get some IDs. Martin explained that we could obtain the documents we needed from some rather shady English blokes in Santa Monica. A green card and social security card, which would allow us to start applying for jobs and earn some much-needed cash would set us back around $500 dollars. But the Geordie said, 'Fuck that'! 'We will go straight to the main man', where we could get the IDs for about $60 – 100 dollars for the pair.

The main man however was situated in a notorious district of LA called MacArthur Park and to make matters worse we didn't actually know who the 'main man' was. We were going to have to find 'him'. MacArthur Park was a well-known hot spot for the procurement of fake IDs, and a very dangerous area with a history of gangland violence between the local black American and Hispanic gangs. Shootings and murders were not a rare occurrence, mainly resulting from drug wars and gangland feuds! It certainly was not the sort of place for two out of town white boys! But we went anyway!

The main street through the district rose and dipped like in the opening scenes of the TV show The Streets of San-Francisco! On either side of the main road tall tenement style buildings loomed high in the air creating a claustrophobic feel to the place. I didn't need anyone to tell me that this was an extremely dodgy area, I could feel it! It was literally a world apart from the glitz, glamour and sparkle of the shinning skyscrapers of downtown Los Angeles. This was the projects! This was like one of those hard hitting 1980s American gangster movies about hard times and poverty. Everywhere you looked it was drug addicts, prostitutes and 'wise' guys. The truth is, I knew it was going to be rough, but I had not expected it to be this rough. I was beginning to think this really isn't a good idea!

After driving down the main strip for about 10 minutes or so, we came to a set of lights and turned right off the main road into a side street. If I had thought the main strip was bad, well this was something else. It was every negative thought and every negative image you have ever had of life in the ghetto! To say it was bad, well it doesn’t even come close! As we came to a stop at another set of lights there was a tap on the passenger side window of our station wagon.

A Hispanic looking guy on a bicycle with mad hair and no teeth said, 'You want IDs'! Jesus was it that obvious! It looked like the main man was going to find us. Why else would two white boys be in this part of town if it wasn't involving something dodgy! Nervously but with my best poker face so as not to look like a victim I indicated that we did indeed want IDs. 'Next corner, next corner' he repeated as he rode off and disappeared out of view. As we again turned right the Hispanic guy was waiting on his bicycle and indicated for us to pull over. At this point, I am thinking, ‘Am I going to get IDs or a gun to the head!

'What you want, what you need'? Everything about the man was nervous and rushed, his nervousness was making me nervous. The Geordie being more experienced in this sort of thing, took control of the situation and told the man what we needed and negotiated a very reasonable price of $60 dollars for both the green card and social security card. Martin also made it clear we wouldn't be parting with any money until we had received the goods. 'Okay, Okay, buddy no problem'! A bargain, as long as we didn't end up being dumped at the bottom of the lake in MacArthur park.

The twitchy Hispanic guy told us to wait in the car while he went to sort it out, the Geordie and me sat in the car, not speaking, both suddenly very serious and understandably very worried. The man returned a short while later and said we were good to go! He needed my name and my date of birth, as they would appear on the documents. Okay so far and fair enough! Then he said, 'I' had to accompany him to a one-hour photo shop for the picture to be taken for my green card. It was at this point that I began to get seriously concerned for my safety. This was an extremely dangerous and dodgy situation,. Apart from the Geordie, no one else on the entire planet knew I was here! And this toothless and clearly crack addicted Hispanic guy wants me to take a walk with him! To a very dodgy looking little one-hour photo shop, no bigger than a doorway on a crack infested, drug riddled, prostitute ridden, gangland hotbed of a street. 'Okay, let's go'! I said, just wanting to get it over with as quickly as possible.

The one-hour photo shop was run by a group of Chinese people, the 'main man' turned out to be a no-nonsense and very serious looking Chinese woman. I was taken through the shop to a little room situated at the back of the premises. I was now alone and out of sight of the normal living world. I was an illegal immigrant engaging in an illegal activity, I was aware that if something were to happen to me ...then no one would ever know the outcome of my demise. It's fair to say I was a 'little' nervous, in fact it's fair to say my arse was going 10 to the dozen!

However my council estate up bringing kicked in, I staunched it, I kept my nerve, I didn't let it show how concerned I really was, not even when I heard the 'main man' lock the door! I was told to sit on a stool in the middle of the empty room so as to pose for the photo for my green card. The Chinese woman barked at me 'Look up, you look left, you no smile' I remember thinking don't worry, I have no intention of doing so!

A few moments later she unlocked the door and I was (thankfully) asked to leave, I can assure you she didn't need to ask me twice! The now very fidgety Hispanic guy told me to return to the car and wait until my documents were ready. I made my way back to the car and got in without saying a word to the Geordie, he just looked at me as if to say, 'you alright'? I made no comment.

As I waited, I began to feel a bit braver now that the worst of my ordeal was nearly over. I had told the Hispanic guy 'don’t take too long'. 'Okay, Okay, I be quick' he assured me. I could see he was eager to seal the deal, so he could get 'another' hit!

Me and Martin waited for almost an hour parked up in the side street. It felt like an eternity. Just up the street from where we were parked there was a liquor store which had iron bars across the windows. From the moment we had pulled up, we had been aware of the group of black and white crack cocaine addicts, dealers, pimps, whores and hustlers who obviously spent their days standing on 'their' corner probably as the Americans would say 'turning tricks'. As me and Martin endured our tense wait sitting in our station wagon, each and every one of the hoods and hoes took a turn in casually taking a stroll past are parked vehicle obviously checking us out! Everyone knew what we were up to! Or at least I hoped they did, I wouldn’t want them thinking we might be undercover cops or members of another gang! Either way, it was bad, and it was uncomfortable. In fact, at one point a cop car drove past and the two police officers looked directly at Martin and me. 'Shit', if everyone else knows what were up to, then surely they will too! I really didn't like this at all, I felt more vulnerable and at risk with every passing minute.

Finally, the mad-haired toothless Hispanic guy returned and alarmingly got straight in the back of the car and sat directly behind me (fuck that!). I didn't like it one bit. He was now visibly more relaxed and calmer than he had previously been and seemed to be in no hurry at all, in fact he seemed to have all the time in the world for us. The deal was done. He had clearly had a hit of whatever the fuck it was he was on. He handed over the goods like he was now a completely different person. Martin looked them over nodded that everything was fine and gave the man the agreed money. The Hispanic guy was eating some sort of snack food from a polystyrene container and began to settle back in the seat! 'So ...you guys from... England, huh'? He enquired. 'Yeah we are mate', I said quite anxiously and just wanting the whole thing to be over. He forked his food and as if deep in thought sighed 'Hmm.... you know Liverpool'? He asked it, like we were all good friends casually chatting over a few drinks. I didn't mean to be so rude, but my nerves were beginning to get the better of me and I blurted, 'Yeah, yeah the fucking Beatles ...now get the fuck out'! The Geordie chuckled (in disbelief) for the first time since we had arrived in this god forsaken hell hole. I actually felt bad as I saw the look of hurt and rejection on the Hispanic guys face by my rather blunt and rude request for him to do one! 'Okay, Okay no problem, my friend' he said as he climbed out of the back seat, looking completely dejected and a little confused. As soon as he shut the door the Geordie put his foot down on the accelerator and we drove off, putting as much distance between us and that shit hole as we could!

The whole experience is, to date, the most dangerous and dodgiest situation I have ever put myself in. I have long-since lost that green card but if you had ever had the opportunity to stare at my face on the front of the card, I guarantee it is the most scared you would have ever seen me look, despite my attempt at the best poker face in history, ...ever!!

When we got back to the Hostel California, I found that for the rest of the day I was in a unusually quiet and funny mood. I drank some beers, but I didn't get drunk! In all, it had been, quite a harrowing ordeal!

Now I had my fake IDs I needed to get working because the money was starting to run low. We had heard that a recruitment agency, specialising in construction work in nearby Culver City was hiring. So, me and the Geordie went along to sign up and apply for work. I think we both felt slightly out of place as we entered a very smart looking lobby area at the end of which was a long counter. Behind the counter stood a very smartly dressed and very eloquently spoken black man. 'Good morning gentlemen and what can I do for you today'? We explained that we were looking for work and wished to sign up with the agency. 'Okay, no problem' he said as he handed us some forms and pens attached to clip boards. He asked us to take a seat and fill out the enrolment forms. I found it surprisingly difficult to fill out the forms because I had to lie about everything; it seemed to take for ever. Every now and again I would look up from the forms and catch the black guy staring at us. It didn't feel right, but I put it down to nerves.

When we were done, we presented are completed applications to the counter. The man thumbed through the forms and finally said 'Okay, that all seems to be in order'. 'Okay guys, I need to see some forms of ID'. Me and the Geordie both slapped are IDs down on the counter in front of him, he looked down at the counter and with his finger pointed to each document in turn as he looked back up at us and said 'Okay, that's fake, that's fake and that's fake and so is that one'! 'Look, I appreciate what you guys are trying to do, but take my advice and get rid of them, because you are both going to get yourselves in a whole lotta trouble'! Before kindly adding, 'Would you like me to tear up these application forms and put them in the bin for you'? Are faces were so red we could have lit up a darkened room, as we simply mumbled 'Erm yeah, Okay' as we made some barely audible apology, grabbed our fakes off the counter and scarped out the front door. F..... UCK!

I was totally demoralised; I couldn’t believe it. After everything I had been through, and the very first time I use them, I get sussed! The Geordie undeterred said, 'Don’t worry, we will get photocopies of the fakes and use the photocopies when we apply somewhere else'! Actually, it was not a bad idea!

I still felt down about the whole thing. I needed to earn some money! I was sick of drinking (but not entirely). And for the first time since being in America I had a true proper hankering for a big fat joint of weed, but I didn't have any and what's more I didn't know where to get any. It had been a tough few days so, to cheer myself up, I went for a walk alone along the board walk on Venice beach.

As I strolled along with the hot Californian sun beating down on my head and the cool pacific sea breeze on my face, I noticed in the distance what appeared to be a Rastafarian; unbelievably he was wearing what I might describe as a 'tea cosy' on his head (in this heat)! He was walking in my direction! I don’t go in for racial stereo types (hmm), but could it actually be possible! Was this really going to happen! He was accompanied by a young woman with a child in a buggy. As the distance between us closed, I began to stare directly at him, after a few seconds he noticed and stared back. As the distance between us shortened still, I never once averted my gaze, nor did he! I just knew! And so did he! As we got closer along the boardwalk, I continued to stare at him until eventually, as we reached one another, we both stopped. He looked at me in complete amazement and with a look of joyous surprise said, 'You want bud'!! It was fucking unreal! I spoke with an almost identical look of amazement and unbelievable joy on my face and said, 'Yeah, I do'! The smiling Rasta, hesitated for a moment, frowned and said, 'You got something to put it in'? I said I didn't, so he suggested I hold out a dollar in my hand, which I did. He then placed possibly the biggest and best, $20 dollar deal, I ever got in the entire time I spent in the United States of America into the dollar bill in the palm of my hand. I quickly closed my hand around it, fearing it might be lost to a sudden pacific gust of wind! I could have kissed the fucker, I couldn't thank him enough, I all but bear hugged him on the board walk. We both smiled as we shock hands and our heads in joyous disbelieve at what had just occurred and then carried on are separate ways!

I fucking love it when things like that happen... It made my day! I don't know if you have ever tried to roll a joint on a crowded beach but believe me it's a bit of a bugger! Sand, wind and inquisitive kids and then there's your David Hasselhoff types! It ain't easy, but I managed it anyway and what's more, I sat and brazenly sparked it up. I was in a world of my own as I sat happily puffing away and gazing out across the ocean. I thought about where I was! I thought about where I was from! I thought about my poor old mum. I pictured her with her back to me as she stood at the kitchen sink doing the dishes, what life has she ever had? The thought upset me, so I pushed it away. Once I had smoked the joint I lazily got to my feet and instantly felt the effects of the weed, it was strong stuff! I trudged my way across the sand and back on to the board walk where I plodded along before stopping and treating myself to a very quiet pint in a beach front bar, before slowly, very slowly, heading back to the hostel. I told the Geordie all about my miraculous good fortune and then lay on my bed where I slept till late that evening!

I woke up at about nine o'clock to find Martin had gone out for the night, so I rolled myself another joint (observing rule number 2!), before going downstairs and out the back of the hostel to a little seating area where I could smoke my joint undetected. It was dark outside but being California, it was still quite pleasant and warm. I sat down on a chair amongst some potted palms, I hadn't noticed the girl sitting on a bench opposite me, in the dark and with her feet tucked up under her. As I lit my joint and the spark from my lighter lit up my face, she said 'Good evening!' scaring the life out of me and making me jump. Noticing she had startled me, she chuckled to herself. We both smiled as I said 'hello' in return.

She looked like the hippie type, she had long scraggly dark hair and was wearing a tie-dyed t-shirt and faded flared jeans, a pair of sandals lay on the floor in front of her. I gathered from her accent that she was German. Having taken a couple of pulls on my joint, I extended my arm in her direction offering it to her. But she held up a roach (end of a spliff) indicating that she had just finished one herself! As I sat smoking, we made some small talk, where we had been, were we were going, that sort of thing. She was not a particularly attractive girl, but she was very pleasant all the same.

Both being young, there was some mild harmless flirtation, but nothing that suggested anything was leading anywhere, which was okay because it was all very relaxed and chilled. As we chatted, I noticed a small amulet hanging on a chain from her neck, still playing the subtle flirtation game I asked, 'What's that'? She took it in her right hand and held out in front of her and rolled it along the chain back and forth as women do and said, 'it is a little Buddha, and it represents luck' 'You rub its belly in a circle three times and make a wish and it will come true!' and then she offered it up to me 'You try', she smiled before adding quite seriously 'You cannot wish for money'!, 'And you cannot reveal, what you have wished for, because then it won't come true ya!'. Not wishing to offend and just in case there was a chance this encounter might indeed lead somewhere! I went along with it! After everything I had been through over the last few days I could have done with some luck, so I rubbed the little 'fuckers' belly and wished that I would soon get some work! That's not wishing for money is it! I was stoned and I felt a bit silly, but it was just a harmless bit of fun. I finished my joint and put it out in the plant pot next to me, it had been nice talking to the German girl. We bade each other 'Good night' and made our way back inside and went our separate ways.

I awoke the next morning to banging on my bedroom door. When I opened it, it was Karl the little black bloke from reception, (the one Klaus had threatened with the sack, for being so stupid!). 'Hey Pat, do you want a day's work doing removals'?

I was stunned! 'Oh my God'! I could have kicked myself! If I had known it was going to work, I would have 'wished' for, …well you know! The German bird and so forth!

Of course, it was a coincidence (or was it!). I had put the word about in the hostel a few days earlier that I was looking for work. Karl was working the front desk when a bloke from a removals company just up the road had come in explaining that they were short staffed and did he know of anyone who might want a day's work, cash in hand. And fair play to Karl he had thought of me.

30 minutes after my rude awakening, I was standing outside on Lincoln boulevard waiting for a big American haulage truck to pick me up. I didn't have to wait long, before the big truck pulled up alongside me and the passenger door opened. I looked up into the cab and two Mexicans stared back down at me. 'Hey are you Pat'? 'Yep, that's me'! I grinned. 'Okay then, get in, ...let's go to work'!

Bert and Ernie were great! Bert (the driver) was a big heavy, thick set man while Ernie was of slight build, of average height and had a pencil moustache. Bert looked like someone's dad while Ernie looked like he used to be (or was) in a gang but had left his bandana at home because he was working! I liked Bert and Ernie from the off. It was plain to see that they were just two ordinary guys trying to make a living, they were friendly and polite, and they were very interested to know all about me! Who I was, where I was from and what it was like. As we chugged along in the truck Bert explained the job. We were moving a rich bloke from Beverley hills to West Hollywood, and they hoped I was fit because there would be plenty of heavy lifting. (careful what you wish for!).

We pulled up at a house in a very smart looking district of Beverley Hills. The house was situated on a slight bend in the road, built over four floors and into the side of a hill (or rock face to be exact), it was very impressive. We had stopped in front of a set of large electric double garage doors, which as they opened revealed a very large 'basement' garage which had enough room for at least ten cars. The first thing that caught my eye was a love chair suspended from the ceiling next to an elevator, if you're old enough to remember the 1980s American TV show 'Hart to Hart', then it reminded me of when Mr Hart, would pull into his garage in the opening credits, climb out of his Mercedes and take the elevator up to the house, to see Jennifer! Mrs Hart, (the two of them together? Well, it doesn't bear thinking about?).

The three amigos! Me, Bert and Ernie took the lift up to the first floor of the house. As we stepped out, I immediately realised I was in for a hard day's graft, because everything in the place looked big, expensive and heavy! The living room or living space, was stark white and round in shape with a circular sunken floor which housed the seating area, including the white custom-made leather couches. The curved exterior walls were all made of glass, affording spectacular and uninterrupted panoramic views of Los Angeles and the surrounding suburbs. The house was incredible! In fact, the best way to describe it, would be, a round (upside down) four tier wedding cake, stuck to the side of a cliff face?!

The owner of the property, a well-groomed middle-aged man, walked us around, so as to instruct us as to what was going and where. I hardly heard a word he said as I took in the lavish splendour of the man's house.

The 'piece de resistance' of the home was to be found on the top floor in the master bedroom. As I entered the room the first thing to catch my eye was the mirrored ceiling above the king size bed. Then I noticed next to the ornate oak headboard there was a couple of steps leading up to a closed door. Intrigued, and without thinking I asked the owner, 'What's behind the door'? Thinking it was probably just another en-suite. The owner of the house smiled, somewhat smugly and said, '...take a look'! To be honest I felt slightly embarrassed, because I got the feeling that Bert and Ernie, would not have 'A', asked. And 'B', been invited to 'take a look'.

I walked up the two little steps and opened the door. I couldn't believe my eyes or wipe the smile off my face as I stepped out to find myself standing on a small terrace on the very tip of a mountain! In front of me was a jacuzzi with probably the best view of LA money could buy. In the far distance the skyscrapers of downtown shimmered in the heat. It was breathtakingly beautiful. The owner of the house took great delight in letting me know just how successful and fortunate he was!

A few moments later and it was back to reality as me, Bert and Ernie got on with the back-breaking job in hand, of removing all of 'MR HART'S' furniture. My first impressions had been correct everything was heavy, big and awkward. As we worked our way from the top down, moving the furniture and putting it in the truck I noticed on one of the walls a hand-written song by, a well-known British superstar, framed below a gold disc, then a little while later I saw a magazine with a picture of the owner of the house on the front cover. It turned out he was in fact a record producer and as the day went on it also turned out he was a bit of an arrogant wanker! This may seem like an unfair judgement call, but as I removed some cushions from a small settee next to his bed, I discovered a 'Jazz' mag hidden underneath. I chuckled to myself and remember thinking 'Yep, don't matter where you live, don't matter how much money you got, we all like to 'bang' one out now and again! Obviously, I said nothing, but then I didn't need too, just knowing was enough! So, I just carried on with my work, happy in the knowledge!

It took a long time and a lot of hard work emptying the house of its contents and loading them on to the truck. At one point I caught Bert and Ernie sitting down on the job (having a breather), they both looked embarrassed at having been caught and as a way of deflection said, 'Hey, Pat, you wanna take a break'! 'no let's just keep going' I said without hesitation. 'Man you Brits are re..al good workers, huh'! they both agreed as they got to their feet (Ernie helping Bert). Unbeknown to them this was not the case, the truth was, I had ran out of cigarettes and was gasping for a fag, so I wanted to get the truck loaded, so we could stop off along the way to the next house and I could buy a packet of smokes!

The next house in West Hollywood was just as impressive as the first in its own right! A mock Tudor single story sprawling mansion with well-maintained and manicured lawns. A completely different world for the likes of me, it too was unbelievable. We began to unload the truck at the new address and as I walked into the large living room of the vast property I was shocked to see the record producer standing legs apart with a glass of wine in his left hand and with his right hand pointing his finger and waving it from one side of the room to the other, while Bert and Ernie were holding aloft a heavy looking leather arm chair and were literally following his finger, walking from one end of the room to the other while the producer was saying, 'I... think...'? I couldn't believe the gall of the man or the stupidity of the two Mexicans. As I say, a different world for the likes of me! A short while later I returned to the same room carrying a stack of boxes. As I entered, the record producer, waving his finger from side to side said, 'erm, ... I...think'. 'PLONK'!! I dropped the stack of boxes in the middle of the room, turned without looking at him and left. As I was leaving, I thought I heard him say, '...oh, ...Okay'!

It was a long day before it was finally over. The record producer chatted with me for a while, he asked me where I was from. When I told him, he said he know it, because he had passed through it on his way to Watford Football Club, with his mate, Elton John. He said it, in that naff, English accent Americans try to do! I smiled politely. As the last box was unloaded from the truck and taken into the house, I left the two Mexicans to sort out the paperwork and went and sat in the front of the truck. A little while later the producer came to the front of the truck and, to give him his due, he shook my hand, thanked me for my hard work and gave me a $50 dollar tip. As he did this he quickly glanced over his shoulder, before whispering, 'I wanted to make sure you got it'! It was actually very nice of him, and I made it clear I appreciated it.

I think, being young, I didn't always appreciate the subtle cultural differences, just like Klaus, the producer, was a nice guy, just different to what I was used to. By the time Bert and Ernie had dropped me off back at the hostel, I was tired although I felt better for having done a day's work. I had earned $100 dollars wages; I had been given a $50 dollar tip and I had seen how the other half live. I had also really enjoyed working with the two Mexicans.

(I don't think Bert and Ernie were their real names!). All in all, it had been a good day.

****

Me and the Geordie had begun to frequent and had become something of regulars in a bar in down town known as GABE'S, so named after the legendary owner, Gabriel, who (so we were told) had once been a big league American football star. Not that it meant anything to the Geordie or me! Gabe was in his late fifties, fat and balding and what little hair he did have was slicked back over his head. He was a likeable man, a lot of fun and a real show-boater. He also ran a great bar! Every evening Gabe would schmooze from table to table with a bottle of something or other and give everyone free shots (a good businessman too!). He made sure everyone was included and made to feel welcome! At the 'actual' bar, instead of bar stools Gabe had installed horse's saddles! Which looked great and were a lot of fun, but a bit of a bastard when you had had one too many, as you would find yourself clenching your knees in an attempt to stay on!

Wednesday night was karaoke night, and one of the barfly's, a stereotypical American bloke called Buck, was a regular performer and would sing such classics as Bowie's 'Star Man' and the Mamas and Papas 'California Dreaming'. Buck would get up on stage and screech and scream his way through each rendition. Buck was also the only person in the bar who didn't know that he couldn't sing! He was fucking awful!

The whole pub was in on the gag and whenever he finished 'murdering' whatever song he thought he was smashing; he would receive a standing ovation of rapturous applause. All would be whistling and cheering and if someone was new to the bar, they would instantly be let in on the joke having been told, 'Quick, start clapping and cheering'! Poor Buck, he honestly thought he was the nuts!

The Geordie, however, was in fact an excellent singer! He endeared my mother to him one night for all eternity, when I had phoned home and the Geordie had drunkenly snatched the phone out of my hands and sang a beautiful rendition of, 'My lovely Rose of Clare' down the phone to her (I think they both ended up in tears!). Martin's mum was however a huge Elvis fan so as a young lad the Geordie had been brought up on it, as a result he was a fantastic Elvis impersonator (he was actually really good!). Whenever he got the chance, he would get up and sing, and what's more the Americans lapped it up, they simply loved to listen to the English guy sing Elvis! Well everyone except Buck of course, who would just shrug his shoulders and say, 'Yeah... it was Okay, ...I guess'.

Wednesday night at Gabe's bar, was also the night the 'Bikini Babes' hit town! The bikini babes were a troop of 'ex' strippers (past their sell by date, I know that sounds sexist and very harsh, but it is also a fair description). Who would tour the bars and pubs creating a bit of excitement; they would sell raffle tickets and frolic with the customers and generally generate a good fun atmosphere. It was all fairly innocent and tame really. It just so happened I was doing a turn on the karaoke, when the 'Babes' descended on Gabe's bar. I was singing, 'I'm Too Sexy' by Right Said Fred (yes, it is a bit cringe worthy!), but the 'Babes' loved it, they were all over me like a rash (literally!). It was a lot of fun for a 23yr old lad! Although obviously Buck thought I was shit!!

It was in, or rather out the back of, Gabe's bar one night that I tried cocaine for the very first time. I had had a lot to drink, but I knew perfectly well what I was doing; I was curious, and I wanted to try it! Me and the Geordie had sneaked out the back of the bar and were hiding in a discrete corner. As we huddled together the Geordie dipped a front door key into the bag of white powder, (the front door key to his mum's house he told me!). Having been dipped in the bag, the groove running the length of the key was now filled with cocaine. The Geordie explained, 'hold the key up under your right nostril! Don't fucking blow it off! Press your finger from your free hand against your left nostril and as you draw the key across and under your nose, sniff like fuck'!! Which I did! I didn't feel any different, so I did another one. Still nothing! So, I asked for another, I couldn't really understand what all the fuss was about! Over the next two hours me and Martin wore a path out the back door of Gabe's and finished off two bags. I had been drinking all night but strangely I didn't feel particularly drunk. I recall as I drove home through the empty streets of Los Angeles at about 2.00am, I actually felt quite good, invigorated even! I had the English rock channel playing on the radio and I can remember blasting out Oasis's 'Champagne Supernova' as I drove past Venice high school, (Rydel High in the musical Grease!). I remember thinking that it was pretty cool! I also remember feeling 'really' fucking pleased with myself!!

Despite the copious amounts of alcohol I had drank the previous night I awoke felling like I had received some form of (good) electric shock treatment. My batteries seemed to have been recharged, and I didn't appear to have the usual hangover. I still however, made myself a cup of strong bitter tasting coffee, because by now I had become accustomed to the taste and actually rather enjoyed it! I was slurping my coffee when Karl the 'receptionist', told me someone had left a note for me at the front desk. 'For me'? I said, suggesting that perhaps he had made a mistake.

Intrigued I made my way to the front desk and found to my surprise a note from Diane, the Geordie ex! She had heard that we were 'back in town'. (Diane had asked for me because her and Martin were no longer talking. I didn't pry as to why!). She had left the note along with a phone number explaining that there might be some decorating work for us. I told the Geordie about the note, (No, she didn't ask for you!). And then rang the phone number.

When the call was answered, the person on the other end said, 'Ello'? Instantly I recognised that we both shared the same accent! The bloke was called Phil, he was from my hometown! When I asked where abouts and he told me, I said, 'Ah the No 4 & No 12, (referring to the buses). I had obviously jogged a memory as he excitedly shouted, 'Fucking hell mate .... yeah that's right! Fuck me it's been a while since I've got the No 4 or 12 up from town'! Needless to say, the job was ours! It was a God send and we started the very next day. Two weeks painting and decorating in Beverley Hills!!!

The next morning me and the Geordie sat side by side in our Ford station wagon, bumper to bumper, stuck in the hot and sticky early morning rush hour traffic on the Santa Monica freeway. The radio was playing 'We built this city' by Starship and I couldn't stop grinning. It felt like we were two bona-fide American dudes making our way to work, and I loved it!

The house we were working on was huge. But despite its size and grandeur and compared to my work back home (and the recent days removals with Bert and Ernie), the Beverley Hills job was a doddle, dare I say even enjoyable! The money wasn't the greatest, but at least we were earning. In fact, if circumstances had been different, I 'might' have been tempted (but probably not!) to do the job for nothing! Just for the experience of being granted access to such splendour and opulence. Everything about the place was a statement, everything screamed look at me! And it was virtually impossible not to.

It was near the end of the first week's work that the Geordie received word from an old friend who he had previously worked and travelled about the states with. Martin's friend was an Irish bloke called Eddie McCormack, who was now living in Florida. He told Martin that there was plenty of work and things were pretty good in the Sunshine State! 'What do you think'? asked Martin, with paint brush in hand. 'Shall we go'? We're running out of money here. I know Eddie will put us up until we get on our feet; he's a good bloke is Eddie'. 'And he's gonna love you with a name like yours'! added the Geordie, for good measure!

My original plan had been to work my way up the west coast, not across the deep south. But as much as I loved it in L.A. I was growing restless, I was by now 'chomping at the bit' to get moving; I wanted to see America! So, I thought about it - for all of two 'nanno' seconds. And said, 'Yeah, fuck it, why not'! And so, it was decided, we would finish the Beverley Hills job, pack up our stuff and head 3000 miles east!

The last Wednesday before we were due to leave, we decided to go to Gabe's, for a farewell drink with the locals, who had in part become friends. I was tempted to tell Buck that when it came to karaoke, he 'sucked'! But I didn't want to spoil it for everyone else, so Instead I just shook his hand and said, 'It was nice knowing you', which to be fair to Buck, it was. We had a great night at Gabe's, everyone was buying us drinks and wishing us luck! It was such good fun that we stayed much later than we had intended as we still had work in the morning, but we were enjoying ourselves too much to really care. When we eventually left the bar in the early hour's we were both fairly drunk!

As we drove home through the empty streets we started 'bickering', I don't remember what about, but we were giving each other a fair bit of stick when out of nowhere...... 'BANG'! We had crashed our station wagon into the only fucking roundabout in the whole of Los Angeles. The whole city is on a grid system, there are no roundabouts, except for that one! (as a matter of interest, It's just a couple of blocks up from Venice beach). Stunned into silence we both looked at each other, wide eyed, opened mouthed and in utter disbelief and then we burst out laughing. We couldn't help it! The truth is we were lucky there weren't any cops about! We stuck the car in reverse, separating ourselves from the roundabout, and quickly drove off heading for the sanctuary of home!

The next morning, we surveyed the damage, 'she' was a fine automobile alright. Apart from a bit of a crumple on the right-hand wing (or fender as the Yanks would say), the only other issue was now you could no longer fully open the front passenger door. (a bit like the General Lee!). I think we both felt a bit sheepish as we drove to work, even more so when we passed the scene of the 'crime' and saw that some official had put warning tape around the damaged 'direction of flow' sign on the roundabout!

We only had two days left to go, but I didn't think the Beverley Hills job would ever end. I was so eager to get going, I was like an excited child who goes to bed early on Christmas eve, so it will be Christmas morning sooner!

The job ended and Phil, invited us to his home in the valleys, a leafy suburb on the other side of Tapanga Canyon. Apart from speaking to him on the phone, neither me nor the Geordie had actually meet Phil. When we eventually arrived at his house, he greeted us with a warm welcome.

Bottles of Budweiser were passed around as he told us he was pleased with our work. He owed us $800 dollars each for our two weeks work but gave us an extra $100 each because we were Brits and undeniably because he and I were both from the same town!

As we drank our beers we told him of our plans to head east. Then me and Phil, started to talk of the pubs back home that we had both frequented and of the people (and lunatics) that were known to us both! Phil told us how he had ended up in the States. He told us how he had been in the navy, but had become disillusioned with it all, so 'fed up', he had 'jumped ship' 10yrs previously and had never looked back.

I think it was quite nice and novel to have someone in his living room with whom he could talk about the 'old place' and also that they actually knew what, who, and where he was going on about. I thought I sensed a sadness in his eyes when he explained he couldn't ever risk going back 'home', in case he got caught! He explained he had a missus and a couple of kids, his own business (decorating) and a good life. He said America had been good to him, even if it didn't know it! He then asked if I smoked 'Bud' (weed). I nodded that I did. He told me he wasn't much of a puffer but had brought some to take with him when he went to Las Vegas for the (then) recent Mike Tyson VS Frank Bruno fight.

He suddenly looked a bit shifty as he pulled a small wooden box out from under his seat and from it extracted about an ounce of weed wrapped up in tin foil and said, 'Ere you can have that', before dropping his voice to a whisper..... 'my missus don't like having it in the house'! Needless to say, I was delighted. It had been equally as nice for me to meet and chat with someone from back home. A little part of me wished I had meet Phil sooner, I had enjoyed his company.

As me and the Geordie got up to leave, I shook Phil's hand, thanking him for the beers, I told him how much we appreciated the extra money and how it was good of him to give it. I also thanked him for the weed (which I suspect he was glad to be rid of!). As we drove away from Phil's house the Geordie remarked how we had gone from being virtually skint, to having a couple of beers, been handed $1800 dollars and a huge lump of weed! We were in high spirits indeed as we drove back through Tapanga canyon, on a warm sun-drenched Californian evening.

As soon as we got 'home' I went to our room and rolled a sneaky joint of Phil's 'Bud'! And then smoked it out the back of the Hostel by the flowerpots. It was good shit! Our last night in LA, our last night in the hostel. Me and Martin sat drinking a couple of Miller Lights under the huge picture of the challenger space shuttle, we were soon joined by Klaus. He looked visibly upset as he helped himself to our beers and said how sorry he was that we were leaving. 'If you are ever in trouble and you need somewhere to stay you will always be welcome at the Hostel California' 'ya'!

Being a hostel there was always a quick turnaround of people so there wasn't actually that many goodbyes to make, although I got the impression everyone knew it was a big deal that Pat and Martin, the two English guys, were leaving! Which was actually kind of nice. I did however make a special point of saying goodbye to Karl the 'receptionist'. I apologised to him for all the abuse me and Martin had given him 'every time' we had come home late and very drunk and for all the times he had been threatened with the sack. Karl smiled and said, 'it's okay Pat, I know you are a good guy', shook my hand and wished me luck! As we shook hand's I felt obliged to say something back, so I said, 'As Americans go, Karl, you're not a bad one'. He looked confused and said, 'I am not American, I am from Grenada!' I grinned and said 'Grenada'? 'Where the fuck's that'? 'It must be a right fucking shit hole of a country, if I've never heard of it'! Karl let go of my hand, rolled his eyes and laughed!

The next morning the Geordie and me were both up early. We settled up what we owed at the front desk and then threw our rucksacks in the back of the station wagon. I had hidden the ounce of weed in with my socks and pants in the middle of my rucksack, (just in case!). Despite it only being 6.30 am we sounded our horn in a triumphant double blast as we left the hostel and pulled out on to Lincoln boulevard, and then immediately pulled into the garage next door feeling a little bit silly! We put $60 dollars worth of 'GAS' in the tank, brought 200 Marlborough cigarettes and then headed for the I,9, interstate heading east out of Los Angeles. As we got on the freeway, I quipped to the Geordie, 'It's been quite the pardy'! We both smiled as we drove on and as the City of Angels diminished in the background behind us. I thought of the contrast between its vibrant, breath-taking beauty and its dangerous ugly underbelly of vice and crime. As we hit the wide-open road heading for the Mojave Desert, I had never felt more alive! And I had never felt more free!

CHAPTER FOURTEEN

I HAD NEVER BEEN IN A DESERT BEFORE. When I hear the word desert, I immediately think of the Sahara or the Gobi, camels and head-scarf's, an oasis with a single palm tree, or a mirage of a coca cola vending machine sitting on top of a sand dune, but you haven't got a coin to purchase the lifesaving beverage inside. The Mojave was not what I imagined, not the parts I saw anyway.

The first thing that struck me about the place was just how vast it was, I had never been in such a huge open space. At first it appeared empty only it wasn't empty at all. It was full to the brim with awe and wonder, the earth's natural beauty at its best. As I looked across the vast desert landscape, I could see mountains in the far distance, I had only ever seen these types of images on TV before.

We drove for hours through the scrub lands and cactus strewn landscape of the Mojave before the road began to rise and fall and then it just rose as we reached the southern tips of the Sierra Nevada mountain range. Our station wagon began to struggle and strain from the heat and the gradient of the climb. It wasn't long before steam began to rise and spew from under the hood of the car. Panic began to set in as it dawned on the Geordie and me, the severity of becoming stranded in this barren wasteland. Through fear alone, we pushed the car to its limits, before finally conceding and bringing the car to a slow stop on the side of the road next to two huge bleached white boulders. There was not another car or another living sole insight in any direction. Me and Martin both had concerned looks on our faces as we stepped out of the car, the heat of the midday sun immediately drained us as we walked to the front of the station wagon and lifted the hood to inspect the damage. As we did so we were immediately engulfed in a huge hot, hissing cloying cloud of steam. It took our breath away. Grimacing we both began to wave away the steam. We looked at each other with the defeatist look of finality upon our faces, we were out of water. How could we have been so stupid!

A little further up the road I could see what appeared to be two concrete cylinders at the side of the road. I gestured to the Geordie and we both began to take a stroll (it was too hot to walk?). After a few hundred yards we reached the two large concrete cylinders. I stepped up on a rock and peered over the rim of the huge container, 'water'! Thick, dark green water, which had a thick soup like layer of every conceivable dead insect coating the top! I looked back at the Geordie with a smile on my face and simply said180
bless America'!

Happier, we 'strolled' back to the car and grabbed a couple of empty plastic bottles before returning to the concrete cylinders. With the bottom of a plastic bottle I gingerly swept aside the offending soup-like layer of dead creatures and attempted to fill a couple of bottles with the green liquid, and without actually getting my hand wet. I failed. Once both bottles were filled, we made our way back to the car. We decided it might be wise to allow the engine to cool down, so to pass the time we climbed up upon the two huge boulders at the side of the road (we had one each!) and took in the view of the mountains and the scrub lands of Arizona in the far distance. We sat smoking and chewing the breeze until we could take no more of the midday sun!

Once the engine had sufficiently cooled, we poured two bottles of the fowl smelling and rather rank looking water into the radiator, I remember thinking this can't be good for the car! We repeated the process of refilling the bottles (just in case) and put them in the back of the car. Thankfully the station wagon started up without protest, so we pressed on, grateful of the cooling breeze now coming through the open windows as we made our decent out of the mountains and into Arizona.

As we drove on through the desert, I saw a road sign which read, 'TOMBSTONE 10 miles'. 'We gotta go there' I stated excitedly. Martin instantly agreed so we left the interstate and followed the directions. The road ambled and meandered over hills and around huge cactus, hundreds of years old. This was real wild west country at its best. I couldn't help but think of my dad; he would have loved it here. He loved to watch the old westerns on TV, Bonanza and the High Chaparral where among his favourites, which meant I had to watch them too, although, as a kid I always preferred Grizzly Adams. My dad also loved to read; I think he liked to escape into a book. So, when I was a kid it was my job (I inherited it from my sister Bridie) to go to the mobile library on a Monday after school and get my dad his large print westerns. His eyesight wasn't great, neither was the selection, as you can probably imagine. If I made the mistake of bringing him back a western, he had already read (which was highly likely), I would get hit down on the head with it! And duly sent back round to the library. My dad would have loved this place; he must have imagined it a thousand times as he read his books!

After a few miles of winding back roads we came to a small tarmac area at the foot of a cactus and boulder-strewn hill. We pulled over and got out of the car. There wasn't a cloud in the sky, nor was there a soul about. There was nothing but the big hill in front of us, so we began to climb it. It was hard going in the hot arid heat of the afternoon; in places it was hard to get a decent foothold on the crumbling rocks and dust. It took us about 30 minutes to reach the top.

When we got to the top and peered over the ridge of the hill, we were both stunned into silence! The scene laid out before us took our breath away. It was beautiful, it was incredible. I was almost moved me to tears as I looked out across the vast Arizona desert. The hill we had just climbed was in fact the crest of a mountain. From my vantage point high above the desert, I could see for miles and miles in every direction. I felt humbled, I felt small and for the first time in my life, I felt incredibly insignificant. It was so vast, so open and so wild I couldn't help but sense my own vulnerability. In the distance towered a huge rock formation, (one of many), which looked like a mountain that had been cut vertically in half. One side was a mesmerising sheer rock face, while the other was a sharp incline which swept out at the bottom and at its base sheltered a lush green meadow which was in total contrast to the red and yellow sandstone of its surroundings. Amidst the lush green I could just make out the silver glint of an Air-stream motor home parked on the outer most edge of the meadow, next to which ran a road which stretched out away from us for as far as the eye could see before eventually disappearing into the distance. I remember wondering where that road led! Neither the Geordie nor myself said a word, we just sat staring for the best part of an hour. The only sound being the desert wind blowing gently against my face.

I felt alive. This was how I had imagined my adventure to be! As I sat atop of that mountain, I wondered why people tolerate living their lives in drab, dreary surroundings. The sort of places where you look out of your window, directly at another window. The sort of places where you hardly ever notice the sky! The sort of shitholes that just drag you down. I now know it's because they have to, I just didn't know it then!

Reluctantly we began the climb back down 'the hill'. It was just as hard coming down the crumbling rock and dust as it was going up! 10 minutes into our descent and I thought I heard something on the ground by my feet. Startled, I snapped 'What was that'? I stopped moving and so did Martin as we both listened and surveyed the ground around us. 'Might be a rattle snake, and ye divini want to get bit by one of them like,' offered the Geordie helpfully! The climb down took on a new level of seriousness and urgency that we both pretended not to acknowledge. Safely back on level ground we walked back to the car, I got in the driver's seat and lit a Marlborough cigarette, sitting back I took a deep drag and thought about how truly great life really is!

It was getting dark by the time we reached Phoenix and the out skirts of the city. Both tired and in need of some refreshments, we pulled into the first liquor store we saw. As we pulled up to the kerb we noticed some dodgy looking blokes mooching about in the shadows by the doorway, I didn't have to ask to know the Geordie was feeling as uncomfortable as me. Undeterred and with a false display of confidence we got out of the car and walked the short distance to the store. Once inside we bought some food, some cigarettes and a crate of Budweiser because it was on special offer! We left the store with our provisions and purposely 'ambled' back to the car but without making eye contact with the local hoodlums who we could sense were sizing us up from the shadows. Only when we were safely back in the car did we relax. Just a trip to the shop! But It had been tense with a very real nasty vibe. We headed back for the interstate and pushed on as we still had the best part of 2000 miles to go before we reached Florida.

To save money we decided to sleep in the car. Not the safest option, but definitely the cheapest. We 'now' decided the further out of the city the better, so drove on out into the desert. Eventually we stopped at an unmanned roadside rest area (vending machines, picnic tables, toilets etc).

Away from the city It was now pitch black and as I stepped out of the station wagon, I looked up and saw a million billion stars. It was as the Americans would say, 'Awesome'! The stars in the desert are something else; I have always enjoyed looking up at the night sky. Back home if I wasn't out on the piss with my mates, I would be at home smoking dope. Remarkably my mum tolerated this, but only after I convinced her I wasn't going to throw myself off a block of flats having smoked the said marijuana. I wasn't allowed to smoke it in the house due to the pungent smell, so I would spend hours standing in the alley at the side of our house smoking weed and looking up at the stars and pondering. Aware that man has done the same from time immemorial. But the stars never looked like this!

The Geordie grabbed the crate of beer while I rummaged through the socks and pants in my rucksack until I found my bag of weed, then the two of us walked off into the desert away from the main road and totally ignoring the huge sign which informed the ignorant of all the species of spiders, insects and snakes that would fuck you up! Not long after, we came to a clearing and plonked ourselves down. We cracked open a couple of beers and I rolled a large joint. As I sat on the desert floor drinking my beer, chuffing my joint and looking up at the stars, I noticed a blue dot moving slowly across the night sky. It was a comet, a 20-mile-wide ball of ice with a blue tail, hurtling through space! And as I have since learned, supposedly a thousand times brighter than Halley's comet. Apparently 'Halle Bopp', won't be seen again for another few thousand years! So, I was kind-a glad I hadn't missed it! As I sat happily puffing away and drinking my beer watching this marvel in the sky, I was blissfully unaware (as were most people) that 300 miles away in San Diego, California, 40 members of the Heaven's Gate cult were embarking on a mass suicide, believing there was a space ship following Halle Bopp and that by killing themselves they would leave their earthly bodies behind and enter a new existence up in the heavens, with their alien friends. 40 members of the cult drank a poisonous concoction thus ending their lives. Their bodies were all found lying side by side, wearing the same (jump suits) clothes and all were wearing brand new trainers! Obviously, most would agree these poor unfortunates were all lunatics or simply brain washed, but then again, how do we know they didn't catch their spaceship? By contrast, that night sat in the desert, I didn't have a care in the world!

We slept in the car, Martin in the back (the estate bit!), me on the back-bench seat. It was very comfortable, in fact no different from kipping on a leather settee. When I awoke the next morning, I washed away the grogginess of the previous night's beers in one of the rest room sinks. 'Refreshed' we headed off looking for some breakfast (pancakes and eggs!).

A few hundred miles later, we had reached the Badlands of New Mexico and the prairies. I have never been any where so flat. I was reminded of a joke I once heard. The American comedian Rich Hall said: 'Where I come from in the states, it's so flat you can watch your dog run away for three days'!!

I thought this is probably where he's from! It was also constantly howling a gale. I thought about all the films I had seen as a kid, depicting the early settlers making their way west in long wagon trains, they must have spent weeks, months even, with nowhere to shelter from the cold winds and dust storms, not to mention the tornado's. And no rest areas either!

Next it was Texas. A huge cheer erupted in the front of our station wagon when we saw a bullet hole ridden sign declaring 'Welcome to Texas'! I immediately started bellowing in my best American drawl, 'All my ex's live in Texas... that's why I hang my hat in Tennessee'. Then Martin started listing all the things that are bigger in Texas than anywhere else: cars, hats, burgers, BBQs, cigars, steaks, ranches, cow horns, country and western, bigotry, murder-rates and Jesus. In fact, the only thing we could think of, that was smaller in Texas than anywhere else, was the whore house that Dolly Parton worked in! It was a great buzz just being in Texas. Two things that really surprised me about Texas was the amount of ostriches I saw and the fact that Texas has almost 400 miles of coastline.

Not long after leaving California, we had lost the radio signal for the English rock channel we enjoyed listening to. After that the only thing we could pick up was Country & Western music. 'Secretly' I have always liked country music! I think it's due to being brought up listening to Irish music at home; it's the next natural step (they can be quite similar!). However, most of what we picked up was new stuff, I liked the old classics, the sort that you would hear drunk people singing! The new stuff just didn't have the same appeal. So when we saw the sign for El Paso and the Geordie immediately started singing the Marty Robbins classic ...'El Paso', it was a welcome break from the new (shit) hip stuff playing on the radio, the only problem being the Geordie sang it all the way to fucking Baton Rouge, (700 miles!), well almost!

As you know, me and the Geordie were illegal immigrants in the US, so it was a bit of a shock when the road we were on suddenly and without warning narrowed down and we were soon confronted with the El Paso border control. We just hadn't seen it coming, before we knew it we were in a line of vehicles being funnelled down to security checks. I have always fancied going to Mexico and now here I was within a couple of hundred yards from it! To our right there was a wire fence about 15ft in height with razor wire along the top of it. On the other side of the fence there was a shanty town. I could see graffiti on the sides of the hills (written all over the rocks); it was all in Spanish, but I guessed it was all derogatory. Our car was now in a queue. The Mexican passengers from the vehicle in front had been asked to step out of their car while presumably their papers were examined, and their car searched. That's when I noticed that the border patrol officers not only had guns, but some also had dogs! I thought about the bag of weed stashed in my ruck sack! I thought about our fake IDs! I thought about a deportation prison! I thought of the John Lennon protest song I once heard, called 10 for 2, about an old hippie who got 10yrs in prison for being in possession of two joints. I was no 'Pancho Villa', but if I got caught, I was fucked! The Geordie had stopped singing!

The Mexicans and their vehicle had been pulled over to one side. Now a very serious looking and armed Texan border patrol officer was stood in front of our car, he held his hand up and out in front of him, indicating for us to stop! He then scrutinised us both individually through the front windscreen for what seemed like an eternity but was probably no more than a couple of seconds. He saw, staring back at him, two white (ashen) faced 'Americans', sitting in a Ford Station Wagon with Colorado tags on the front. Satisfied that we were not a couple of 'Bert & Ernie's'! he stood aside and waved us through the El Paso border control point. Like a couple of naughty schoolboys, we nodded our compliance and drove on. I looked in the rear-view mirror and saw the Mexicans getting a hard time. Fuck me, that was a close call. I must remember to offer a prayer of thanks to 'Jesus Malverde', (the patron saint of drug smugglers!). I've still never been to Mexico!

That night we treated ourselves to a stay in a motel just outside San Antonio. It was typical roadside fare, although it was clean, and the bed sheets were fresh. I had a welcomed shower, sat on the end of the bed and then switched on the most violent TV I have ever seen. Every channel (apart from the God ones, which only showed the odd crucifixion!) showed images of guns, shootings and murders. I was actually taken aback by its brutality. Texas is 1 of 30 states in the US that has the death penalty. It also has one of the highest murder rates in the US, (60% higher than average.). So, it doesn't seem like much of a deterrent! I am not sure where I stand on the debate concerning the death penalty, (I think for the most heinous of crimes, especially concerning children), all I know is, those that receive it, tend not to re-offend! It was however a strange notion, knowing that if you were to do something 'really' wrong - the government might 'legally' murder you (presumably while everyone cheered!). I turned the TV off and went to sleep.

I woke up the next morning feeling refreshed, although I am sure I heard gunshots being fired in the distance at around 2.00am. I hadn't bothered getting up to investigate, instead I had just pulled the duvet up a bit higher around my head. We had breakfast, mooched around for a bit and then set off again. We drove through San Antonio and then Houston. We had been on the road for hours and were again in the middle of nowhere when we came to a cross-roads on the interstate and saw a sign for KFC. Hungry, we pulled off down a dusty slip road to find the KFC and a petrol station and nothing else in any direction for miles. I could see a battered up old Ford truck parked between the two. I wondered how the employees got to work, did they all come in the truck? And if so, where from? We really were in the middle of nowhere, proper tumble weed territory!

We had some food and then pulled in next door to the gas station. As we did so, I noticed a lone figure standing by the entrance to the slip road leading back onto the interstate. He looked like an old hippie, he had wild shoulder length salt and pepper hair and a scraggy old beard. Beside him at his feet lay a battered old grey duffel bag, he was standing with his thumb out and looking in our direction with a hopeful plea on his face. I pretended not to notice him as Martin filled the tank. Nor did I look back in the old hippie's direction as I sat in the car while Martin went in and paid for the fuel.

When Martin returned to the car, I saw him look across to the hopeful hippie before he turned to me and said, 'Shall we give the poor cunt a lift'! Shocked, but without the slightest hesitation I said, 'Not a fucking chance, I don't want that fucking loon in the car with us, are you fucking mad'! The Geordie, 'hummed and argh'd'. 'We can't leave the poor fucker stranded here; he could be stuck here for hours if we don't give him a lift. I know what it's like, I hitch hiked through the Yukon in British Columbia'! I suddenly felt embarrassed by my lack of empathy and compassion for the hitch hiker, so I quietly (and reluctantly) murmured my agreement. The Geordie shouted, 'Oi mate, where you headed'.

The old hippie sprang into action, now ecstatic, he grabbed his duffel bag up from the floor and hurried towards us. He said he was headed for a place called Pineville, in northern Louisiana. I explained we were heading east but would take him as far as we could. I wasn't totally comfortable with it.

As the three of us pulled back on to the I,9 the old hippie said, 'My name's Nathaniel, but everybody calls me Nate'! And then didn't stop talking for the next 150 miles. Nate said he had been to a rainbow festival (dancing naked around a fire no doubt) up in the woods! He said all he had eaten in the last two days was an orange and a bagel, he said that bit.... like he was dying! We shared our snacks and cigarettes with the famished hippie. Fed, warm and comfortable in the back of our station wagon our guest fell into a deep slumber and didn't stir for a further 200 miles. I was glad of the peace and quiet.

Eventually we came to the junction on the interstate where our guest was due to depart our company. 'Na... tha...n... iel' I cooed, the way a doting mother might gently wake her sleeping child, which raised a smile from the Geordie. The old hippie stirred, and then looked at me wide eyed, momentarily confused as to his whereabouts. 'Nate this is it mate; this is where we go our separate ways' I stated more firmly. We pulled the car over at the junction with the I,9 and the 49 heading north, and the three of us got out. 'Hey, I really appreciate it, fellas. It was fun travellin wit y'all'! As he said this, he walked towards me and attempted to embrace me with open arms. I really didn't mean to offend him; I had done it before I realised. I instinctively smacked both his arms down and away from me and then shot my hand out indicating a firm handshake would be suffice! He looked hurt and offended as he said meekly, 'oh, ...oh okay'.

Feeling embarrassed I feebly offered 'good luck mate'! He threw his duffel bag over his shoulder and walked around to the other side of the car towards the Geordie, as he approached he went to open his arms, hesitated, thought better of it and held his hand out to the smiling Geordie. As they shook hands the old hippie looked over at me, smiled and gave a little shrug of his shoulders!

We drove away leaving our new 'friend' on the side of the road heading north as we continued to head east. After about 10 minutes I started saying to the Geordie how much I missed old Nate. I kept turning in my seat looking at the space in the back of the car where he 'used' to sit as I pretended to give out a little sigh! ' ...I miss his smell'! I finally declared, and then that was the joke over.

****

Plantation houses, Gumbo and paddle steamers. Welcome to Louisiana! Music is very emotive. You can move people with music, you can evoke feelings and you can jog memories. Whenever I hear Kris Kristofferson's, 'Me and Bobby McGee', it takes me straight back to me and the Geordie driving through the swamplands of southern Louisiana. 'Busted flat in Baton Rouge.... headed for the train... feeling just as faded as my jeans... Bobby thumbed the diesel down... just before it rained...took us all the way to New Orleans'.

It was a happy relief as I had been listening to the Geordie sing 'El Paso' for the last 700 miles (almost!). Now the landscape had changed, we were no longer in the wild west, we were now winding our way through the deep south. To the north of the state it's mainly farming land, cotton, and sweet potatoes. To the south, swamps, bayous, and tall bald cypress trees with their tangled roots exposed just above the water line. Everything was covered with hanging vine moss and the whole place seemed to be shrouded in a fine mist, giving it a mystical eerie feel. There was also the constant chorus of bull frogs croaking.

I tried Louisiana 'Gumbo' for the first time in my life. If you have never tried it, then I fear your missing out! It's a kind of hodge podge soup (or stew), consisting of all the days (kitchen) leftovers. It was really, '…. kind-a gurd'! The Louisianan's take their Gumbo very seriously and regularly hold, fiercely fought, 'Gumbo-titions'! (May the best 'Mama' win!).

Apart from the major towns and cities we passed through, most of Louisiana seemed impoverished (the parts I saw anyway). You could see deprivation everywhere you looked, in fact in some places you could feel it. It was as if the rest of America had forgotten about it. On the plus side we were able to fill the tank of our station wagon up for 99cents a gallon!

As we on drove towards Baton Rouge we crossed the mighty Mississippi river. We both got quite excited at the sight of, 'Ol' Man River', it was muddy brown, half a mile wide and fast moving. From our vantage point up on a huge iron bridge, we could see the iconic paddle steamers making their way up and down the river constantly fighting against the strong currents and swirls, it was an amazing sight to see, but you wouldn't want to swim in it! Me and the Geordie did actually board a paddle steamer, not that it was going anywhere! It was moored up on the side of the river and was in fact a floating casino! (it has something to do with the state gaming laws!).

As you are aware money was tight. The Geordie, who never missed a trick, suggested we should 'hit' the casino and 'pretend' to gamble! 'if you're gambling they give you complimentary food and beers, to keep you there'! he had said with total conviction. We boarded the steamer and stood out like sore thumbs, looking like a couple of blokes who had been sleeping in a car, which indeed we had! It cost $10 dollars for admission, and once inside, I lost $60 dollars while 'pretending' to gamble and didn't even get offered so much as a packet of crisps let alone a free beer!! Dejected and feeling like a right pair of mugs we left and headed for the nearest McDonald's. Having enjoyed our 'happy meals', we then grabbed a six pack each from a liquor store and drove out of the city eventually finding a rest area where we parked up, drank our beers and spent the night in our car.

The next morning, we drove into the state of Mississippi, the Bible Belt, the true deep south and also Ku Klux Klan territory, (I hope they don't burn Paddy's and Geordie's!) (They probably do!). To be fair Mississippi is a beautiful state, lush green dense woodland and forests (great for hiding bodies, just like the river!). It was exactly how you would imagine the deep south, and a stark contrast to the wilds of the wind-swept west. As we motored along, I saw a road sign for Biloxi, Mississippi. I remembered years earlier seeing a film called 'Biloxi Blues', starring Matthew Broderick, (of Ferris Bueller fame) and suggested to Martin that we stop off and take a look, so we did!

Like a picture postcard, we both instantly fell in love with the place. All the little wooden houses had white picket fences around perfectly manicured lawns. Nearly all the houses had swing chairs on the front porches and most flew the American flag with pride from the front of their homes. On the green in the town centre next to a very grand municipal library building stood a picturesque bandstand, and in the harbour brightly coloured fishing boats gently swayed in the wash of the Gulf of Mexico. Me and the Geordie couldn't help but get excited by the intoxicating beauty and tranquillity of the place, so much so that we momentarily forgot about Florida and even enquired about jobs on board the little fishing boats!

As Martin and me, had travelled across the United States there had been many places we had wanted to stop off and stay a while but couldn't. Money was one consideration, I have always regretted not exploring more, but our funds dictated how much we could or couldn't do! The other consideration was this, two English blokes in a sleepy backwater little town can cause quite a fuss. Being illegal immigrants, we did not want to run the risk of bringing too much attention to ourselves, it was a very real concern. One night over a few beers the Geordie had told me the story of how he had been working in a petrol station in British Columbia, Canada. He said how he loved the job, the stunning scenery, and how he got on really well with the guy who owned the place and was allowed to live in what he described as a beautiful loft apartment above the garage. He was truly loving life and as he told me, was 'living the dream'! One day a car pulled into the garage and Martin went out to fill the car with gas. The driver spoke to Martin and when he replied, the driver commented on the Geordie's accent. 'Where are you from', enquired the driver. Martin explained that he was English. 'That's real neat', said the driver, 'but how are you able to work here in Canada'? 'Can I see your documentation'! It transpired the driver of the vehicle was an off-duty police officer. The Geordie was arrested and given a choice, 24 hours to leave Canada or be held in custody until deportation could be arranged! So, with just a few hundred dollars in his pocket the Geordie had done a runner! Which is how he had come to be hitch hiking through the Yukon, and also why he had felt 'obliged' to give 'ol' Nate' a lift! With that in mind we reluctantly decided to give Biloxi a miss (such a shame). Before long we were back on the interstate heading for Alabama! Alabama, the heart of Dixie, and we barely stopped. The finish line (Florida) was within our sights. At its narrowest point 'Ol' Bamy' is only 100 miles wide between the Mississippi state line and the Florida state line. We passed by the city of Mobile situated just north of Mobile bay, a huge expanse of water which filters down into the Gulf of Mexico. I didn't know at the time but the Madi-gras was first held in Mobile Alabama, before eventually moving to and becoming synonymous with New Orleans. After three weeks on the road and having travelled 3000 miles we finally crossed the Florida state line into Tallahassee. A huge sign at the side of the road welcomed us to the 'Sunshine State'! I was 23yrs old and aware that in just three weeks I had seen more of the United States than most Americans would see in a lifetime. We crossed over vast concrete bridges that seemed to be barely above the water line as we made our way through Tallahassee and into Pensacola.

Eventually we stopped for gas and refreshments at a shopping court. As we stepped out of the car an old lady looking at the Colorado tags on the front of our station wagon quipped 'My, my, you boys are a long way from home'! I startled the old girl with my British accent and a wry wink when I said, 'Yes love, a lot further than you think'!

There was a payphone outside one of the stores. Martin thought it would be a fun idea to ring Klaus the worlds shittest wizard and let him know we were now in Florida! The Geordie stood inside the phone box all smiles as he waited for the German to answer. 'howa Klaus, were in Florida! 'weh'! I could hear shouting coming from the other end of the receiver and something about 'You fucking English bastard' and then something about 6.30 am? Me and the Geordie looked at each other before bursting out laughing. We hadn't considered the 3-hour time difference between both sides of the states. However, we knew all too well that the crabby German hated to be disturbed when he was sleeping! It was a nice idea, but it hadn't gone to plan. Martin hadn't got the, 'Oh my God, really?' that he had been hoping for. The Geordie hung up and I said, 'Fuck him anyway, the skinny anaemic German looking cunt'! Next it was a call to Eddie and Nula to let them know we were in Florida and to expect us some time the next day (we still had 300 miles or so to go). They said they were looking forward to seeing us both and would put the beers on ice!

Happier and more relaxed we made our way down through the Florida turnpike. We drove for most of the day until we were exhausted, and it was beginning to get late. The sun was going down so we pulled into a roadside bar to rest for a while and have two beers each!

We both got really pissed! I think it was due to tiredness, excitement and the realisation of what we had just achieved. That and the fact we were both greedy bastards! It wasn't until we got back in the car that we realised just how drunk we were, our driving was nothing short of dangerous. It was apparent to us both that we needed to get the car off the road quick, before we got arrested, as we were swerving all over the place. We pulled off the main road and onto a dirt track which we followed for a short while before eventually parking up in a field. When we turned the engine off, we could hear the night-time chorus of hundreds of crickets and through the beam of our headlights we could see mist rising from the grass. As the mist rose it gave the illusion that the car was sinking! Alarmed and fearing we had driven into a swamp, I said 'We're fucking sinking'! 'What'? Said the Geordie. 'We're fucking sinking'!! Martin laughed, 'No we're not'! 'We are, we're fucking sinking'! I don't like to admit it, but I think I may, have had a 'mini' panic attack! As I took a bit of convincing that we were 'not' in fact sinking. Eventually and in a state of drunken stupor I fell asleep.

The next morning, I was rudely awoken by the sound of a truck and an angry American shouting in our direction! My head was banging and with one eye open I looked around trying to make sense of my surroundings and in the general direction of the noise. I stepped out of the car and held my hand up shielding my one open eye from the glare of the morning sun. There was a man standing half in and half out of a big Ford pick-up truck. 'Hey, what the fuck are you guys doing in my back-garden man'!

As he shouted this, I noticed for the very first time, the back of a house, a fence and an open gate! Trying to gather myself, I blurted 'whaa...t'. My mind raced and then in my 'best' British, I began to apologise. I said how sorry I was and how I hadn't meant to intrude. I explained how I had been looking for a friend's house, but not being from around 'these parts' I had become lost, exhausted from a long drive I felt for safety reasons I should park up and that I had not realised I was in fact on somebody's property! Not for the first time my accent had thrown the situation in my favour. The man looked momentarily confused, he looked like he wasn't sure whether to believe me or not. Had I been an American, it may have become violent! Had I been an American, he might have called the police! Had I been an American, shots might have been fired! But I was a hopelessly lost Brit! And as he was still trying to make sense of what he was seeing and hearing he actually began to give me directions which I didn't fucking need! I couldn't apologise or thank the man enough as I leant back in the car. It hummed of stale beer and to my amazement the fucking Geordie was still asleep! I shook him violently by the shoulder, 'Huh', 'Wake up' I barked! 'What?', I shook him again 'We're in someone's fucking back garden'! 'Huh?', 'We're in someone's fucking back garden and I think the cunt might have a gun! The Geordie eyes widened as I jumped in the driver's seat and started the car up, while trying to look as composed as possible. I turned the car around and headed for the open gate with my arm out of the window waving and thanking the bemused American as I put the pedal to the metal and left him in a cloud of dust.

Back on the freeway we headed south towards Orlando. The roofs of the cars in front shimmered in the 90-degree heat creating a mirage affect. It was certainly the sunshine state, perfectly clear blue skies with not a cloud insight. At about midday we picked up the sign for Juno Ridge, the town where Eddie and Nula lived.

It was blisteringly hot as we wound our way through the dusty back roads, which began to twist and turn the further away from the freeway we got. Soon we began to pass lots of orange groves; I had never seen oranges growing by the side of the road before! Every few hundred yards a strategically placed sign stated that it was a federal offence to pick the fruit and would result in a $500 dollar fine (which to me, just made it all the more tempting!). As we turned a tight bend in the road, I saw a ramshackle wooden shack, a little kid was playing out the front, while a line of washing hung between two trees. Next to the shack was a small pond which had a horse standing motionless (apart from the swish of its tail!) in the middle of it, trying to cool itself down. It was an unexpected, but fantastic sight to see, something reminiscent of a scene from Huckleberry Finn!

At last we turned onto a long tree-lined avenue with white fencing running either side of its entire length. 'The Gallops', was the stud farm where Eddie and Nula lived in a trailer close to the stables. Nula worked with the horses while Eddie worked as a carpenter on construction sites in the local area. The place was beautiful, smack bang in the heart of Florida, it was surprisingly 'green'! Which is probably why it reminded me of the English countryside, only it was hot!

We received a very warm welcome indeed and were greeted with open arms. Excited exchanges were made and true to their word the beers had been kept on ice! Nula had prepared a meal which had been simmering and bubbling away in a slow cooker all day awaiting our arrival. I don't wish to appear ungrateful, but it soon became clear Eddie was not with her for her cooking skills.

The first thing Eddie McCormack ever said to me was, 'And how did you get a name like that with an accent like yours'? Smiling I replied, 'I think it all boils down to geography Eddie'!

I instantly liked Eddie and Nula; it was clear they were nice, decent genuine people. Eddie (like my dad) was from Kerry and had a similar accent which instantly endeared me to him. However, unlike my dad, he was about 5ft 10, skinny with scruffy hair and a ginger beard. Nula was a Kiwi, of average height, slight, blonde and not unattractive.

Over dinner Martin told them of our antics in LA, and told them about our dash across the states. They told us how they had come to be living on a stud farm: Nula had been offered a job as a stable hand; she had a passion for horses. A passion that had been forged and nurtured growing up in her native New Zealand. They told us how we had missed all the excitement. And had we arrived a week earlier the place would have been crawling with cops! As Eddie passed the beers around, Nula went on to explain how a few hundred feet away in the next trailer (there were only two on the stud farm) two farm hands, who were the best of friends had been drinking and playing cards, when an angry dispute erupted. It quickly got out of hand, a gun was pulled, and one of the farm hands had been shot dead!

Eddie had all his correct papers and a green card and was in fact a registered alien permitted to work in the US, however Nula was not! Understandably it had been a tense situation with so many police officers and investigators asking questions, but thankfully she had not been found out. Even the owner of the stud farm (who did not live on site) had become a bit jittery. As all this was revealed to us, Eddie didn't look the slightest bit bothered as he drained his beer and reached for another! Nula continued, she said she had told her boss that a couple of friends were coming to stay. She said he was totally cool with it but had hinted that in light of recent events it might be a good idea to keep a low profile and avoid any unnecessary antics!

Then Nula excitedly went on to tell us of all the plans she had for us and where we were going to go! We could go here, there and everywhere. 'Disneyland is a great night out for adults with lots of bars', she announced. I immediately became uncomfortable and felt incredibly awkward and looked directly at the floor. Martin shifted in his seat and began the agonising explanation of our situation. We had only $400 dollars between us, how we had struggled to get work in LA (failing to mention it was because we had been flat out on the piss!). And how we had made our way to Florida due to Eddies promise (Martin had played his trump card) that there was plenty of work!

There followed a brief moment of awkwardness as Eddie and Nula exchanged glances, Nula was clearly annoyed, but fair play to the Irishman he immediately said 'Arghh, you will be working and on your feet in no time, fuck Disneyland and fuck Mickey Mouse'!! He laughed as he passed the beers around again! I was glad our situation had been made clear and was now out in the open. Both Eddie and Nula were excellent hosts and to their credit never mentioned our predicament again.

They had both at some point during their travels been in similar situations. A little while later, me and the Geordie were momentarily alone, so I whispered, 'Fucking hell that was embarrassing'! Referring to our revelation. 'Don't fucking worry about it' said the Geordie, 'I remember her when she was a penniless waitress in Tennessee'! As the night went on we all became very drunk, beer after beer flowed. At some point a bottle of whiskey was opened, after which I don't recall very much at all.

The next morning, I awoke with a real humdinger of a hangover! I also had a black eye!! I was furious! I could recall hardly nothing of the night before. I remember drinking the whiskey, I have a vague recollection of being in the shower, but nothing else. The fucking dirty northern Geordie cunt had given me a dig!

Angry doesn't quite cut it, I was livid! I was full of rage. I grabbed him by the scruff of the neck and began shaking him awake, while calling him a 'fucking cunt'. I must have looked like I wanted to kill him (which I did!). 'You fucking wanker, fucking hit me when I'm paralytic drunk you fucking cunt'! He was now wide eyed and genuinely looked worried and started to blurt, how I had passed out and had then began to puke all over myself and then Eddie and Nula's trailer. He said he had become embarrassed and then angry with me, he then stated the precarious nature of our predicament, before adding, 'These people are putting us up! and you're being sick all over the fucking place'! 'YES, he had a point'! But I still wanted to punch his fucking lights out! I would never have done that to one of my friends, never! I was furious, but for the next few weeks we were at the mercy of our hosts! After the story Nula had told of the shooting – I had no choice but to let it go, I was not fucking happy about it. I did let it go, but that didn't mean I was going to forget!

Not long after Martin's rude awakening, Eddie and Nula got up (perhaps they heard the commotion!?). I was extremely embarrassed; I was aware my behaviour had been appalling and to make matters worse they didn't even know me! What must they be thinking? I couldn't apologise enough. However, my first impressions of Eddie and Nula had been correct. They could not have been nicer, telling me not to worry, 'These things happen' added Eddie, matter of factly, before making us all a fry up. They never mentioned it again. The Geordie apologised. I remained quietly livid, but I didn't let it show. I understood, but I could not accept. (he was fucking out of order!).

****

We had arrived at the stud farm on a Friday so could do nothing about our work situation until the Monday. We passed the time strolling around the extensive grounds admiring the horses and getting bitten by horse flies. They 'nipped' like a bitch; on occasions they even drew blood! I narrowly missed a foal being born by seconds, having reached the paddock a moment too late to see it actually 'plop' out, but it was still in its (amnion) birth sack, which its mother was tentatively licking from the unsteady foal. We fished for freshwater bass from the jetty down on the lake behind the stables. I caught a 3lb bass, let it go and a couple of minutes later I caught another 3lb bass, I was convinced it was the same fish! It was beautiful to just sit and watch the lake as it changed with the sun going down, occasionally a turtle would poke its head above the water do a flip and be gone again, much to my delight!

We spent the evenings sat on the front porch of Eddie's and Nula's trailer drinking beer (obviously I took it easy!) and hatching a plan of action concerning employment. We had photocopied our fake IDs and, I have to say they looked very convincing!' On the Monday morning and with 'documents' in hand we headed a few miles back down the road into Juno Ridge and headed for the nearest labour pool. In the US the labour pool is the equivalent of our employment agencies. Being out in the sticks as it were, we didn't anticipate any problems using our ID's, assuming that whoever was behind the counter would not be as clued up on immigration matters, as say the smartly dressed, well-spoken black man had been back in LA.

We immediately struck gold! As we entered through the front door and walked up to the counter, the Geordie said, 'Morning mate we're looking for work'. Upon hearing the accent, the 'Hick' behind the counter beamed with delight and said, 'Hey, my grandmother's Scottish'! The Geordie did not correct him and neither did I.

We immediately baffled the poor man with our 'complicated' paperwork and were promptly signed up! We started work the next day. It was clear we had instantly become 'Brad's' favourites. It's quite simple how the labour pool works. First name down on the list in the morning, gets the first job that comes in. Some jobs paid better than others, and due to our 'Scottish' connection we got our pick of the jobs, regardless!

One day we would be installing a sprinkler system in somebody's front lawn. The next a refurbishment project or labouring on a construction job. For a full week we earned between $250 - $280 dollars, not a lot, but it was a start. We both enjoyed the work, the pace was nice, you could always rely on the weather and it was good being somewhere different every day. Every morning we would leave Eddie and Nula's, stop off at the store, buy a cup of coffee and a packet of smokes, turn up at the labour pool 'choose' which job we fancied and then head off to work.

One day I was working on a refurbishment job doing a rip out. I was standing on the very top of a pair of steps, pulling at a piece of timber that was tightly wedged in at ceiling height, when it suddenly 'snapped' out of place and whipped me just above the eye leaving an inch long gash above my right eyebrow. It instantly produced a lot of blood! The American bloke we were working for suggested he run me up to the local hospital to get stitches, adding, 'it looks kind-a nasty'! But I protested, 'No... no... I'm fine, honestly,' it's just a scratch'! I said, not wanting to go to the hospital due to my immigration status! With his hands on his hips the American gave me a slow nod of admiration and respect and said, 'Ahh... tough guy huh', 'Man, you Brits are built, re...al, strong'! It actually hurt like fuck, and I still have the scar to this day!

As soon as me and the Geordie received our first week's pay from the labour pool, we did the decent thing and offered Eddie and Nula money for allowing us to stay at their's. But they wouldn't hear of it, Nula said they didn't have to pay rent as the trailer came with the job, she said we should keep our money until we were on our feet. As a gesture of good will and to show we appreciated what they were doing for us, we (for the duration of our stay) supplied the beers! In hindsight it may have been cheaper just to pay them rent!

Ever on the ball, the Geordie suggested we apply for Florida ID card's, adding that they might come in handy for blagging our way into jobs. We made an appointment at the local government building in Juno Ridge, which turned out to be a concrete hut with a tin roof! I used my British driving licence and my fake social security card as a means to establish my identity (the lady dealing with my application didn't batter an eyelid, as she seemed more interested (excited even) that I was British! In fact, she couldn't stop smiling at me!). I filled in a couple of forms before having my picture taken and then 30 minutes later I was handed a plastic card depicting the state of Florida, my smiling face, the words 'Sunshine State' emblazoned along the top and to my surprise, in the bottom right hand corner it had the word 'RESIDENT'. I felt as happy as I looked (with my big beaming smile) in the picture on my new ID card. Apart from the year, the date of issue stamped on the reverse of the card read the same as my date of birth! This was because It was also my 24th birthday!

Later that day we decided to celebrate the special occasion by having a few beers (obviously) and then during said celebrations Nula presented me with a surprise birthday cake! It had a number 2 and 4, birthday candle stuck in the top of the cake, it also had a huge green shamrock on the face of it! I was really touched by her kindness; it was very thoughtful and a very nice thing to do (even though I wasn't too sure about the shamrock!). They sang Happy Birthday, and generally made a huge fuss. It was lovely! Later that evening, I sat on the front porch of Eddie and Nula's trailer, drinking, smoking weed and eating cake with a Geordie, a Paddy and a Kiwi (no joke!). We all enjoyed great banter while watching the Florida sun set over the lake on the other side of the paddock. Life was good!

We had been working for Brad at the labour pool for a couple of weeks when we got lucky. A group of us had been sent to a concreting plant called Durabeam, who made concrete posts, pillars and beams for bridges, for the highway's agencies and some of the attractions at Disneyland. The factory yard was immense with the vast majority of the works carried out, outside, due to the hot dry climate. Everything was oversized, huge jigs and rigs for pouring concrete were set about the place and huge reels of steel cable to be used as reinforcement bars for the concrete post, pillars and beams towered over us. The whole place had a bleached white look about it due to all the concrete and the glare of the sun. Virtually everything on site was made of concrete even the tables and benches in the works canteen were made of concrete, lending a hostile prison yard feel to the place. The yard was so big that they had beaten up old cars (with no doors on them) dotted about the place, so if you wanted to go to one end of the complex to the other, you just jumped in a car, drove to your destination and then walked away abandoning the vehicle, it was very novel!

The Florida heat regularly hit 90 degrees during the day; as a result we started work early before the sun came up and while it was still cool. This was also the preferred time of day for the mosquitos, midges and hordes of other insects to swarm and be most active! The poor Geordie was eaten alive and for the duration of our time at the concreting plant looked like he was suffering from a dose of 17th century smallpox! I, however, apparently smell like shit to a mosquito, because I hardly got bitten at all. 'Hooray'!

As temporary agency workers we were required to wear yellow hard hats, while the full-time employees of Durabeam wore blue ones! After only a week, me and the Geordie were getting good reports concerning the standard and rate of our work. Everyone on site wanted to meet the two British guys, we were causing quite a stir! Stereotypes can be very harmful they can also be very beneficial. It was universally agreed the two Brits were great workers, were not afraid to get stuck in, learned quickly and got on well with everyone. We were soon visited by the top bosses, who were also keen to meet the two British guys! It's fair to say me and the Geordie both possessed excellent people skills. We quickly ingratiated ourselves with the bosses, winning them over with our colloquial British charm. They praised our British work ethic and to our surprise said they would like to take us both on, full time, once (by law) we had served out our one month with the labour pool. As quick as a flash the Geordie said, 'No need we just told the labour pool we were leaving today, as we were going to head for Orlando to try for more money, but if you are offering us jobs we can start direct for you on Monday, if you like'?

I had to hand it to the Geordie he was sharp! Obviously, we had told the labour pool no such thing. The bosses said, 'Well, okay then, that's great, erm, you can start direct for us on Monday then, I guess'! There were smiles and handshakes all round, then one of them said, 'Obviously you have to have drug tests... standard policy, you understand, State law an all'. 'Yeah of course, no problem, we both just passed our drug tests for the labour pool, so whenever you're ready. That's great'! Chipped in the Geordie cheerfully. Yet another lie!

Me and the Geordie were delighted, our wages had just gone from $280 a week to $400! We were really pleased with ourselves. 'That's fucking great Martin, but what about the drug testing'? I asked in a concerned manner. 'Don't worry about it', said the Geordie, 'it will take them weeks to sort it out. If we get pulled, we will just leave!'

The following Monday morning we pulled up for work in our station wagon, as direct employees of Durabeam! As we got out of our car, we said good morning to the agency lads by the front gate and then put on our 'blue' hard hats. One of the agency lads said 'Hey, what the hell... man'. The Geordie gave him a stern look and said 'Shuddup, yer stupid looking cunt yer'! We never got any come back from Brad at the labour pool, and for the two or so months that we worked for Durabeam we never got collared for our drug tests either! The extra money we earned allowed us to move out of Eddie and Nula's trailer and into an apartment in the next town of Leesburg!

The address of our new apartment was 112 Lee apartments, West Dixie Avenue, Leesburg. West Dixie Avenue was a beautiful, sleepy, tree lined avenue of weeping willows, well presented houses, manicured lawns and white picket fences. As we slowly drove up the length of the avenue It didn't take us long to locate our new abode! That's because it stuck out like a sore thumb, what with being the only run down looking 'shithole' on the whole fucking street!

It was a dump. It was situated on the corner of a quiet crossroads next to a stop sign. At one end of the street there was a café, a launderette, a 7-11 store and a lake which had a sign which read

'Please do not feed the alligators'! At the other end of the street, three blocks away, was the main high street which ran through the centre of Leesburg. The high street consisted of four stores and two bars, one which was called the Crickets, but which we quickly re-named as 'the Rickets', due to the condition of most of its clientele!

Having found our new gaff! we pulled into the drive and were greeted and interviewed, by a slim young woman with shoulder length blonde hair who looked like she had been raised in a trailer park. That's not a slur, lots of people in Florida live in trailer parks. In fact it's no different to me being working class and growing up on a council estate back home (well maybe a bit different!). She said her name was Tracey-lee. Like a lot of people we meet she was momentarily taken aback by our Britishness, there was even some mild flirtation, before she regained her composure and snapped back into business mode and said, 'It's yours if yo wan it. Two weeks in advance and a week up frern'! ($450). Before adding, 'And if y'awl don't pay yo rent, I'll pack yo shit myself'! She then tilted her head to one side, placed her hand on her hip and looked at us defiantly, indicating (I assume) that the ball was now in our court. 'We will take it', we both said in unison with beaming smiles.

Lee apartments was a timber framed block of four flats (2-up, 2-down). We were on the top floor. The communal hallway was, as you would expect 'dingy', the flat wasn't much better! The purple front door opened into a large living room which had large windows on the two external walls and a ceiling fan in the centre of the room. Both windows had fly screens on them to keep the bugs (in) out! The kitchen and bathroom were side by side and both situated directly off the living room, so you had to walk through either to access the large bedroom which alarmingly only had one double bed. 'Baggsy settee'! I shouted. I did not like the look of the bed at all! The sofa was large and actually quite comfortable, even if it did resemble the kind you might find in a taxi rank waiting room! (eventually we brought a fold out camp bed from an advert in the local paper - 'Baggsy fold-out camp bed'!). Our new neighbours were dubious to say the least. Directly below us was a Hag of a woman, who had a habit of shouting and, looking back, was probably heavily addicted to crack! Opposite the Hag lived a girl in her early twenties, who at first glance seemed quite attractive but on closer inspection, is probably best described as trailer trash! On the top floor and directly opposite us lived two lesbians (bingo!). Frankie and Daisy.

Daisy was very attractive and very feminine. In fact, she was drop dead gorgeous!! Frankie, on the other hand was a total freak, she was definitely the male in the relationship, if you like! She was flat chested, she had short jet-black hair (she later told me she was half Sioux Indian!) and she was constantly squinting! I couldn't get my head around it; I couldn't understand why Daisy was with her - surely she'd be better off with me! (I mean Daisy obviously!). Any way who am I to question love! Despite my first impressions, I instantly took a shine to Frankie, she was a fantastic individual and great fun to be around. It turned out Frankie was one of life's beautiful people, she was decent, genuine and kind. No matter what, she was always smiling. We became good friends. Now I think about it she looked like a young Keanu Reeves and even spoke with the 'Hey dude, what's up' kind of accent. Despite our flat being a total shit hole and despite our neighbours, I instantly loved the place, it felt like a home! Me and Martin were now living like two normal Americans. We had our apartment, we were going to work in the mornings, we were paying rent and doing grocery shopping, it felt pretty good.

Most evenings Frankie and Daisy would pop in for a drink, it was always great fun. At the weekends Eddie and Nula would visit and the four of us would inevitably get rat-arsed, I felt comfortable and

I felt settled. Having a permanent address also meant that my mum and poor old 'M' could now write. Emma sent me a belated birthday present, a couple of books. She said it was the only thing she could think of sending that was light and legal! I also received a letter from my mum. It didn't say anything in particular, just how she and her friend Jean Ellis had been to bingo round at St John's church, but they hadn't won! That sort of thing. The letter from home upset me, it was the first time since I had been away that I felt truly home sick. I hadn't realised, but I missed my mum, I missed my family and I missed my friends. I'd, had a pang of homesickness once before when I had been watching the local news on TV. There was a report from London, and as the reporter spoke into the camera, a red double decker bus went past in the background, but apart from that, this was the first time I had actually felt sad!

****

Me and Martin were eating dinner in the flat one evening (we were fairly drunk), when a cockroach ran over my bare foot! I was (at first) horrified, however I managed to overcome my repugnance and caught the little 'bleeder' on a magazine and began toying with it! Truth be known we were both devastated at the prospect of having cockroaches in the flat, so to lighten the mood and whilst still toying with the little creature I said, 'Can we keep him Martin, can we'!? You know as a pet'! We both laughed, although the laughter was short-lived when I later discovered one in the bottom of the fridge, on its back and spewing out eggs!!

Florida, (due to its tropical location) is the bug capital of America, and to be fair a Floridian finding cockroaches in his home is a bit like you or me finding ants in the cupboard. However, it didn't stop the both of us from feeling sick to the core! It just so happened the TV was on in the corner of the room and as if by magic an advert for 'roach killer' came on. It was one of those hard hitting, hard-sell aggressive type of adverts the yanks are famous for:

Roaches carry diseases, FACT!
They multiply quicker than rabbits, FACT!
They are almost impossible to destroy, FACT!
They can withstand a nuclear attack, FACT!

The advert finished with a rather disturbing image. It was a silhouette of a toothbrush in a glass, then you see the silhouette of the cockroach and its little legs as it climbs up the brush before coming to a rest on the head of the brush and nibbling at the bristles!!!

'FUCKING SOLD!'

The next day me and the Geordie paid $40 dollars for a pack of gas canisters that promised to annihilate the shit out of our little friends! In each room you had to open all the doors and drawers, let a canister off and then repeat the process throughout the property and then leave, not returning for four hours! This was not a problem for us, as we just headed for the Rickets! We returned from the pub some six hours later barely able to stand, as we entered the flat, we mockingly called out to our friends to see if any had survived before collapsing on our respective beds and passing out! When I woke the next morning, I found the odd dead one here and there but no living ones!

A week later me and Martin were out drinking when a huge storm erupted, you could feel the static charge of electricity in the air with each lightning strike. The whole area seemed to shake with the roar of thunder. I saw some very impressive storms while I was in Florida; it wasn't uncommon to see lightning striking across the night sky as opposed to down it. When we returned home to our flat we discovered the storm (or static charges) had awoken tiny fly like creatures, which seemed to be coming up from the floor boards, I literally had to flick them off my bed before climbing on (not in) and passing out! We soon got used to the bugs! And they soon got used to us!

It was hard going, working outside in the sun all day at the concreting plant. The heat and the dust made for thirsty work, so naturally we always finished the working day with a few beers. This particular day we had picked up a case of (Busch) beer and a bite to eat on the way home, (we had stopped cooking since the roach in the fridge incident!). Once home we had sat down in the living room, the ceiling fan blowing a welcomed cool breeze down onto us and cracked open the first (and best) of the ice-cold beers. Shortly after getting settled, there was a knock at the front door.

I opened it to find Frankie standing before me in floods of tears. Concerned I asked, 'What's the matter Frankie'? 'That fucking bitch Daisy has dumped me and ran off with her friend', she sobbed. I instantly felt her pain and sadness for I, too, would have been gutted if Daisy had dumped me (my God she was hot!). 'Come in and have a beer Frankie, don't worry about it! She's just some bird, there's plenty more fish in the sea, eh'! Frankie smiled at my reference to 'some bird', walked in and plonked herself down on the sofa next to Martin while I took the chair at the table. I handed her a beer and me and the Geordie listened as Frankie slagged Daisy to the hills. 'And she's shit in bed!' shouted Frankie in anger. With a raised eyebrow I said, 'really, now that does surprise me'! The Geordie smiled, but Frankie didn't notice, as she produced a bottle of Jägermeister from the inside pocket of her jacket. The evening took on a lighter mood as the beers flowed and we drank the medicinal syrup Frankie had offered us. Me and Martin soon cheered her up with our tales and exploits of our travels and stories of back home. When the night came to an end and Frankie had reluctantly gone home, I remember drunkenly climbing onto my bed and as I drifted off, thinking, 'Poor Frankie, I'm really going to miss that Daisy'!

****

Me and the Geordie had been in Florida for seven weeks before we saw our first alligator! It was 10am on a Saturday morning and as usual the sun was splitting the trees! We were heading over to Juno Ridge, to pay Eddie and Nula a visit, in the hope of convincing them to come out drinking with us (almost certainly a sure thing!). We were driving past Lake Harris, one of the larger lakes in central Florida (there are thousands). Martin was driving, as I lazily gazed out of the passenger window across the shimmering water of the Lake. That's when I noticed what at first appeared to be the ridges of two knobbly motor bike tyres sitting just above the surface of the water line! 'GATOR', I shouted excitedly! 'Quick, pull over Martin'! I had been itching to see a 'real life one', since we had arrived in state. Excitedly we both jumped out of the car and ran down to the water's edge, it was incredulous, less than ten feet away from us was this prehistoric monster casually swimming along the edge of the lake. I wouldn't like to happen upon a lie, as to how big it was, 10ft? 15ft? I don't know, all I know is, it was bigger than me and very close! Had I been brave enough I could have poked it with a stick!

We followed the alligator along the water's edge for quite a while, both in total awe of the amazing spectacle in front of us. It swam slowly, writhing through the water in a snake-like movement, its two eyes and the tip of its snout were visible just above the water line. I sensed it 'knew' we were there, it knew we were following it. At one point it stopped dead in the water and half-turned its head in our direction; perhaps eyeing us up as a potential threat. I stared it out! 'Defiantly' I stared directly into its eyes! I have done the same with cats and dogs before back home. They usually buckle and look away quite quickly leaving me the victor - the Alpha male! However, the alligator did no such thing and held my gaze, before 'I' quickly buckled and looked away!

I remembered hearing somewhere that alligators (and crocodiles) can launch themselves at speed out of the water and are also quite quick across land! I tell you, if that thing so much as flinched in our direction, I was going to kick the Geordie in the bollocks and run like 'fuck' (zigzag fashion)!! However, the alligator rightly deduced that there was no threat and that we were indeed just a pair of sightseeing mugs, before becoming bored of us and resuming its leisurely swim along the water's edge. It had been an exhilarating buzz, and very exciting to be that close and for so long! Without realising it, we had walked quite a distance and could now see at the far end of the lake a little harbour with fishing boats (for hire) and a bar with a neon sign outside which indicated it was open, this was also an exhilarating and exciting buzz for me and the Geordie, so we wasted no time in going back to the car and taking a drive down to the bar at the end of the lake!

We pulled into the parking lot and as we stepped out of our station wagon, we heard 'Hey what the fuck, it's Pat and Martin, weh'! It was our old friend 'Brad', from the labour pool sitting at a table outside the bar with a lady friend. He waved and indicated for us to join him. It was a pleasant surprise; Brad was a nice guy. We joined them at their table and ordered some beers. Brad explained to his lady friend who we were and he also mumbled something about us ditching the labour pool and going to work direct for Durabeam, but we ignored it and talked over him and it was instantly forgotten! We excitedly told him about our encounter with the 'giant' gator! He seemed disinterested saying, 'Oh, that's neat', before casually adding, 'Yeah, you get a lot of them round these parts, we use to catch them when we were kids! They're a real pain in the ass man, they keep knocking my bins over and scattering rubbish everywhere'! Me and the Geordie guffawed into our pints! We spent a pleasant couple of hours sitting in the sun and drinking with Brad and his friend. It was turning out to be a really good day. Then Brad whispered, 'Hey you guys want to come back to my trailer for a smoke'? I thought, excellent, I am going to get to smoke some weed as-well! 'Yeah that would be great, fucking love to'! I said eagerly as I drained the beer from my glass. At this point Brad's lady friend looked at me with some uncertainty, she gave me a quizzical look, before saying, 'Erm, when he says a smoke, he don't, erm mean, 'you know', a smoke'!? She looked slightly embarrassed and said, 'He means a smoke'!

It took a couple of seconds to register what she was implying, and then it clicked! 'Oh... a smoke'! 'Nah..., thanks all the same but that's not my thing, I appreciate the offer and thanks for being up front about it, but we won't be joining you'! I was gob-smacked! Not for a moment did it ever occur to me that 'Brad' was using Crack cocaine! He certainly didn't look like a crack-head; I was totally stunned. Just for the record and in case you're wondering, I never did, never have and never would go near crack or heroin! I am bad enough with fags, booze, and weed! I actually felt sorry for Brad! But each man must choose his own path! Me and the Geordie 'chose' to get back in our car and get the fuck out of there!

We eventually meet up with Eddie and Nula in a bar called the Lake Jem pub, halfway between Leesburg and Juno Ridge. In safe company with good friends, we drank and sang the remainder of the day away and all got completely wasted! The Lake Jem pub was a great little bar slap bang in the middle of nowhere, but full of great characters. My favourite, being a huge man called I.C, an ex-Chicago cop, he had some great stories! He told me when he was a young man, he wrote a love song. Everyone agreed it would be an instant hit, but try as he might, he just couldn't get a record deal! 'What was it called' I asked innocently? 'it was called, I love you so much, I could shit'! bellowed, the laughing American as he slapped the bar, howling at his own joke! I instantly liked the man! He went on to say that he was now retired from law enforcement, but now ran a café in Leesburg! 'We live in Leesburg' I told him, 'on W. Dixie Avenue'. He looked at me astonished and said,

'My café is the one at the bottom of the street, ya dumb ass, come in and have breakfast on the house, we do the best 'grits' in the whole of Florida'! Smiling I said, 'Yeah, that's great mate, but what the fuck are grits'? Which brought rapturous laughter from everyone at the bar, partly due to my British accent! 'Well, come on down and find out for yo self son'! replied the smiling hulk of an American! (Grits are rotten! A cross between porridge and cold semolina! If you have never tried them, don't bother!). 'Where abouts on W. Dixie do you live'? enquired I.C, before adding, 'Hey not that fucking shit hole of a place on the corner'?! I almost spat my beer out laughing! And jokingly said, 'Yep that's our little piece of paradise! and if you ever need somewhere to st...'! I.C didn't let me finish and in an English accent (the best I had heard) said, 'f... ark.... orff'! The whole bar was in fits of laughter. As Saturdays go it had been a great one! I don't remember getting home!

Sunday. After the laughter! Dare I say it, me and the Geordie had established a bit of a routine! Sunday was washing day. I hated it, it meant a stroll to the launderette at the bottom of the road, (opposite I.C, s café). I would nip in to the 7-11 store buy a packet of smokes and a big gulp (large bucket of coke with ice and a straw) ask for a rake of change and then go and sit in the launderette nursing a hangover, sipping my big gulp and watching my dirty underwear and socks as they tumbled and rolled in the noisy machine in front of me. The practicalities of life! Although I must admit it was always nice walking back up the road with the sun shining on my back and a rucksack full of clean washing! I recall little lizards (geckos) darting across my path as I made my way home. There is a photo somewhere of me sitting on the loo in our flat, I'm as black as the ace of spades due to working in the sun all day, I'm smiling and giving the thumbs up at a little gecko perched on the bathroom wall beside me, I remember being drunk and excitedly calling the Geordie, who for some reason happened to have a camera handy, and caught the moment for all prosperity.

Little glimpses of the past, those are the moments I cherish the most!

That morning while I had been in the 7-11 store, I had also brought a $15 phone card, with the intention of phoning my mum (I usually phoned about once a fortnight) but hadn't actually gotten round to it. Sunday evening me and the Geordie headed for the Rickets for a couple of drinks. Happy hour was from 5 till 7 on a Sunday (it's true!). A pitcher of Miller Light and two glasses cost $5 bucks, instead of $7.50. I think this was to entice people in for the Sunday night disco, a sight to behold in the Rickets, I can tell you. We were on our second or third pitcher when I remembered I had the phone card in my pocket. Having had a couple, I thought I would give my mate Simón, back home a call. I hadn't spoken to any of my friends in England since I had left for the states. I stood in the hallway of the pub and dialled the ridiculously long number and waited for Simón Pompidou to pick up. I smiled to myself, when he answered the phone like I had just woken him up, (ello?), I hadn't, he was just very stoned! He soon perked up though, when he realised it was me and that I was ringing from a pub in Florida, 'Pat, how you doing'!?, He hollered down the phone. I quickly began to tell him my exploits (you only get 10 minutes with the card). What I had been doing, the places I had been and the things I had seen. It was great to hear a familiar voice. 'So, what's been happening back home'? I asked. That's when he told me Molloy's dad had died! The news knocked the wind out of my sails, I was gutted, I was gutted for Steve! I had always, had a lot of time for Shay, he was a good man. I was sorry I had missed his funeral and that I hadn't been there for Molly. The ten minutes were up! Despite the sad news, it had been good talking to Simón, but after the call I was left feeling somewhat subdued. I returned to the table and sat down with the Geordie. I told him about Molly's dad, then out of politeness he feigned concern and understanding, but that was okay. We drank two more pitchers of Miller Light before the

DJ had finished setting up his turn tables, the Rickettes was beginning to fill up for the Sunday night 'ye-ha'! By the time the music started me, and the Geordie were both glassy eyed and well on our way!

Through the smoke and flashing lights of the disco I noticed her standing by the edge of the dance floor. She looked about my age, she had auburn hair and she was attractive. Having had a few I decided to chance my arm and go over and say hello, I asked her name. 'I'm Brandy' she said shyly. 'Yeah I'm Randy'! I replied chuckling at my own wit, however I immediately felt embarrassed because she didn't get the joke, and why would she! Hence, I felt a bit silly and she seemed a bit confused when I said, 'No, its Pat, my name's Pat'. There followed a brief moment of awkwardness between us and then I surprised myself by asking her if she wanted to dance (I never dance!). She then surprised me by saying 'Okay, sure'. I don't actually know how to dance, so we smooched our way through an hour of rock, hip hop, funk and of course Motown!

Eventually (thankfully) we sat down at a table and I went to the bar to get the drinks in. 'Where's Martin'? I asked the barmaid. She smiled and said, 'Your buddy told me to tell you he's gone home, and he said, good luck'! Before she gave me a sly cheeky wink. Fair play to the Geordie, after all it was the decent thing to do! Me and Brandy had a great night laughing, joking and flirting. She asked me all about my life in England and seemed genuinely fascinated. She told me about her life in the US, how she had a good job working in a bank, in nearby Ocala, before adding in a slightly more serious tone that she had her own place! The hint wasn't wasted on me! When the bar closed, we got a cab back to her 'trailer'! A friend of Brandy's (a young hippie-ish guy) asked if he could get a lift in our cab, as he lived in the same trailer park. Obviously my first thought was 'fuck off mate', but he seemed genuine enough. I didn't have a clue where we were going, but eventually we arrived at Brandy's trailer. I was understandably disappointed when she invited the little hippy in. However, every cloud has a silver lining, he had a big bag of weed and rolled a joint before inviting me to do the same! I quite liked the little fella, we actually started having a bit of a laugh. Brandy cracked open a bottle of bourbon and then produced, from a tank in the corner of the room a boa constrictor, which she then draped around my neck! So, there I was, sitting in a trailer in Florida on a Sunday night, joint in one hand, glass of bourbon in the other, a snake around my neck and Brandy sitting next to me on the couch stroking my inner thigh! I felt like the king of kings!

It was totally surreal! It didn't take long for the little hippy to realise it was time for him to go, thus leaving me and Brandy alone at last. With the snake safely back in its tank (no it's not a euphemism!), me and Brandy gravitated towards the bedroom, once there we kissed and caressed one another and slowly began removing each other's clothes before reaching the bed. We were young and it was sublime! I think an English guy was a first for her! An American girl was certainly a first for me! Now I don't wish to be vulgar but there's really only one way to tell it! We were naked on the bed, engaging in and I feel confident in speaking for us both when I say, also enjoying, a very popular position, (especially amongst our canine friends!), when Brandy did something that has remained etched in my memory ever since. As we were 'going for it' she turned her head back to face me and in her soft southern American drawl said, 'Pay ...trick, you are no longer a stranger'! It was one of those beautiful rare moments when you realise that life doesn't get much better! Naturally I couldn't help but feel rather 'magnificent' and 'exceptionally' fucking pleased with myself!

It's hot in Florida! (of course!). As such Brandy had an air conditioning unit on the wall above her bed, presumably to keep her cool during the long hot Floridian nights. It just so happened that the positioning of the air conditioning unit dictated that with every backwards thrust of my amorous intent, I got a shot of cold air on my bare arse, which unbeknown to Brandy brought a brief wry smile to my face! Forward thrust, the expected grimace! Backwards thrust, a wry smile! It was actually very distracting, but, being the type of man, whom if I take a job on! ... I like to see it through to the end! I had little choice, but to ....'grin' and 'bare' it!! Brandy was an amazing girl! Being young we fooled around until the early hours, while I did my best to finish off her bottle of bourbon. I have a vague recollection of leaving with a phone number and the promise of staying in touch! I had no such intention.

Things were going good for me and Martin. We were settled. We had a routine! We had a flat, a car, and we had a regular wage coming in, as a result we became complacent. Our weekends were mental, and every night was like a Saturday! The Monday morning after my night with Brandy I didn't go to work, I couldn't, I was to hungover! I told Martin to tell 'em' I was ill. The following Monday neither the Geordie nor myself went to work, we couldn't, we were both hungover! We told 'em we had car trouble! We didn't make it in, the Monday after that either; we had no excuses so when we turned up on the Tuesday, we simply just shrugged our shoulders. Our tardiness hadn't gone unnoticed. They let it be-known it simply wasn't good enough. For over two months we had been the blue-eyed boys at work, but we had now fallen out of favour, because to put it mildly, we were blatantly taking the piss! As a result, the matter of our impending drug tests which we had so far managed to evade, was now being put to us on an almost daily basis. There was no way we would pass them! Things were hotting up for us at Durabeam, so when Eddie mentioned the bloke he worked for was looking for a couple of guys to join his 'crew' (construction), the Geordie and me decided it was time to jump ship, before we were pushed! So, we did!

Eddie's boss was a Filipino guy called Gus, he was a nice enough bloke, but he was somewhat erratic. His personal life was a chaotic mess; he had three women on the go and about 12 kids to support (in Florida if you don't pay your child maintenance, you go to jail!). However, Gus was more interested in getting us to party with him and his brother back at his place, than he was in actually doing any work. Obviously, this was great fun, and nor did we need much encouraging! But it also meant that sometimes Gus struggled to pay us what he owed. Some weeks (if indeed we got a full week), we would be short and then on others he would give us extra in case he didn't have it the next! Gus was constantly robbing Peter to pay Paul. Me and the Geordie knew if we stuck around long enough, we would eventually get stitched! All this coupled with me and Martins excessive alcohol fuelled weekends meant that we had started to miss the rent on our flat. Tracey-lee was not impressed.

We finished work one day and had a couple of beers at the Rickets before heading home. When we arrived home that evening, we found an eviction notice had been pinned to our front door! In a show of bravado, we immediately started to mock and joke about the notice, I said with a broad grin, 'Oh... my god, I don't believe it, my first 'ever' eviction notice'. I then held it aloft like it was the world cup or a lifetime achievement award! The truth was we both knew things were beginning to come on top and it wasn't good.

The Geordie went to see Tracey-lee and smoothed things over by telling her some cock and bull story about us being owed money from our boss (not a total lie!) and that we would pay, what we owed, in full on the following Monday (a total lie!) and then make sure we stayed on top of the rent. Tracey-lee accepted this story. The Friday before 'the' Monday Gus paid us what he owed us in full. We went home packed our few possessions into the back of our station wagon and quietly slipped away under the cover of darkness heading for Orlando! Eddie and Nula were the only people who knew we were going. I never said goodbye to Frankie! Looking back, I now realise it wasn't a very decent thing to do, but we were young, and everything was just a game to us. At that time in my life I never considered the consequences, or the impact of my actions on others. I wasn't a bad person, I was just naïve, and if I am totally honest, I was also immature.

Having spent over three months living out in the sticks, being back in the city was exciting, as new beginnings often are. Our plan of finding a youth hostel to stay in spectacularly backfired, because there wasn't one! So, we had to book into a motel. This was a real concern because we didn't have a lot of money, plus the only labour pool we could find was not hiring (karma perhaps?). In our wisdom we decided it would be a good idea to visit a few bars to see if we could find some locals or better still a few Brits who might be able to point us in the right direction.

But we had no luck, we only succeeded in getting drunk and digging into our cash reserves! I was starting to worry about our predicament and aired my concerns to the Geordie. Having been in similar situations and on numerous occasions, he just laughed and said, 'If you think this is bad, just wait until your down to your bottom dollar'! (obviously an American expression). I think it's fair to say, 'sometimes things have to get worse, before they get better'! On our third day in Orlando, the car finally died! It refused to start! We had crashed 'her' into the only roundabout in LA, I had poured fowl smelling, rank looking green liquid into her in the Sierra Nevada's, she had caught fire in Mississippi, and had since used more oil than gas! And bare metal grinned through the front right-hand tyre. We had driven her across the entire united states of America, and through two different time zones. She was totally kaput! I thought of our promise to the three Kiwi lads and winced! We phoned a breakers yard and scrapped our faithful friend and received $60 bucks! We stood and watched as 'she' was dragged on to the back of the tow truck and then decided it was only right that we have a final drink on 'her'. As it was, we only had 200 dollars to our names, so this brought the grand total of our combined fortune up to $260. When the tow truck was no more than a dot on the horizon the Geordie and me walked away and headed for the nearest bar with the intention of spending the $60 bucks! We awoke the next morning with only $80 dollars and a handful of change between us! I was distraught. What were we going to do? Even if I phoned home and tried to get some money sent it wouldn't arrive in any kind of time to do any good and where would I get it sent to! Martin said, 'There's only one thing for it, we will have to give the Salvation Army a try'! I looked at him like he had just lost his fucking mind! And said in no uncertain terms, 'You can fuck right off, if you think I'm sleeping in a fucking homeless shelter. Its 'not' fucking happening'! He wasn't joking when he said, 'Well Pat, its either that or the street mate. And it's dangerous on the street'!

It took a while for it to sink in. That this was actually happening. Had I been in England and in the same predicament, I think I would have been suicidal, on the verge of giving up! I had heard stories in the pubs back home of blokes who had gone to work in Germany, had drank their digs money and had been forced to spend a few nights sleeping rough, until they had got paid! This brought me little comfort. I tried to console myself with the fact that I was a young man who had embarked on an adventure where anything could happen, in short, I decided that this did not count as real life! Plus, no one knew me, so it was not as cringeworthy as it might have been in different circumstances!

Our only saving grace was that unbeknown to me and the Geordie, the local religious community, organisations and churches of the down town district of Orlando, had been rallying, collecting and raising money for years and had just built and opened a brand new facility for 'Men who had lost their way'! The place was state of the art and what's more it was spotless! It was better than any youth hostel I had ever stayed in, although it did not have the eclectic mix of young international backpackers I was used to. Instead it was a mix of cut-throats, tricksters, bums and vagabonds, and two Brits! The ethos of the place was to help men re-establish themselves and get back on their feet, who had lost their way. Alcohol (and drugs) were not allowed, and anyone under the influence would not be permitted.

It was with a heavy heart and a real sense of shame, that the Geordie and me approached the front desk and explained our situation (except the bit about both being illegal!), to a very 'serious' looking man, sporting a mullet and a handlebar moustache! He asked to see some form of ID, and then asked us to sign a register. And then in a deep southern accent, he said in turn to each of us, 'Have 'you' accepted Jesus Christ as your saviour'? I just wasn't expecting it, it momentarily threw me! I quickly thought of all my options before finally and firmly stating in a matter of fact fashion, 'Yes, ...yes I have'!

I may well yet burn in hell for all of damnation, because I didn't mean a word of it. I don't wish to mock religion. After all, it was good people of faith who had tirelessly raised the funds for what was in fact a fantastic facility, I am sure it has saved many a poor man. I for one was extremely grateful for it. A facility run by people, who when I needed it, offered me shelter, safety (I hoped) and comfort. I didn't realise at the time, but I had been humbled by it and I have remained grateful ever since. It was a really nice building, the whole place sparkled and smelled clean. Unfortunately, the same could not be said for most of the 'guests'.

Despite the dormitory style accommodation and the strangeness of my new surroundings I slept very well. The beds were new, and the sheets were fresh and clean. The next morning having washed we were given a fine breakfast followed by coffee and orange juice. The place wasn't at all like I had at first expected, in fact it wasn't bad at all. However as grateful as we were, we had no intention of staying a moment longer than was necessary (obviously!).

At 9.00am the next morning we stepped out of the 'Sally Ann' and into the hot Florida sunshine. Now installed with new vigour and a real sense of urgency we paced (or tramped if you like!), the streets of down town with a steely determination regarding our employment prospects. We knocked on a lot of doors and got a lot of No's before our diligence paid off.

Late that afternoon, we approached a large construction site on Orange avenue in the heart of downtown Orlando. We had asked if anyone was hiring. They were! Yet again our Britishness had opened doors that may have otherwise been closed. We managed to blag our way through a brief interview and questioning regarding our right to work in the US (necessity being the mother of all invention, especially lies!). And were then taken on by a firm called EAST-SIDE glass, which installed windows and cladding to the exteriors of large commercial buildings. The building in question being a twenty-eight-floor skyscraper with two four story wings coming off either side at the bottom (shaped like bull horns) around a large circular courtyard. Unbeknown to us and rather cheekily, we had just secured jobs (illegally!) working on the brand-new Orange County, 'Police Head Quarters' building. We started work the very next day!

When we returned to the salvation army building that evening and told the staff our good news, they and some of the 'guests' seemed genuinely impressed with our ingenuity and determination! So much so that the next morning after an early breakfast the Geordie and me were surprised to be both handed a pack lunch of 'baloney' (spam) sandwiches and a carton of orange juice each, I couldn't help feeling like we were taking the piss!

The man that interviewed and ultimately hired us was also our on-site boss, or 'Boss Hog' as the yanks would say. Our first morning on site we were to meet him by a block of port-a-cabins at the base of the building. He was a tall gangly looking bloke from Alabama called 'Scooter' (real name unknown). His second in command (foreman) was a short stocky guy in his late 50's/early 60's who was covered in tattoos and looked like he had been left out to bake in the sun for the last forty years. His skin looked like cracked leather! His name was 'Bones' (real name unknown).

Between them 'Scooter and Bones' had a 'goffa' called Jerry (his real name). Jerry was of average height and a bit fat. He had bulbous, bullfrog eyes, a ginger mullet and a ginger moustache, but despite these afflictions he was convinced he was the coolest kid on the block! Jerry was also the biggest bullshitter I have ever meet, but still I could not help but like the man. His stories were pure fantasy. Drive-by shootings, gang wars, drug feuds you name it, Jerry had done it. Oh, and the women, well you couldn't make it up! Unless of course, ...you were Jerry! He was the sort of fantasist that believed his own lies, you could see his eyes darting around as he made shit up in front of you. But what truly endeared me to Jerry was his child like innocence, he really thought I believed it!

After having being introduced to the 'boys', we asked 'Scooter' what he wanted us to do? 'Nothing.' he barked. Instead he told us to, 'Go make yo self's familiar and say hi to all the guys'! 'I will put y'all to work tomorrow, when yo found yo feet'! Me and the Geordie did as instructed and took a walk around, before taking the hoist (which went up the outside of the building) to the 26th floor! After the 18th floor it was just concrete slabs and concrete pillars because the windows and cladding that would eventually enclose the building had not yet been fitted. It was a strange sensation standing on the 26th floor with no sides to the building, needless to say we didn't venture to close to the edge for fear of a sudden gust.

It was amazing, looking out over the entirety of Orlando, to the north, east and west all you could see was the lush green tree canopies (it was fairly flat). Every now and again there would be a small patch of the canopy missing indicating a lake or homestead, but to the south, were the buildings and skyscrapers that made up the Orlando sky line. Me and the Geordie decided this would be a good spot to have our lunch. We sat and ate our 'baloney' sandwiches, watching the sun glint and shimmer of the city skyline. We had well and truly landed on our feet with this one! It was obvious to us both that this was the type of job where you could easily hide! In fact, as jobs go, it turned out to be a doddle, some weeks the hardest thing we did was walking down to pick up our pay checks. Despite this, we were constantly praised for our work ethic 'you guys'!

On the first Friday after we had begun working for the company, me and the Geordie negotiated a small advance on our wages to see us through until the following week, when we would receive our first pay check. Being a Friday most of the lads were heading to a bar around the corner from the job, it was called 'Hoops Tavern', however it was not a gay bar as the name might suggest! (it had a basketball theme!). Me, Martin, Scooter, Bones, Jerry and a few others enjoyed a pleasant few hours drinking and generally having a good laugh. It turned out one of the lads sitting at our table was in fact a crack cocaine user, he looked haggard and tired, it was hard to not feel sorry for the man. Scooter and a few of the others were giving him a hard time, telling him to sort his shit out or there would no longer be a job for him. Scooter then turned to me and in a joke reference to the man's crack addiction said, 'Hey Paay...trick! You know any 'rock stars' coming from England an all'!!

To which I replied in my best clipped English, 'Not really, ...but I did once bump into Mick Jagger in a fish and chip shop'! The whole place fell about laughing, the Americans loved it! Me and the Geordie were in!

I was on my 8th bottle of Budweiser and could feel myself starting to suffer the effects of the booze. So, I whispered to the Geordie, that maybe, considering the 'NO ALCOHOL' rule back at the Salvation Army, it might be wise for us to make a move.

We said our goodbyes and began to walk the few blocks 'home'! As we did so, we practised composing ourselves and acting like we had consumed no alcohol whatsoever in an attempt to appear sober, which was difficult because we couldn't stop giggling! Upon entering the salvation army, we were as usual confronted with the very serious, mullet sporting, moustache wearing, droll American behind the counter. With a face like stone, he looked up and drawled, 'Have you accepted Jesus Christ as your saviour'? Smiling and in an attempt not to breath my strong alcohol smelling breath on him, I quickly covered my mouth with my hand and with a certain amount of sarcasm to my voice said, 'Yes, ...yes I have'!

Once inside the Geordie and me stifled more giggles as we negotiated our way around the heaving mass of vagabonds, bums and cut-throats, then in an attempt to stay out of everyone's way, (in case they sussed that we had been drinking). I headed for the toilets, the Geordie headed for the showers! The toilet and shower block were situated side by side and encompassed in the same area. As I entered the toilet block, I was confronted with a row of around 12 cubicles, I selected the third nearest one, entered and sat down, I didn't need the loo, I was simply hiding! I hadn't been hiding for very long when I heard one of the overhead showers come on and somebody preparing themselves to wash.

A moment later I heard the Geordie begin a very convincing and rather moving rendition of Elvis Presley's, 'In the Ghetto'. The ceramic tiled walls of the shower block enhanced the acoustics and the Geordie's singing rang out loud, around the shower and toilet block. As I sat in the cubicle, I smiled to myself as I listened to the Geordie's rendition. When he reached the end of the first verse, I could not resist, so I boomed in 'my' best Elvis voice the classic chorus line, 'IN THE GHETT....O'!!! I had a huge smile on my face, when I heard Martin snigger to himself and then carry on with the second verse, '...'and if there's one thing, that she don't need' ...'!!! As the Geordie sang, I prepared myself, in anticipation, waiting for him to get to the end of the second verse. As he finished and just as I was about to 'boom' the immortal line, ...I got the shock of my life. When the 'whole' toilet block erupted in unison and sang, 'IN THE GHE....TTO...OOOO'!!!

Unbeknown to the Geordie and me, about seven of the other cubicles were occupied and had been listening to me and the Geordie the whole time. A chorus of American bums (literally) had all joined in, it was pure magical! It was excellent! It was one of those rare fantastical times in life, when strangers spontaneously join together in a shared moment of unity! Had that moment been rehearsed a hundred times, we would never have got the timing as perfect as it was that night. To this day it remains one of my fondest and one of the most memorable moments of my life! We never got caught for having been drinking either!

The weekend was quiet! (drinking was not allowed!!) Not really a problem because we didn't have the funds anyway. So, Saturday we just mooched about. Sunday, however, was a bit more eventful as everyone was 'forced' to attend church! Jesus Christ, what a sorry sight we were. A band of tramps all attempting to wear their Sunday best, which quite frankly would have been 'best' going straight in the nearest bin! At 9.30am we were all marched along the pavement to the church building next door. Another stipulation of staying at the salvation army was everyone was required to wear a shirt and tie to church! Me and Martin could not stop smiling at the absurdity of our situation, as we plodded along at the back of a long line of hopeless hobos.

As we entered the church, I saw an old black man, with hardly a tooth in his head, standing just inside the doorway. As each one of 'us' shuffled past him I could hear him saying, 'tie'? got a tie? what about a tie! ...yo need a tie, wanna tie, ...would yo 'like' a tie'! As I approached, he grinned a toothless grin and I beamed a massive smile straight back at him! ...I 'didn't' have a tie! 'well sir...ee, have I got a tie for you'! He beamed with delight and seemed really pleased with himself as he dived his hand into a cardboard box full of ties and pulled out two and held them up for my inspection. 'Which yo want'? he said, as he looked at me quizzically, waiting for me to make my decision. One was a fairly normal looking blue tie (not bad!), the other was a fucking joke! A clown wouldn't be seen dead wearing it, it was a purple belly-warmer, with huge yellow polka dots on it. It was so wide you could have laid it on the floor and had a fucking picnic on it! I reached out my hand, … .and took the purple belly warmer one with yellow polka dots! The old black man still smiling, nodded his toothless head in agreement, suggesting that 'SIR' had made an excellent choice! I looked at the Geordie, his shoulders were bouncing, and he was crying!

We duly took our places (at the back of the church), among the worshippers and resisted joining in with singing, 'can he, could he, would he...... yes he did'!! The following Sunday neither the Geordie nor myself attended church! Instead we spent the entire day in the pub getting shit faced and sporadically bursting out with, 'could he'? Would he'? '.... singing can he, could he, would he, ...yes he did'!!!

We had stayed at the salvation army for a total of ten days and we had been grateful for it. With our combined first full weeks' pay from EAST-SIDE, we had moved into a small apartment. Conveniently it was only a couple of blocks away from the job and more importantly only a few blocks away from the city centre and all the bars! Our new abode was small in comparison to the place in Leesburg, although it cost the same (but did not have a roach problem, which was nice!). The main living area contained two single beds, however unlike the dubious looking bed in Leesburg, these beds seemed pleasant enough, so I was happy to claim one! Off to the left-hand side of the main living space was a small kitchenette and off to the right was the bathroom (shower only). Small but perfectly formed, it suited us fine! Its close proximity to 'everything' was a huge bonus. Not having a car caused us no real problems, which is a rarity in the US. There was even a free shuttle bus (for the tourists), which ran 24-7 around the downtown area, so getting about was hassle free.

Work was going really well; we had settled in quickly. We were both generally accepted as 'one of the boys' and 'part of the gang', we were constantly praised for our British work ethic and got on well with everyone on site. Also, there was 'no' drug testing! EAST-SIDE was registered in West Virginia, so did not come under Florida state law concerning the routine testing of employees, which was a relief! We were both amazed at the speed with which our fortunes had changed, in a matter of weeks we had gone from being destitute to having the world (or so it seemed) in the palm of our hands.

****

The night life in Orlando was superb, most of the bars and pubs had happy hour style promotions to lure in the tourists; needless to say me and the Geordie soon sussed where to go and when! We lived for the weekends, Friday being 'the' one! We would finish work at four in the afternoon and head for the check-cashing store; it cost ten dollars to cash our five hundred-dollar checks. Then we would walk the four blocks to Dennis Scots sports bar, and take up our positions at the bar! From 4-30 until 5pm we drank dollar Budweiser! Then (I still can't get my head round this next bit!), a bell would ring indicating the start of the 'free' bar from 5 until 6, it's amazing how much you can drink in an hour especially when you have no shame! From 6 until 7 it was then a free buffet of subs and crawfish! And then at 7 o'clock on the dot, the place emptied! 'Fluterd' and 'stuffed' it was then off to another bar around the corner, which did five bottles of 'bud' in a bucket of ice for 10 bucks! There were lots of bars and lots of promotions! Most Saturdays I awoke unable to lift my head of the pillow and with no recollection of getting home, but a quick shower would wash away the cobwebs and clear the head, ready for the Saturday shift (in the pub!). Eddie and Nula visited regularly and would join us on our excursions around the city, they often stayed (crashed) at ours which was nice. It evened the balance! We made a fuss of them whenever our pockets would allow. We all became regular faces in a number of the bars in downtown. Our favourite haunt was a bar called 'Scruffy Murphy's'. Firstly, because the Guinness was exceptional, secondly because it was the only place we could get a decent authentic fry up; proper sausages and real bacon! Believe me, the fry up was important, especially if you wanted any chance of lasting the day! We had really landed on our feet, things were going from strength to strength, we even got Eddie a job working for EAST-SIDE.

Eddie had (as we predicted), been stitched up by Gus! Gus had disappeared owing Eddie two weeks wages! It now meant every Friday me, Martin and Eddie would cash our checks and head for Dennis Scots sports bar, they were great times. Nula wasn't happy though! So, on a rare occasion (on a Friday), we would jump in the truck with Eddie and head up to Juno Ridge and stay at theirs, which meant a day's drinking in the Lake Jem pub with my friend I.C! They were good times indeed!

Scruffy Murphy's was our second home. We were on first name terms with all the staff and all the regulars. I had also become aware that the Geordie was quite taken with one of the barmaids, but was being very coy about it, bashful even! She was an English girl, from Birmingham. I would often catch Martin and 'Trudy' making eyes at each other when they thought no one else was looking. I never mentioned my observations!

One particular Friday night me and Martin were sitting at the bar, when Trudy mentioned she needed someone to cover her Saturday day shift. 'I can do it for you Trudy'! 'I worked loads of bars in London, like', said the Geordie innocently, but whilst also letting her know he was a well-travelled and experienced man! I just smiled above the rim of my pint glass. 'Awh, thanks Martin, you are lovely', cooed Trudy! As per usual me and the Geordie left Scruffy's that Friday night very late and a little worse for wear!

The next morning, I was surprised to see the Geordie up so early and so full of beans. He was very keen to 'get to work', so as not to let his, 'Trudy' down. It was blatantly obvious he really liked her, but he was carrying on like he was 'just' doing a favour for some bloke! I went along with the charade. 'Well, you gotta help out now and again haven't ya'! stated the Geordie matter of factly. I sighed an exaggerated David Essex/stroke cockney style, 'ye...ah', and smiled to myself. It goes without saying that I too was 'going to work', I was going to plonk myself down at the bar and keep my buddy company on his one and only ever shift behind the bar of Scruffy Murphy's!

When we arrived at the pub, we noticed a large scorch mark on the pavement and halfway up the wall outside (next to the entrance). As we entered, we saw all the staff huddled together talking excitedly with, Donal the landlord at the far end of the bar. 'What's up'? I asked. One of the barmen called Steve, began to explain that after me and Martin had left the night before, there had been a 'terrorist attack' against the pub! A car had driven past just after 1.00am and had thrown a petrol bomb at the front door! Fortunately, no one had been hurt and no real damage had been sustained. He went on to elaborate that the police believed there was a political motive, due to the fact that Scruffy's was an Irish establishment. 'That's terrible' I said, before adding '...Can I get a pint of Guinness please'!

I don't know if the incident had scared people away, but it was unusually quite in Scruffy's for a Saturday. The staff had all left and Donal the landlord had gone to the station to talk things over with the police, leaving Martin (with a tea towel slung over his shoulder), alone behind the bar. There were only a handful of customers in, scattered about at various tables, and 'only' me sat directly at the bar. I was chatting away to the Geordie about how 'good' it was of him to cover for Trudy at such short notice, when the front door of the pub flew open and in came the ....'Channel 9 Eye Witness News Team'!

There was a whole entourage of sound men, lighting, and camera operators and a very sure and confident reporter holding a microphone. They headed straight for Martin behind the bar, leaving a trail of wires and cables in their wake. 'Excuse me, Sir', said the reporter, 'but were you here last night when the 'TERRORIST ATTACK' took place'? And then thrust the microphone forward towards the Geordie. Martin visibly reddened and said 'No... no... I wasn't'. 'Oh' said the disappointed reporter. 'Well, ...is there anybody else here who witnessed the attack'? 'I' said the Geordie. 'Him' and gestured towards me sat at the bar! I nearly spat my fucking beer out! Before I had time to think the reporter and his entourage were on me. The guy with the camera on his shoulder was pointing it right at me. The sound man held the fluffy thing on a stick above my head. The lighting man directed the bright light towards my face. I was literally caught in the spotlight! I was surrounded with nowhere to go. The eager reporter thrust the microphone into my face and excitedly asked 'Sir, can you tell us what happened during the TERRORIST STRIKE'!

I shifted in my seat, I paused for affect, then staring directly into the camera and with a very serious look on my face said, 'It was terrible'! 'To think I could have died'. 'To think you can be wiped out.... just like that', I clicked my fingers to express just how quickly a life can be taken! 'Here one minute', I shook my head, '...and gone the next'! 'It was...', I hung my head and again shook it in disbelief, before slowly bringing it back up and staring directly into the camera with an expression that said I was struggling to make sense of what had taken place, before finally adding, ' ...It was frightening.. is what it was'!

'CUT', shouted the sound man! The camera man lowered his camera and the grinning reporter said, 'Thank you sir, you were great, that was awesome'! And with that, the Channel 9 Eye Witness News team, were gone, as quick as they had arrived. Me and the Geordie burst out laughing, 'You fucking cunt'! cried the Geordie in disbelief! 'I can't believe you fucking went along with it, that was fucking excellent'!!! We couldn't stop laughing! Martin finished his shift and joined me at the bar and played catch up, we were still sitting there at 6 o'clock, when Steve the barman who 'had' actually witnessed the attack on the pub walked in for his evening shift. He looked totally gob-smacked and said 'You fucker, I couldn't believe it, I was at home eating my dinner watching the news and then 'you' came on, I nearly spat my dinner all over the table when you said you 'nearly died', you cheeky cunt you weren't even there'!! Me and the Geordie were in fits, we had to hold on to the bar! So, there you have it! Just because it's on the telly, don't mean it's true!

As the evening drew on, Trudy had joined us at the bar and had even laughed at the first two telling's of my earlier antics! As the drinks flowed and as Martin and the lovely Trudy began to cosy up to one another, I did the decent thing and made my excuses and left. I called into every bar I passed on the way home and actually quite enjoyed my solemn excursion. It was nice to be on my own for a change. I'm not sure what time I eventually got in, but I am sure I flaked out as soon as my head hit the pillow. I awoke to an empty apartment; the Geordie had not come home. Wahey!

Life was good. Dare I say it, the Geordie and me had yet again established a routine. We worked all week, finished at four on Fridays, cashed our checks and hit the bars. Eddie often joined us on a Friday and often to poor old Nula's dismay! He would also, quite often, get too drunk to drive his truck home (which to us meant unconscious) and would end up crashing at ours before waking up early on a Saturday morning, distraught and full of remorse, before rushing home to Nula!

On one such Friday the three of us had finished work, hit the bars and started some pretty heavy drinking. At some point in the evening I had bowed out unable to carry on and had waddled home leaving the two of them to carry on without me. I woke up the next morning feeling relatively fresh due to my 'early night'. Martin and Eddie were both awake and sitting at the table in our tiny room. Eddie had a black eye! Martin was looking sheepishly at the floor! I was instantly outraged, I was furious, it was obvious what had happened. Directing it straight at Martin I jumped up off my bed and said, 'You fucking cunt; what the fuck do you think you're playing at, you fucking mug'! I had not forgotten or forgiven the Geordie for giving me a dig! But I was actually more enraged that he had hit Eddie. 'You're fucking out of order'! I could feel my fist clenching, I wanted to bang him straight in the face. Eddie was clearly very embarrassed and said, 'Leave it... leave it', he gestured with his hands for me to let it go, as did Martin. Not for the first time in my life, I felt it was 'my' duty, as though it was 'my' responsibility to stand up for Eddie (to stand up for the victim, to be the protector). Poor old Eddie. I had Eddie sussed, the first time I ever meet him, I instantly felt like I knew him. He was Irish. I grew up in an Irish household, I knew the culture, I understood the do's and don'ts. I understood the unwritten rules of conduct and behaviour. I really wanted to go 'fuck it' and just give the Geordie a dig anyway! But I couldn't. Eddie had made it clear he wished for it to be left alone. I knew I had to respect that, or I would have only caused him further embarrassment. Looking at the Geordie sitting in the chair, sheepish, remorseful and hanging his head in shame, I couldn't help but also see the 'victim' in the perpetrator. After all, hadn't my dad been the same.

When we had first embarked on our American adventure, I had looked up to the Geordie. I had been happy to follow his lead, believing he was a top bloke! I had thought I would have liked to be more like him, he was after all living the life I had only ever dreamed of. Martin, Eddie and Nula, were all in their early thirties while I was ten years or so their junior. I was, or had been, in awe of them all, especially the Geordie. But now I was disgusted with the Geordie's behaviour. More than that, I was embarrassed by it. I didn't like it and I didn't want to be part of it! Yes, it's true my upbringing had been rough, I had witnessed violence, anger and rage. But despite this, (both!) my parents had installed in me, from a young age, a sense of decency and kindness. I had morals. You don't hit mates! You look out for one another, if a mate starts acting like a dick, you give him the benefit of the doubt. You certainly don't hit a bloke who is so drunk he can't defend himself, it's not the done thing. It's just not on!

I had not been the same with Martin since we had first arrived at Eddie and Nula's, and he had given me a dig! I was now beginning to think he was a bit of a cock! And I was now beginning to think he was a drunken bully; I despise bullies of any shape or form. I was starting to think I would have had a better time travelling alone, perhaps I would have had a better experience, a more pleasant adventure.

There had been another incident between me and the Geordie a couple of weeks prior to Martin' and Eddie's 'scuffle'. Me, Martin, Eddie and Nula had been sitting at a table outside a bar in downtown one evening having a couple of drinks. The Geordie had leaned back on his chair and had nearly fallen off, naturally I laughed! As he sat forward, he 'cuffed' me around the head, like I was some sort of disobedient child. I instantly shot my beer glass down on to the table and jumped to my feet, 'Don't, fucking do that'! It was perfectly clear I meant it, all three were suddenly quiet! 'I'm not drunk now, you cheeky cunt'! There was an alleyway directly beside where we were sitting, I gestured towards it. 'Come on, you're the big man, let's go and sort it out, right fucking now, come on, I'm more than happy, lets fucking go'! I was furious! He instantly buckled, 'No', 'no... leave it', he murmured. 'yeah that's what I thought Martin'! I took my seat, and said no more on the matter, I didn't have to!

He wasn't the first person to confuse niceness for weakness, nor would he be the last. I have said it before, I don't like violence, but I don't like being treated like a fool either. He annoyed me, the most annoying thing being there was no need for it. Now it was getting to the point where he was actually offending me! That's how I felt when I saw Eddie's eye. Yet again I had to let it go and yet again it blew over and things returned to normal, although I was beginning to think my American adventure may be coming to an end. Familiarity, breeds contempt! He had given me a dig and got away with it. He had cuffed me around the head, and he had got away with it. He had given Eddie a dig and got away with it. Did he really think he was going to get away with it again? Why is it people insist on taking the piss?

Now, you know, and I know! That it was all going to come to a head between me and the Geordie, so I will get straight to the point! It was a Saturday, we had spent the day drinking in Scruffy Murphy's, it had been good fun and we had enjoyed a lot of banter with all the regulars. Me and the Geordie were both very drunk when we eventually left at around 1.00am. For some reason we had ended up directly across the street from the pub, standing in a small courtyard which had a couple of stores on either side.

I know the Geordie started it! I was not an aggressive or argumentative drunk, far from it, I had in fact always been a fairly happy drunk! Precisely what happened I'm not sure, but I am guessing in his drunken state, the Geordie 'thought' he was going to give me a push or a dig! Clearly that was not going to happen. I remember giving him a couple of shots to the head, before grabbing him and throwing him against the wall, where I suppose I intended to finish the job! Unfortunately, in my drunken rage I hadn't realised that it wasn't a wall but was in fact the large glass plate front window of the (closed) pizza shop. There was a huge crash and the sound of glass smashing, as I put him straight through the window! I had by now completely lost it and was still gunning for him! Within seconds I had jumped through the gap where the window had been and again had hold of him, I couldn't believe the audacity of the man for having started on me, I had grabbed him by the collar and had began hitting him again. We both ended up rolling around in the shattered glass on the floor of the pizza shop. The shop alarm was ringing, and unbeknown to the two of us, a crowd had gathered outside the pub upon hearing the commotion! Also unbeknown to the Geordie and me was that there was a police station at the other end of the street from the pub (neither of us had ever got that far!), so the police had arrived within minutes (on bicycles)! They broke up the fight and dragged us out of the shop and then kept us separated while they attempted to ascertain what had happened! I (we) had sobered up a bit by this point! And

I remember the guy who owned the pizza shop had turned up on the scene and was going mental! 'What about my window', he was shouting, I heard one of the police officers saying to him, 'Look it's just two drunk tourists, just claim it on your insurance, okay'! The man was fuming! One of the police officers then attempted to interview me, but I did the old classic of pretending to be, 'still' very drunk and as a result was struggling to understand his questions! He had pulled my wallet out of my back pocket and looked at my Florida ID card and had seemed satisfied he now knew what had gone on when he said, 'So your name's, Patrick Delaney, hey', as if this explained everything (might he also suggest I join the Irish guards, so as to be with my own lot!)! I nodded that it was, I then became quite alarmed when he pulled out my social security card and started saying a bit more seriously, 'What's this'! He repeated the question a couple of times whilst holding it in front of my face, but I persisted with my charade of being very drunk and did not answer! The police ascertained, we were two friends, on holiday, who'd, had too much to drink and had unintentional broken a window! They decided as such, that there was no point in taking the matter further and to our relief and utter astonishment, told us to 'Do one'!

Neither of us could believe we had gotten away with it; had we been Americans we 'would' have gone to jail. As me and the Geordie walked away muttering low inaudible insults at each other, the crowd outside the pub began to disperse, I looked over my shoulder and cringed when I saw a couple of familiar faces shaking their heads in disbelief!

The next morning there was an awkward silence and an atmosphere you could have cut with a knife in our tiny little apartment. We both had cuts and grazes to our knees and legs, but otherwise, I was unmarked. We sat at the table and both sported the sulking, pouting expressions of two little boys who had just been told off!

I held firm and said nothing. Eventually the Geordie raised his head to look at me; I winced when I saw his black eye and fat lip.

Then the Geordie said, 'Look I'm sorry for starting on you last night, like', 'I know I can get a bit arsey in the drink, and that, ... erm', he trailed off. It was now my turn to say something, 'Look Martin, I get the impression that you might think I am some sort of a southern Jessy, just because I don't get all aggressive and boisterous in the drink, but that's not my style. I thought we were mates and where I come from, mates don't start on each other, mainly coz its tramp-ish! The first time I let it go, but only because I had no choice! There was no way you were ever getting away with it twice, you do understand that don't you'? The Geordie looked at me, grinned and said, 'Yeah... but you didn't have to throw me through the pizza shop window, you could have just had a quiet word in my ear like'! I gave him a puzzled look and sarcastically said '.... But I'm sure I whispered something to you on the pizza shop floor'! We both laughed, the way men do when they are both embarrassed and wish to just brush something under the carpet. There was a brief moment of silence before I slapped both my thighs and said, 'Anyway, fancy coming for a pint'!

The fight had certainly cleared the air between us, I was man enough not to mention it again, so I continued to carry on exactly as before. I was glad the Geordie now knew why he had got away with giving me a dig, because I had allowed it! I had no interest in trying to make the Geordie feel uncomfortable or awkward in any way. I was not interested in male bravado, because it's exactly that! Bravado! Self-praise is no praise! But I was aware the Geordie had a new respect for me, not because he now knew I would have it with him. I think it had finally dawned on him, that I was actually a decent bloke, I had tact, there was no need for him to try to assert his toughness, in an attempt to protect himself! I had no interest in trying to embarrass or undermine him in anyway, I just wanted everyone to get along and have a good time. I think actions speak louder than words. As a result, I think he admired me. He no longer wrongly believed I might be a southern Jessy; he now realised I was in fact the manliest of men. I was quietly pleased, but not smug! Despite these changes, despite the fact, things were good, and everyone knew where they stood, I still hadn't, nor ever would, forgive him for giving me a dig! I let it go.

Me, Eddie and the Geordie were all getting along well, the job at EAST-SIDE glass had been an absolute god-send. I actually enjoyed it. And I loved Florida; every day was like a perfect hot summer's day back home. I especially liked the warm evenings, sitting out the back of our apartment wearing just shorts and a T-shirt and drinking cold beers. We still visited Scruffy Murphy's every week-end, although immediately after the incident between Martin and me their had been cursory glances and comments made and a few questions asked, but we both made it clear that, 'What was done, was done' and the issue had been dropped. Life was, yet again, good, we were poodling along quite nicely. However, I still couldn't shake off the idea that I may be better off without the Geordie. The idea had even crept into my head that it may be time to go home! However, this was easier said than done, because we were living week to week and drinking every penny we earned. Getting the money together to leave, would be the same as getting the money to arrive! (and I was not going to receive a tax rebate!). Sometimes you need a bit of a 'nudge' to get things going!

****

Having arrived for work one morning, Scooter informed me I was to work with Jerry (the bullshitter) for the day up on the 24th floor. As me and Jerry made our way up to the 24th, he began telling me some cock and bull story about a load of weed that had come his way, due to some very elaborate and dodgy gangland dealings! So naturally, I asked 'how much for a quarter of an ounce'? I was just playing along I never expected to get it! '40 bucks' said Jerry, 'I can have it for you Friday'! 'Yeah'! I said somewhat disbelievingly, 'Okay that'll be great'. And then I thought no more of it. Me and Jerry had been given the task of dismantling a scaffold tower situated 'outside' on the balcony of the 24th floor. The balcony ran around the entire exterior of the building. The scaffold tower in question was approximately the same width as the balcony, but the working platform of the tower (the bit you stand on) was about 6ft off the floor and a good foot above the concrete perimeter wall of the said balcony!

I was wearing a safety harness and aware that in the unlikely event that something should go wrong, the harness would undoubtedly save my life - but I was also mindful that if I should fall, the 'snap' of the harness against my 14 stone weight would probably break my back! As I scaled the tower and clipped myself on to a strategically placed anchor on the exterior face of the building it came to mind that I was also an illegal immigrant and in the event of an accident, I would not receive a penny in compensation. Obviously, I did not disclose my thoughts to Jerry who, incidentally, had both feet firmly on the ground!

Once I was stood on the working platform of the tower, I set about dismantling the very thing I was standing on, 24 floors above the ground!! I could feel the wind as it pushed against me as I started to undo the handrail which faced into the building and then passed it down to the ginger bullshitter. Then, with some trepidation, I turned facing outwards from the building and began to undo the handrail facing out from where I was standing, I had a spectacular (and uninterrupted) view of the city (like a man on a ledge, in a Hitchcock thriller!) It was surreal. I was concentrating on looking straight ahead but eventually braced myself and looked directly down passed my feet, 24 floors to the street below. For a moment my head swam, as my eyes focused on the scene. The vehicles looked like matchbox cars and the throng of people resembled an army of ants marching to and fro! I then passed the handrail (I was now standing on a tower with no sides!) down to a very serious looking Jerry. As I did so, I made a very loud and long drawn out 'RASPBERRY' sound, indicating the very precarious nature of my current situation! We both immediately burst out laughing! I loved the fact that the raspberry had said it all! I loved the fact, that although me and Jerry came from completely different backgrounds and were in fact worlds apart in lots of respects, we both knew, we both understood, no words had to be spoken! Humanity at its best!

The next day (Friday) Jerry (true to his word!) surprised the hell out of me, by bringing me in an 'actual' bag of weed. He was acting quite shifty, before, 'nervously' and 'hurriedly' stuffing the bag of weed in the front pocket of my T-shirt, 'There you go buddy' he said as he patted my pocket and simultaneously blew a raspberry whilst looking at me for approval with his big bullfrog eyes (some gangster huh!). Smiling I said, 'nice one' before giving him his $40 dollars. I liked Jerry.

That Friday started the same as was typical of all the other Fridays since I had begun working for EAST-SIDE Glass. I had cashed my check, I had made a pig of myself at Dennis Scot's sports bar, I had gone for my bucket of bud and then I had made my way to Scruffy Murphy's! At some point in the evening I had decided I could drink no more, so a little worse for wear, I had left the Geordie propping up the bar on his own and had stumbled out the door, staggering down the street heading for home. I did pretty well! In fact, I almost made it all the way!

I have a vague recollection of 'walking' down a tree lined avenue of weeping willows and manicured lawns and then, I stumbled! Try as I might, I just could not get upright again. I must have made a sorry sight as I flayed and rolled about in my endeavour to right myself and get back on my feet. Eventually splayed on my back and in somebody's front garden I passed out!

Presumably, the owner of the property or a concerned neighbour had phoned the police to report a man laying motionless in 'their' front garden. Had they not seen me stumble, they might have been forgiven for thinking I was dead. I am not sure how long I had been laying there before the police arrived. I came to, as I was being helped to my feet by two police officers, one of them was asking me my name! I must have told them because I remember, amidst the red flashing rotating lights of the squad car one of the officers saying, 'Where do you live Patrick'? I managed to explain 'just round the corner'! I really had 'nearly' made it!

To give the two officers their due I recall they were very pleasant, caring even, and polite. I too was polite, I think despite my drunken state, I felt embarrassed and ashamed and I think they picked up on it. Our conversation was almost genial in its manner, they indicated no harm had been done and that they just wished to give me a lift home to ensure my safety. How nice! I honestly thought I was going home! They explained that as a matter of procedure and before they could put me in the police car they had to ask me if, I had about my person any weapons or narcotics, 'No, of course not' I said helpfully. I was actually a little offended, because by now, I had thought we were friends! One of the officers then said, 'Okay, Patrick, we have to search you now. Before we can put you in the car and give you a ride home...okay?'. 'Yeah, of course, no problem mate' I said with half closed eyes, as I gently swayed from side to side. The officer began to pat me down, as he did this, he patted the front pocket of my T-shirt and with two fingers extracted a bag of weed! I had genuinely forgotten I had it!

Everything immediately changed! 'Okay buddy, you're going to jail'!, barked the officer, as he quickly spun me round and handcuffed my hands behind my back. Because of my state of drunkenness and due to having watched many an episode of 'COPS', I found this last statement extremely funny. So funny in fact, that I started laughing and singing the theme tune ... 'Bad boys, bad boys, what-cha gonna do, what-cha gonna do, when they come for you, bad boys'! I thought it was hilarious that, 'I', Pat Delaney, was going to jail!

I remember being put in the back of the police car; I remember the steel grill that separated the officers from their prisoner (me)! I remember one of the officers calling something in on his radio, 'male, blah blah, Caucasian, blah blah'. After that ...nothing!

I woke up laying on a cold concrete bench. I looked around the room with one eye open, squinting against the glare of the clinically white walls. It took a moment for my eyes to adjust to my surroundings. There were five other men in the room, I thought one of them must be a painter and decorator because he appeared to be wearing white overalls. I sat up and felt the cold of the concrete as my feet touched the floor. Looking down I saw that my shoes and socks had been removed, I noticed that the belt that had gone through the loops in the waistband of my shorts had also gone. The man that looked like a painter and decorator was now shouting at the wall and to no one in particular, 'That's it, she's gone, I'm fucking leaving her, the fucking bitch'! When I looked at him again, I could see that his 'decorators overalls' were actually, a white paper jump suit, he had obviously had more than his shoes removed! I had no recollection of getting there! I didn't know what I had done! I had never been there before, but I knew exactly where I was! I was in jail!

A little while later a civilian worker appeared and I was given a pair of prison issue plastic flip flops! I had at first declined them with a look of disgust as I wondered whose and how many feet had been in them before mine, but I had changed my mind when the man offering them said, 'Yo sure'? 'Floor gets awful cold'. I grimaced as I slipped my feet in.

Waking up in a police cell was not a new experience for me. It had happened on a number of occasions back home. However, back home I would be arrested and put in a cell, alone. In those days you didn't receive a caution or a fine, in fact I think it was generally accepted that young working class males tended to get pissed up at the weekends and if they were a handful or acting the goat, then they got thrown in the cells until the next morning when they had sobered up.

I don't think I, (we, those) were ever thought of as anything other than youngsters who'd had too much to drink. I certainly wasn't ever criminalised for it, it was just the norm, it was part of British culture, I don't think even the coppers thought that much of it! Then when I had sobered up enough (alone), I would be informed by a duty police officer of what a 'cunt' I was and then told to fuck off. Usually I would head to the pub and tell my friends all about my exciting experience! Basically, back home I knew the score, here I didn't. This was different! I was in an American jail. I wasn't frightened nor was I concerned about my safety as I was too busy just being immensely fucking gutted!

I sat holding my head in my hands. I didn't know the score. I didn't want to ask any questions, in case they in turn, began to ask me questions and discover I was an illegal immigrant. I remember thinking, well you have really outdone yourself this time... 'Way to go Pay...trick'! After an hour or so I was led from the cell (drunk tank) by two police officers who walked me down a long corridor to a room where I had my fingerprints and mug shot taken. I had hardly uttered a word since I had woken up as I did not want to bring attention to my accent! Eventually I mustered up the courage to ask, 'why' I was there. I still did not know!

'Shit', said one of the officers, 'You don't know'? 'Man, you were brought in last night... you were pretty naa...sty'! I was a little taken aback by his last comment but dismissed it! 'so, what happens now', I ventured. 'Shit, you really don't know, do ya', said the helpful officer. 'No, I don't mate, I'm just here on my holidays (fib!), an American jail is a first for me'! He shot me a glance that said 'unlucky', before saying, 'Man, as vacations go, this must be a real stinker huh'! I nodded my agreement, fearing I had already said too much. The helpful officer continued, 'Well, you were brought in last night for drunk and disorderly and possession of marijuana, so you will be up before the judge sometime today buddy'!

This really wasn't going well at all. I was marched down another corridor by the two officers until they stopped by a rack which appeared to contain rolls of fabric?! 'Okay, if you wanna take your bedding'. I was flabbergasted! 'bedding' I said in total shock, 'What, I'm fucking staying'?! With this both officers burst out laughing. I didn't. 'Yeah, I am afraid so buddy,' said the friendlier of the two.

It got worse! All my clothes were taken (even my pants!), I was made to shower using a de-lice-ing soap (obviously I didn't have any, it was just standard procedure for all prisoners!) and was then issued with an orange press-stud jump suit to put on. I was then marched with my bedding roll tucked under my arm to a cell containing 20 inmates! All I kept thinking was if they find out I'm an illegal immigrant I am fucked, and then I thought, if they find out I'm working on their brand new police headquarters I am really fucked, just for the cheek of it!

I entered the cell, it had twenty bunks and at each end of the cell was a stainless-steel toilet bolted to the wall. There was no cubicle, there was no curtain wall, the 'pan' was literally bolted to the wall! I remember thinking I could probably do a couple of months without taking a shit!

The front of the cell faced the corridor and an observation booth 'manned' by a huge black woman in uniform. The cell didn't have bars like you might expect, instead it was one large piece of (toughened) glass. As I entered, everyone turned in my direction. The officer offered a well-rehearsed, 'make yourself at home' as he closed the door behind me. Most of the 'residents' were of black and Hispanic ethnicity with just a few whites, whom all sported the standard mullet and moustache. So, there I stood, in my orange dungarees and plastic flip flops! I was 24yrs old, I was white (although I had an exceptional tan!), I had broad shoulders and big arms and unlike everybody else, I had a shaved head! If there was ever a case for 'not' judging a book by its cover then this was it!

There was one empty top bunk about three quarters of the way along the cell. I walked to the bunk and put my bedding roll on it and simply thought 'fuck'! I stood there for a moment deep in thought. How the fuck am I going to get out of this one? What's the procedure? Do I keep quiet and hope I just get bumped along until I eventually pop out the other end of the system? What are my rights, do I have any rights? How long will they keep me here? As I was digesting all these thoughts, I heard 'Whatch...yo looking at'! I had been so deep in thought I hadn't realised that I had in fact been starring directly at a tall skinny black bloke who was lying on the bunk beneath mine. Without thinking and without hesitation I (rather aggressively), blurted, 'What do you fucking mean, what am I looking at'!

I wasn't attempting to act tough, it's just how it came out! His eyes widened, my accent had startled him, he hadn't been expecting it, my appearance didn't quite fit the bill either! Unsure, he immediately diverted his eyes and looked away, before turning on his side and away from me. He never spoke another word.

I had been lying on my bunk for a few hours when the cell door opened and an officer read out a list of names to go up in front of the judge, I was one of them. About twelve of us were ordered out of the cell and marched down the corridor (in a blaze of orange!) and led into a court room. We were all made to line up against the right-hand wall of the room as each man was called in turn to take the stand at the front of the room and in front of a big TV screen! A TV judge was another first! I presumed he was in another room somewhere in the jail. As each man took his turn on the stand and his crime read out, the judge asked, 'And how do you plea?' Before delivering his verdict. It was serious stuff.

My heart sank when a huge hulk of a Hispanic guy took the stand and I heard the judge say something along the lines of 'We are going to detain you until we can establish the authenticity of your identity. Some of your papers are questionable to say the least'! I am sure the colour must have drained from my face as I stood there waiting my turn, all the time thinking 'I'm fucked'.

Eventually my name was called out and I took my turn on the stand in front of the TV. My crime/s were read out for the judge. 'And what are the circumstances of this crime', he mumbled to somebody out of view. However, before he could finish what he was saying, my survival instinct kicked in and I started to babble! I apologised for being a poor ambassador for my country. I explained how I had gotten carried away drinking in the glorious Florida sunshine and had been caught up in the holiday atmosphere when I had become intoxicated and had behaved totally out of character (hmm!).

Like the tall skinny bloke on the bunk below mine, the judge seemed suddenly perplexed as what to do with me! 'Yes, yes well erm... I will set bail at erm, $250 dollars and you will appear before me on, erm ...let's see now'. He peered at me above the rim of his spectacles and with a slight grimace, said, 'Will you still be in the States in a month's time'? I instantly promised that I would make arrangements, to make myself available, so as to receive my rightful and just punishment! For good measure, I again stated that I was embarrassed for my poor conduct and had not only let myself down but had indeed let my country down as well! This seemed to please the judge! Of course, I had absolutely no intention of ever turning up for the court date nor did I have $250 dollars!

After the last man had taken to the stand, we were again led back to the cell. I was also informed that I was entitled to make a phone call. I admit the child in me wanted to phone my mum! 'Hi mum, yeah everything's great. Yes the weather is glorious. No, I'm currently languishing in Orange County jail, 20 to a cell. Yeah, mostly Hispanic and black, mum'!

Obviously, I was not going to phone my poor mum, even if it was tempting. Who then, GHOSTBUSTERS!?

Me and the Geordie did not have phones, Eddie and Nula had a phone, but I didn't know the number! The only thing I could think of was Scruffy Murphy's. Somehow, I managed to get hold of the phone number for the pub. I dialled the number thinking please let somebody answer, to my great relief 'Trudy', Martin's 'bird' picked up the phone. I explained my predicament, I asked her to let the Geordie know as soon as possible. I told her my bail had been set at $250 dollars. I also added 'Tell Martin, there is money in my drawer'. This was a lie; I didn't have any money. I knew Martin would know this and just hoped he would be able to sort something out! Please God sort something out, I thought as I hung up the phone.

I was taken back to my cell and upon entering I was given a clear plastic toiletry bag, containing a small bar of soap, a tiny tube of toothpaste and an equally tiny toothbrush. You would have been hard-pushed to brush your teeth with it, let alone make it into a shank! I climbed up on to my bunk and just lay there too gutted to be anything else.

Sometime during Sunday everyone was ordered out of the cell and made to line up in the corridor outside while four officers conducted a cell search. It was a welcome distraction. It had been over 24 hours since I had made my phone call and I had heard nothing back. To the best of my knowledge it was still unknown that I was an illegal immigrant, so I was still hesitant to ask questions.

MONDAY 11AM.
The door to the cell opened, an officer with a clip-board read out two names. 'Ecquildo Marinez and Patrick Delaney'. 'Get yo shit together guys you're leaving'! I leapt off my bunk; I was ecstatic! Myself and a little Puerto Rican fella were led from the cell and marched down a corridor following behind the officer. As we walked the Puerto Rican, who was by now grinning from ear to ear (as was I), gave me a jubilant fist bump! Followed up by some elaborate hand jiving. I was so happy to be leaving, that I automatically hand jived him straight back and to my amazement I seemed to do it in the correct sequence and order! I found this quite amusing, the two of us bowling down the corridor, hand jiving like a couple of 'huggy bears' behind the officer who was unaware of our jubilation.

My clothes, possessions and paraphernalia were returned to me. Once again resembling a human being I signed a form agreeing that yes, I had been treated well and yes, I do promise to show up for court! Then an officer opened an exterior door to the jail and said, 'Okay, off you go, ...see you all next week'!

I stepped out into the Florida sunshine totally elated. A passer-by would have been forgiven for thinking I had just finished a ten stretch, rather than 3 days. Fair play to the Geordie, whatever he had done, he had done good! I wasn't exactly sure where I was, so I just headed off up the street and at the end of the road I turned the corner and saw a 7-11 store and a bus stop. I went into the shop and brought a packet of fags and a big gulp. I hadn't had a cigarette since I had been arrested (there's a no smoking policy in the jail; if you get nicked in Florida, then you no longer smoke!). I left the shop and took my place at the bus stop, at the end of a long line of jubilant men all of whom were chain smoking and grinning! I hadn't been standing there long when I heard the toot of a horn and a familiar voice shout 'Oi, Pat, you drunken bastard, do you want a lift'? I spun round to see Nula in Eddie's pick-up truck, smiling at me through the open window. I ran over and jumped in and kissed her (on the cheek) I was so happy (don't tell Eddie!). As she turned the truck around, I waved and gave the thumbs up to the lads at the bus stop as she drove off heading for Scruffy Murphy's! On the way Nula explained that Eddie and Martin were waiting in the Pub for me. She explained that Martin had phoned them, and Eddie had stumped up the bail money! You really don't get much more decent than Eddie McCormack. I let it be known how truly grateful I was and promised to pay him back with my next pay check, which I did. As me and Nula entered the pub a huge cheer went up from the regulars and staff, the Geordie was grinning and had a look on his face that simply said, 'fu...ck ...in... h... ell'! 'Quick get the boy a pint', he demanded at the bar.

Trudy handed me a pint of Guinness and said, 'It's on the house' and then gently added the way women do, 'Are you okay'? My face erupted into a massive grin as I said, 'I fucking am now'! This was followed by rapturous laughter from everyone in the bar! I was a legend, for the whole day! At one point I said to Trudy in a very serious tone, and for the benefit of everyone at the bar, 'I knew there was something up.... when the letters stopped'! This brought about more hilarity!

When things had quietened down, I told Martin, Eddie and Nula (to the best of my knowledge) what had happened. I told them how my main concern was that they were going to discover that I was illegal. I told them about the TV judge and the court date! It was at this point that I mentioned that perhaps it might be time for me to go home! I was surprised and touched by their reaction to this last piece of information. They looked saddened by my news, especially the Geordie!

The next day I phoned home. I didn't ring my mum; I didn't ring my friends. I phoned my brother. I told him what had happened, I explained that I needed to leave the states. I suppose begging for help is a good away of putting it as any other! My brother was great, he was sympathetic, he was understanding, and he was happy to help. I think he was proud of me, not for having been arrested of course, but for what I had achieved in the last 12 months. Connor was doing well for himself. He had started up his own business in the specialised gas industry and was well respected. As a result (and down to his diligent work ethic), his company was growing from strength to strength. I was (am) proud of my brother and his success.

We had both grown up in the same house, we had both experienced the hardship and pain of our shared upbringing. Being the older brother, I had always known it had been harder for him. I had always looked up to my brother, I suppose hero worshipped. The reality is, I think I saw him as a father figure. His business was doing well, his little brother had just spent a year travelling around the US. I think he felt as a family (as men), we had become established somewhere above what we once were! I think he was glad to be in a position where he could help (bail out!) his little brother! Perhaps he felt this was the beginning of a new era for our family. He agreed to send me a one-way ticket from Orlando to London! I was happy, embarrassed, glad and sad, all at the same time!

I told work I was leaving. Scooter, Bones and Jerry, all said they were sorry to see me go. Although it didn't sit well, I 'lied' and said I had been away from home for almost two years and that I needed to go home as my ‘father’ was unwell! It was all I could think of that sounded credible. I didn't like lying to my work friends, but I had no choice, I couldn’t tell them the truth because It would have jeopardised the Geordie’s position. I felt very uncomfortable about it, but it was a necessary evil.

Having made my mind up to leave, the last few weeks dragged. I just wanted to get on the plane and for it all to be over. I felt guilty and I felt bad for leaving the Geordie on his own! But at least we were established with regards to work and a social scene, this helped some way to ease my discomfort.

A week after getting out of Orange County jail, me and Martin were at home watching the early evening news on the TV, when to my astonishment the huge Hispanic guy who had been detained by the judge due to the uncertainty of his identity, appeared in hand-cuffs on the screen of our television set. His name was Santino Garcia, he had been charged with three murders! I was gob smacked! I couldn't believe I had been sharing a cell with a mass murderer, I had naively thought that all the other inmates were just drunken idiots like me! Ignorance truly 'is' bliss!

I checked the mail everyday anticipating the arrival of my ticket 'to freedom', 'my coupon to scarper'. After almost two weeks of waiting it arrived. I kissed it! And thanked my brother out loud! It had been a tense wait. The departure date on the ticket was for the day before my court date. I was cutting it fine! My concern was that when I didn't show up for court an arrest warrant would presumably be issued in my name. As everything was computerised these days, would it flag up at the airport?! I just didn't know.

With my last week's wages, I brought the Geordie a little stereo, so he could listen to his cassettes! Just in case he got bored with no one to talk to in our (his) little apartment. He was clearly touched by this gesture. I had a farewell drink with the lads from EAST-SIDE, in Hoops Tavern (not a gay bar!), everyone wished me luck and said kind words like, it had been nice knowing and working with me, travel safe and, Yo hurry back now, yo hear! Jerry gave me a bear hug! I was going to miss him.

Eddie and Nula drove down to Orlando to have a farewell drink with me and Martin in Scruffy's. It was emotional, we had all become really good friends, I felt like I had known them all my life, I actually got a bit emotional at their kind words and praise, it was very touching. Eddie insisted that he would drive the four of us to the airport, to bid me farewell on the day of my departure. These were good people indeed!

When the day came for me to leave, Eddie and Nula arrived an hour late to take us to the airport. To make matters worse Eddie was fucking paralytic and refused to let anyone else drive, I remember thinking you have to be fucking kidding me! It was too late to try and organise a taxi, so the four of us all squeezed into the front of Eddie's ford pick-up. Eddie drove like a lunatic, weaving in and out of traffic, I remember some heated exchanges in the front of the cab as I thought to myself, 'Are you deliberately trying to get me nicked! Are you deliberately trying to scupper my bid for freedom'! It was hair raising to say the least!

Eventually we arrived at departures and all in one piece! We had one last final drink together in the bar and then it was time for me to go. I hugged Nula and thanked her for everything. Eddie shook my hand and told me to take care and I thanked him for all he had done for me. I was surprised to see the Geordie was visibly upset, his eyes looked glassy as he hugged me and told me to take care of myself. I felt a tinge of empathy and compassion for him. We had started our trip as relative strangers, but we had been through a lot together (mainly the pizza shop window!) and we had become good friends.

As I stood there in front of him, I briefly wondered if I was his 'only' friend? Unlike me he had only ever phoned home once in the year we had spent together, he had not received any letters from home and he rarely ever mentioned friends. I knew, despite everything, the Geordie was a big softy at heart.

At last my flight was called, we all promised to stay in touch, I picked up my rucksack, threw it on my back and walked away leaving Eddie, Nula and my good friend Martin behind. I didn't look back and I never saw any of them again!

As I took my seat on the plane, I felt a sense of relief wash over me. I had mixed emotions. My American adventure had not been what I had expected it to be, but then, when does life ever turn out how we imagine it? To quote Charles Dickens:

'it was the best of times; it was the worst of times'!

I was glad I had done it. I was aware that if I hadn't done it then, at that time, then I never would have done it at all. When I got back home 'life' would surely stick its claws into me and I wouldn't be going anywhere! Our plans rarely turn out as we expect them to. Along the way we get pushed and pulled in all manner of directions. What I thought I was going to do was only a fantasy. The adventure I had, was the reality. The two can never be the same. I also felt like I had just spent 12 months on the run!

CHAPTER FIFTEEN

IT WAS NICE TO BE HOME! I had declined my brother's offer to pick me up from the airport. Instead I had insisted on making my own way. I suppose, as some sort of (feeble) symbolic gesture, I wanted to complete my journey alone. I wished to cross the finish line unaided!

As I entered my mother's house, she was at the kitchen sink washing the dishes just as I had pictured her when I had sat on the beach in California. All the family were there to greet me, and as I had half expected I returned to a jubilant hero's welcome. They even threw me a surprise party in a local pub aptly named The Phoenix! However, no sooner was I home than it began to feel as though I had never left. Things quickly returned to normal and I began the same old routine.

Emma had patiently awaited my return (bless her!), and so we picked up where we had left off. Despite everything I had felt towards her in the past, it was actually really nice to see her again, I enjoyed the familiarity. I gave her a watered-down version of my adventures! Being a young man and full of gusto, my friends received the full, slightly exaggerated, version of my 'actual' adventures. I knew they were impressed. They marvelled at my tales of adventure and woe! I sensed they held me with a new esteem and high regard. I enjoyed it and I wallowed in my new (albeit, brief!) celebrity status.

I didn't just feel different, I was different! I had changed. I no longer felt like the frightened little boy I once was. I felt as though 'now', I could do anything, I could achieve anything. I had proved myself. I could hold my head high. I had become a man.

So when 'M', suggested we should move in together, I quickly agreed, seeing it as the next obvious step and if I'm honest a quick and easy way of getting out of my mother's house, which quite frankly had become overbearing and stifling. In part due to the fact that my mother was constantly nagging me about my drinking. I didn't know at the time, that 'M', would be no different! In fact, apart from sex and being able to smoke a joint in the living room in just my underpants, living with 'M' was very much like living with my mother! Emma had an annoying habit of turning my music down every time she passed the stereo. She also disapproved of my friends!

The move had happened quickly. Frank and Eunice's son Rick (the head case), had a house for rent. Rick had sorted himself out and had in the space of a few years completely turned his life around. It was hard not to admire the man. The house in question was a little two up two down terrace in an area popular with young couples wanting to get on the property ladder. We arranged a viewing with Rick and his new wife. My first impressions as we walked around the property were not good, every wall was painted a different colour, it looked a bit hippy-ish, so 'I' decided 'M' would not be having a bar of it.

To be polite, I told Rick I would discuss it with Emma, and we would be in touch, thinking that would be the end of it. But as we walked out of the front door I quietly asked 'M', 'so what do you think'? I was surprised when she said with a huge smile, 'It's lovely, I really want it'! I immediately did an about-turn, knocked the front door and when Rick opened it, me and 'M', both said in unison 'We will take it'! Rick just grinned. The rent was £320 per calendar month and as far as I could see the best thing about the house was its close proximity to three local pubs. The nearest (I counted) being sixteen steps from my front door to the bar! And thirty-two on the way back!

It turned out that Emma was quite the home maker. I painted under her direction, which was really the entirety of my input. She did everything else. She chose the furniture, the carpets, the pictures that adorned the walls and the knickknacks that went around the home. Within a few weeks she had created something truly beautiful, even I was impressed. Life was good, it was nice being settled, it was nice being in one place. I liked it! It was the first time I had ever lived with a woman, so It felt a bit weird the first time she did my washing!

It was at about this time that Connor offered me a job working as a pipe-fitter for his company. It was good timing! I had grown tired of the construction industry; I was fed up with chasing my tail concerning money and work. The idea of a secure regular wage coming in made sense due to my newfound status and responsibilities! The job involved working on large commercial projects all over the UK, which meant a lot of working away from home and staying in digs. It appealed to my sense of adventure. Basically, I would go to work on a Monday, and I 'might' come home on a Friday! The best of both worlds. I really enjoyed the work, I found it interesting and it wasn't as heavy going as what I was used to. I also enjoyed the camaraderie of working away from home with the men.

The work involved running pipelines for high pressure gas systems. I've always been quite practical and hands-on, so fitting pipes wasn't a problem. However, being new to the industry, I didn't always fully understand 'why' I was fitting it! So Connor teamed me up with a lad called Fatty Nolan! (Obviously there wasn't a pick on him!).

We would drive up and down the country fitting installations, one week a hospital, the next a university, a laboratory or factory. It was always different, so remained fresh. 'Fatty Nolan', once quipped that we were like industrial gypsies, which was a good and fairly accurate description. I loved the job! It helped that every night me and Fatty would sit at a bar and get completely shit faced, in fact every night was a Saturday night as far as we were concerned. I felt as though I had really landed on my feet!

Six months had passed since I had returned from the US and a lot had happened, new home, new job, new status! America already seemed like a distant memory. It just so happened I was visiting my mother's house one evening when by chance the phone rang on the wall in her hallway. I picked up the receiver, 'Hello'? 'How'a, Pat, how you doin' like'? 'Fuck-in-hell, Martin, how are ya'? I roared in disbelief!

The Geordie explained how the job on the county courthouse was coming to an end, but EAST-SIDE had asked him if he would stay on and go with them to a new project in West Virginia. He had accepted their offer and was excited about the move! He told me Eddie and Nula were well and sent their love, he asked after my mother and 'M'.

I hate to admit it, but after the initial surprise, I was a bit cool with him on the phone, I have regretted it ever since. When I think back to that call, I wish I had been more 'manly' and had not acted so churlish. Was I cool with him because I am now back home, safe and sound? It's true, I felt like my adventure had been marred in some ways by the Geordie's behaviour, but now was not the time to score points. If I'd, had a grievance I should have been man enough to state it there and then, not months later from the safety of my mother's hallway and while he was half the world away! I had let myself down and I (despite everything) had been out of order to the Geordie. He sensed my coolness and the conversation stalled to an awkward and embarrassing conclusion. That was the last time I ever spoke to the Geordie.

And like 'every' other time in my life that I had let myself down or had not done the right thing when it was so obviously called for, I pushed it deep down inside me and forgot about it. Like it had never happened! And that's exactly what I did with Martin's phone call.

I was loving life, it was if 'I' had found the perfect balance. I loved my new job which took me all over the country and I loved the security it offered. I also loved the fact that Emma was not only the type of woman who kept herself looking nice, but one who also kept a lovely home and who would spoil me on my return from working away! During the week I would be in the pub every night with the lads from work. And at the weekends I would be out on a mad session with my real mates! It was just non-stop laughter, drink and drugs!

Me and 'M' got along okay for the most part. She liked to have (her) friend's round, I liked to go out! 'M' liked to throw dinner parties, I liked to get drunk. Perhaps we were a little mismatched? Still, we had a lot of fun times together, but we also bickered a lot, like an old married couple sometimes! But it was all fairly innocent!

I came home from the pub one afternoon and lay on the couch while smoking a cigarette. Emma was pottering around in the kitchen when I must have dozed off for a moment, because my cigarette slipped from my fingers and burnt a 2-inch-long grove into our new 'green' carpet! Right in front of the couch! Being the 'manliest of men', I panicked and quickly covered it up with my 'Viz' annual! I said nothing!

A little while later Emma, (cheerfully) came wandering into the living room, I got up from the couch and disappeared into the kitchen. For a few moments there was silence and then I heard a loud disbelieving GASP! Followed by an angry, 'PATRICK'!!! She stormed into the kitchen with a face like thunder, demanding an explanation. 'Alright 'M', ...there's no need to talk to me like I'm a little fucking BOY'! I countered, with hands up! To which she smugly replied, 'yeah! Then why did you cover it up with your fucking Viz annual'? She had me bang to rights, I had no answer, so I sheepishly lowered my eyes to the floor (like a little boy!).

It used to be J.F.K. but nowadays most people in Britain will say they can remember where they were and what they were doing the day princess Diana died! I do! I remember it perfectly well, because I was on my hands and knees, scrubbing the carpet which went inside the recess, where the old Victorian fireplace would have been. But which now was where 'M' kept a lovely bunch of artificial flowers in a large glass vase!

I had come home the night before and had wrongly believed I was relieving myself in the bathroom but was actually 'pissing' in the fireplace! I'm sure I'm not the first bloke to have made this mistake, but nonetheless, 'M' wasn't too pleased!

Just like she wasn't too pleased the first Valentine's day together in our new home! I 'honestly' believed that now we lived together, we didn't have to 'bother' with all the 'soppy', 'silly' business of cards and flowers and such. I now know that is 'not' correct! I now know that I got it horribly wrong!!! Poor 'M' became quite upset, in fact she went fucking ballistic and called me some rather choice names. I didn't really blame her, after all I had failed to show I cared! But then it got a bit weird, she snatched my cigarettes from the mantlepiece, threw them on the floor and jumped up and down on them in temper, then as I was protesting, she ran off and then re-emerged from the kitchen and began to chase me around the house, whilst hitting me about the head with a lump of raw steak, which I can only presume would have been for my (romantic) dinner! (incidentally Emma was a vegetarian, so it all seemed a tad bizarre!). Anyway, as there was 'no' talking to her?! I decided to remove myself from the affray and took the opportunity to fuck off to the pub... with Neil Duncan! As I walked down the street and away from the house, I could hear her shouting insults at me from the upstairs window!

'Shall I compare thee to a summer's day'!? 'perhaps not'!

I staggered home in the early hours with a crumpled-up valentine's day card stuffed in the back pocket of my jeans. I had the intention of sneaking into the house and getting my head down on the couch, without waking the sleeping 'Banshee' upstairs! But when I got to my front door and after I had checked each pocket at least five times, I realised to my utter dismay that I had forgotten my fucking' keys!! With a heavy heart and a big sigh, I gingerly knocked the front door. (round 2).

She opened the letterbox! ...'What do you want'? Half grinning, I said, 'Well, I think I would very much like to come in... please'! There ensued a bit of back and forth through the open letterbox, until finally I said, 'Fine, I will sleep in the car'! And then moved out of 'eyes' view'! I had no such intention. I also knew she would not be able to just leave it 'at that', so I hid behind a little wall opposite our house ...and waited!

Sure enough, after about five minutes the front door slowly eased open and out popped Emma's head as she quickly scanned the area. Then in the still of night, she gently crept along the pavement towards the car like a silent assassin. Just as she reached the back of the car, I leapt up from behind the wall and bolted for the open door! I saw her spin round in shock and disbelief as I shouted 'Ha'! And then I slammed the door shut! A minute later there was a gentle knock on the door... I opened the letterbox and said, 'What'?

If my home life was 'lively', then my work life was positively 'manic'! Every evening, once I had finished my shift, I would position myself at a bar and commence to get absolutely slaughtered! Drink, work, drink, work, drink. I was living the dream, ...my dream! When I returned home from working away, I didn't have time for 'M', I didn't want to hear about the bills, I wasn't interested in who said what! I just couldn't wait to meet up with my mates down the pub so I could impress them with my work stories!

I think it's human nature not to know a good thing when you see it. It's human nature to push it to the limits, to the brink of destruction! I was having my cake and eating it! What's more I was getting away with it. But nothing stays the same forever!

CHAPTER SIXTEEN

A LITTLE OVER A YEAR AFTER RETURNING FROM THE STATES I received word from Diane, the Geordie's ex. I was pleasantly surprised that she had got in touch, that is until she told me the news! She was crying as she said, 'Oh Pat, I'm so sorry to have to tell you this... but it's Martin, ...he's dead'!

I couldn't quite believe what I was hearing! I couldn't believe he was gone! I was shocked and I was devastated! My companion on my American adventure, we had drank together, worked together, hours, days, weeks sat side by side in our station wagon, we had laughed, and we had fought, the highs and the lows. Who now could I reminisce with in years to come, over a pint in an English pub! I felt a sadness wash over me and in the middle of it all, deep down in the pit of my stomach, I thought of the last time we had spoken, and I felt ashamed.

Diane tearfully explained what had happened. Martin had taken the job that he had excitedly told me about and had moved up state to West Virginia. It was a Sunday and a few of the lads he worked with had decided to go up to some lakes. Everyone was drinking and having a good time, when Martin had decided to go for a swim. He was unaware of the strong undercurrents in the lake and presumably he had gotten into some difficulty and was swept under. His body was found a few hours later, two miles downstream. The poor Geordie.

EAST-SIDE glass had arranged for his body to be flown home. My heart went out to his family and his poor mother, Martin was her only son! 'M' accompanied me up to Durham for the funeral. The priest said Martin was 33, the same age as Jesus when he died. I could hear Martin's mother sobbing at the front of the church and I was reminded of my own mother, when she had sobbed.

After the service I offered my condolences to the family and then Me, 'M' and Diane, left and found a little pub overlooked by Durham castle. Me and Diane reminisced about old times and relayed stories to Emma, but the mood remained very sombre. It had felt strange as I had stood at the back of the church, as if I were intruding on a very personal matter. I had been aware of the odd glance in my direction as some wondered who I was. Life's funny sometimes. I couldn't help thinking that I was the only one there, who really knew him, yet I was the stranger at my friend's funeral.

As the three of us sat just inside the window of the little pub, we heard music coming from outside. We craned our necks and saw some colliery bands as they came marching down the old cobbled street towards us. Each band waving their own particular banner, everyone started to spill out of the pub and onto the street to cheer and wave as they made their way past, except for us three! Soon it was time to head home. Me and Diane made empty promises to stay in touch but of course we never did!

****

Life goes on! Another year passed and me and 'M' were still bickering! Work was becoming difficult; I was drinking heavily on a daily basis; I was constantly hungover, and I rarely remembered anything of the previous night's drinking. My escapades were becoming legendary or, so I was told. I was hardly eating and yet I had ballooned in size and in weight. As a result, my relationship with Emma began to suffer and it wasn't long before the cracks began to appear. 'M' began to tire of me! The poor girl was fed up of living alone in an empty house, I just wasn't there for her. She valiantly fought to try and save our relationship but when she tried to talk sense to me, I perceived it to be nagging, so I would shut down or become defensive and distant. After two lonely years Emma did the inevitable and left me. 'Hell, hath no fury'!

I returned home from work one Friday evening and walked into an empty house, literally. She had taken everything bar the light bulbs. I had been so wrapped up in myself that I hadn't even seen it coming! I put my bag down and closed the front door. I walked into the kitchen and found one plate, a cup, a knife and a fork sitting on the work top.

As I glanced around the kitchen my eyes fell upon the only other thing in the room, a paper-mache zebra, which I had brought for her six months previously! This was significant! It had sent a shiver down my spine when I saw it! Six months previously whilst working away from home I had cheated on 'M', I suppose you would call it an affair, it had lasted for just over a month, the duration I was working in the area. Her name was Gillian, she was a bit posh and told me she was a direct descendent of royalty! Not that I cared, although it was a good story to tell my mates. She was actually quite a horrible person (almost as horrible as me perhaps!). She meant absolutely nothing to me, just as I had meant nothing to her, it was pure self-gratification, for both parties. Of course, I had brought the zebra out of guilt, more original than flowers! Had it been that obvious? Did she know? It really threw me, I thought I had got away with it!

As the years rolled by I would see 'M' from time to time. She remained good friends with my sisters and she kept in contact with my mum, always remembering her birthdays and Christmas, yet, to this day the incident of the zebra has never been mentioned between us!

Selfishly I didn't care that 'M' had left. After the initial shock, I actually felt relieved. I was glad that she was gone, now I could do whatever I wanted! Without constantly being 'fucking' nagged!

Needless to say, it didn't take long for our beautiful home to become a party house for me and my friends and anyone else for that matter who wanted to tag along (much to the annoyance of my neighbours). More fag burns appeared in the carpets but there simply wasn't enough Viz annuals to go around! And the kitchen... well if it had been a restaurant then someone would have shut it down! The place was a shithole! But I didn't care because I was having too much of a wild time!

I became a regular face in the pub next door to my house, so much so that if someone was trying to get hold of me, they would ring the pub rather than the house. I found an answer machine message on my house phone one morning. It was from 'me' saying that 'I mustn't be in'! The sessions in the pub which now involved my good drinking buddy Fitzy, who lived just around the corner, were legendary and increasingly messy due to the involvement of recreational drugs and large quantities of Stella Artois. Whole weekends were a complete mystery to me. It was just fun, fun, fun and more fun! Everything was hysterically funny, right up until the point that I began to piss the bed! And that's when it all began to change!

The first time it happened I had awoken in the early (or wee) hours, soaking wet. Horrified, I had leapt out of the bed, and had stood, cold and naked staring at the soaking wet mattress. At first, I refused to believe it despite the evidence before me. 'Did I spill a drink'? I had asked myself. 'Had I brought a glass of water up to bed and in my drunken state knocked it over?' I was confused, I was repulsed! I was also racked with shame and remorse! As 'luck' would have it I now lived alone! So I told no one of my dirty secret.

Instead I pretended it had not happened. I skulked about like a dog who has taken a shit on the carpet and is now being scowled at by his owner! And just like a dog, I knew I had done wrong!

That next evening, when I walked into the local pub, I asked the barmaid for a pint of Stella and in the back of my mind I was thinking, 'Please don't fall asleep in the pub and piss yourself!' But still I ordered the pint, I felt like I had to, or people might notice something was up! (Just for the record I fell asleep in the pub loads of times, but thankfully never suffered the humiliation of pissing myself!).

My behaviour was becoming unpredictable (not aggressive, just a little bizarre). It now seemed that every time I took a drink, it was pure potluck how it ended up! Every time I took a drink, I seemed to have an adventure, mishap or scrape! One Christmas, (the night before Christmas Eve in fact), I was out on a works do, when one of the lads asked if I could get hold of any speed. Naturally I obliged, and while I was at it, I got myself some too! I ate about 40 quid's worth in one go! I was flying, literally! After the pub had shut and everyone else had gone home, I found I was still buzzing, but had nowhere to go, nor could I sit still! So, I decided to head for the airport 'thinking' there may be an all-night bar! Once there I took a 'mad' notion, handed over my credit card and booked a flight to Dublin! I came down the same time as the plane!

Completely 'Banjaxed', I took a taxi into the centre of Dublin (by now it was early morning!), I found a café, ordered a breakfast that I simply couldn't eat (Instead I just pushed it around the plate), and then found a pub that was open opposite a bus station. I had two pints of Guinness, nipped across to the bus station and brought a ticket heading for Kerry and then went back to the pub for a couple more pints while I waited! The speed had worn off, now on a 'come down', I had a change of heart! I started thinking that turning up in Kerry on Christmas eve with just the shirt on my back and 50 odd years after my dad had left, was probably not a good idea! So, I ordered a cab back to the airport and caught the next flight home! I was back in the same pub as the night before, and just after opening time! I was sitting at the bar drinking a pint when Paul McGillicuddy walked in and innocently enquired, 'what did you do after the pub shut'? He was wide eyed when I showed him my bus ticket for County Kerry!

I was out of control! And I knew it, but I said nothing, I put a brave face on it all and just carried on regardless. Not for the first time in my life I felt like a fraud! I began to feel increasingly uncomfortable, I had about me a sense of foreboding. It was almost a fear of being found out, an unease as if I was going to be discovered, but yet, I couldn’t quite put my finger on what it was that was going to be found out!

It was also becoming increasingly difficult to cover my tracks at work due to my drink fuelled antics. I began to worry that I might piss the bed whilst working away, which I eventually did, bringing yet more secret shame on an already fragile state of mind!

Whenever I worked away from home, 'we' always tried to get digs in a pub or if not a B&B that had a bar; reason being, if you were a 'resident' they would keep the bar open for as long as you were drinking, which was a disaster for me! I remember I was working away with two other lads and we had got digs in a pub, but due to the fact that they were busy the three of us had to share a room. It was only for a couple of nights so none of us were particularly fussed!

We were supposed to work 12-hour shifts starting at 7am, but more often than not we would be in the bar for 6 o’clock each evening. Even then in my late twenties the whole day was about getting the work out of the way so I could get to the pub. It was a shame because the job should have been enjoyable, but instead it became a chore. After work the three of us would sit at the bar and start drinking! Nearly all the other lads I worked with would have two maybe three pints and then one by one they would trickle off up to their respective rooms to get a shower, then come back down and have a meal and maybe another pint. Before heading off to bed!

Not me! I stayed put, as if I was glued to the bar, I just couldn't leave. So, I would sit there all night and get hammered. It was during this particular occasion when I was sharing the room with the two other lads that I awoke in the morning and realised I had pissed the bed! I was mortified, obviously I couldn't say anything to the lads because I was too ashamed of what I had done! I had to keep quiet and pretend everything was normal. To make matters worse, as we were only staying a couple of nights, I couldn't change the sheets either, as they would surely question why!

I went and did an eleven-hour shift, not letting on and feeling like total and utter scum! After work I sat in the bar (unusually quiet and cringing inside), getting drunk and knowing that I would be sleeping in a dirty bed! That night when I eventually went up to my room, I had to sleep in an elongated S shape to try and avoid the damp patch. So great was my fear and shame... I slept in a dirty bed!

Thankfully we were going home the next day. But the fear was I might be sent back there in a couple of weeks. What if the landlady was to say something in front of the lads! Then I would be discovered for what I was. A dirty little tramp!

That experience had a huge psychological impact on my soul! I thought I must be fundamentally flawed in some way! Broken, not quite right. No matter how hard 'I' tried, I would never be like other (normal) people. I began to worry that I might do something 'knowingly' humiliating or wrong, whilst drunk and bring shame on Connor in front of his clients and employees. I felt like I was becoming a liability. So, I did the decent thing and left!

It was pretty much out of the frying pan and into the fire, because nobody knows if you piss the bed when your all alone! Outwardly I brimmed with confidence, but inwardly I felt like I was sinking like a stone!

I concocted a story for my brother, as I couldn't tell him (or anyone else for that matter) the truth. Not that I really knew what the truth was. I told him I'd, had enough of working away from home, I said that I was considering starting up my own construction company, I said the time had come for me to try other things.

My brother asked me if I was sure? He said, 'look, Pat, you're only one week away from poverty, you know'! To which I replied, 'Yeah, and as long as I work for you that will always be the case'. I think I offended him, which wasn't my intention; he couldn't understand why I would just jack the job in! I love my brother and I am very proud of him. There have been many times over the years when we have gotten our wires crossed. This was one of them. He was right. Leaving 'was' a massive mistake, but what choice did I have? I started to believe my own lie about starting a construction company, I clung to the façade of being my own boss. So, this was the story I told anyone who would listen! I secured a £5000 bank loan and brought a fairly decent and newish large transit van for £2000. I then 'kitted' it out with every perceivable tool that I might need. I taxed it and insured it and then I parked it outside the pub next to my house, while I drank the £700 pound float I had left over! Privately and for the first time in my life I genuinely begun to worry about my future, where's it all heading? I'm not sure what's happening to me.

I felt like I was losing myself, if that makes sense. Most of my mates had or were starting to settle down. Jim and Simón were married (not to each other of course!). They both had kids and mortgages. I noticed others were carving out careers for themselves too. Why can't I be like them? Why do I always struggle to make ends meet, despite the fact I earn good money. How comes I'm constantly skint! It begs the question; how do other people manage? Perhaps they are sneaks! I see mates meeting girls and getting all loved up. I think they must be dishonest and weak if they can meet someone and within a couple of weeks be practically joined at the hip! I start to wonder how comes I can't maintain a serious relationship.

Perhaps I am just too 'real' and can't be bothered with the fakey stuff and all that, 'I love you, too' business. I brush all these feelings aside. But deep down I am worried there is something seriously wrong with me. I pose the question, why am I incapable of truly loving another human being? It worries me that I don't know the answer. Perhaps I'm doomed!

****

As happens from time to time, the construction industry experienced a downturn, so I began to struggle financially. It wasn't long before I was unable to pay the rent! I had little choice but to sign on the dole. This also meant I had to tell Rick the head case. I was embarrassed because I had grown up across the road from him and his parents and I didn't want them to think 'ill' of me! It was a relief when Rick turned out to be surprisingly cool about it, basically he said, he didn't give a fuck as long as he got his money. Having had no work at all for a couple of weeks I was delighted to be offered a couple of shifts on site, cash in hand.

It was sod's law then, that at the same time the dole wanted to visit me in my home to establish that I was who I said I was and that I did indeed qualify for housing benefit! This immediately presented me with a problem, a dilemma! I needed the money from the couple of shifts, but I also needed the housing benefit...argh!

It took some doing, but I convinced my drinking buddy, Fitzy, to pretend to be me for the day! I gave him all the information I thought he might need, my date of birth, national insurance number, when I moved into the house and so on. I went over the particulars with Fitzy a couple of times, just to make sure he had got it all. 'Now, can you think of anything else Fitzy'? I had asked, as he scrunched his face up and said, 'Do you mind if I bring a bit of ironing round, coz my iron's broke'! Before adding, '...it will make the ruse more convincing if I'm doing the housework' said Fitzy! 'Yeah, of course, whatever Fitzy, I'm just sorry I ain't got a hoover' I replied smiling!

Fitzy did it! The bloke turned up from the town hall and found Fitzy doing 'his' ironing in 'my' living room! When I got home from work, I asked Fitzy what it was like being me for the day, before quickly adding, 'I bet it was fucking great'! Fitzy conceded that it was ...okay, that is until he opened the front door and realised it was the same bloke from the council that had been to his house two weeks earlier!! Fitzy said he instantly shit himself, fearing the worst, that the bloke had done a bit of a double take! But when he saw the pile of ironing and the ironing board, he 'assumed' all was well, so we had gotten away with it! I was awarded my housing benefit. And Fitzy was awarded a night out on the lash!!

Despite now getting my rent paid, I still struggled. I didn't pay the bank loan and the gas and electric hadn't been paid in months, every penny I had went in the pub. If I couldn't get to the pub, I felt I was missing out, I also feared all the lads would know I was skint and start to suss that something was wrong. I was full of fear. Everything was beginning to come on top. The house was still a dump and I was now scared to open the front door in case it was the bailiffs! I couldn't cope anymore, so I decided to do what all little boys do when the tough gets going. I gave up the house and moved back to my mum's! I was embarrassed and ashamed by my failure, even idiots have their own places!

In an attempt to 'protect' myself, I convinced everyone in the pub, all my friends and even 'myself', that I was in fact moving back to my mum's so I could save enough money to move to Ireland! It was a lie! It would never happen. Although I believed it. I had plucked the idea out of thin air, there may have been some loose thread of an idea that it would be okay to be a piss-head in some sleepy back water part of county Kerry. Maybe I would not be judged so harshly over there, maybe I would be better understood! My poor mum!

CHAPTER SEVENTEEN

I MOVED BACK TO MY MUM'S WITH MY TAIL BETWEEN MY LEGS, obviously it was a complete disaster. I brought with me everything I was running away from! All the chaos of my drinking and drug taking. My mother understandably did not take kindly to me falling in the door drunk at all hours or coming home from bingo on a Thursday night to find me sitting on the top step of the stairs, paralytic, naked and asleep! She didn't mince her words when she told me she wished I was dead, because I would never be any good, 'You're just like your cunt of a father! She had screamed!

My antics didn't go unnoticed with the rest of the family either, everyone had something to say on the matter of my drinking and none of it was good. I couldn't understand why everyone was getting so upset and annoyed with me. I wasn't hurting anyone! I was a nice bloke, I wasn't a nasty drunk like my dad, and I only ever drank the money I earned, so what's the big deal! Surely, I am entitled to have a drink?

Had I been truly honest with myself at this point in my life I would have admitted that deep down I knew I had a problem; I had always known. It was becoming unbearable at my mothers and not just for me; she hinted that if I carried on, I would have to leave. This scarred me because I didn't have anywhere to go. And I had no means with which to support myself.

I had no choice but to curb my drinking, so I 'cleverly' switched to 'mostly' smoking weed! It didn't tend to cause the same noticeable issues, although it did knock the wind out of my sails. Any energy or ambition I might previously have had, was gone! I began to watch passively as life seemed to pass me by!

I had a few attempts at stopping drinking all together. I recall going to the pub with Neil, Jim and Paul. I made out I was fed up with hangovers and wanted to get myself sorted, so I was going to give it a miss for a while. Not for ever, I assured them, just a week or two! I didn't drink alcohol that evening, but I carried out the same behaviour. I matched them drink for (soft) drink, and stayed in a round, trying to impress on them that nothing had changed and there was nothing to worry about! In hindsight they weren't worried or even bothered, it was me who felt uncomfortable with it all.

Sober as a judge I had sat around the table with them and listened as they grew louder and more raucous. They were not talking, they were shouting! The same stories and jokes went around the table all night. For the first time I felt like an outsider, looking in, and all I saw was complete madness. I drank eight pints of coke that night! I remember thinking 'Okay, so there's no chance of me falling over, but there's a good chance my teeth will fall out'!

The next day when I meet up with the lads, they were excitable and were saying what a great night it had been. Looking at them all, like they were mental I said, 'What you talking about? It was rubbish, you just sat at the table for four hours, shouting at each other and taking it in turns to say the same fucking joke'! It was their turn to look at me ..like I was mental!

It had been both novel and pleasant when I had left the pub sober, I had never had that experience before! It was also novel and pleasant to wake up with no hangover, remorse, shame or guilt, although it did feel like I had coated my teeth in shit before going to bed! Nonetheless It had been a worthwhile exercise, even if

I didn't fully appreciate it at the time. My mum was also pleased that I hadn't fallen in the door drunk.

My first attempt at staying sober lasted for a whole week, I was extremely chuffed with myself. However, staying off the drink was not as easy as I had hoped. I soon found that if I was a 'good boy' and behaved myself by not drinking for the whole weekend, then there was a good chance I would 'nip' into the pub, on say a Tuesday, just for a couple, as a reward! Which by the time I had drank a couple of pints usually resulted in me going the whole hog and having a bit of a mid-week session as I tried to make up for what I had missed out on at the weekend!!!

The truth is it had been a rough couple of years. I was tired. I was fed up with all the grief I was getting. Over the next 6 months I desperately tried to behave myself. On, off, stop, start. I had some brief successes followed by yet more failures. I was starting to resent my mother: if she would just leave me alone and stopped fucking nagging, I would be alright, I would be the same as my friends! I started to (wrongly) think that perhaps 'she' was the cause of my dad's drinking, no wonder he behaved the way he did when he had to put up with all this shit! How would I have reacted had she been my wife?

Despite everything, despite the difficulties of having moved back home, things did begin to improve, albeit slowly. The odd weekend off the drink turned into a week, then a fortnight. For the first time in my life I was starting to experience the benefits of not getting constantly shit faced and blowing all my wages, I was starting to enjoy the occasional spell of sobriety, and work was beginning to pick up too! I even lost the bulk of the weight I had put on whilst working for my brother.

Things really were on the up! Connor even phoned me and asked if I would be interested in 3 months work in Aberdeen! I had left his employment because I was worried about causing him embarrassment. But things had changed. I now felt more confident in myself, I felt more in control and sensed that the worst was now behind me. Perhaps it's normal, perhaps most people go through such difficult times? I decided I could do 3 months without causing any harm. So I agreed, I told Connor that I wanted to save some money, so I asked him to pay me just £200 per week cash and save the rest for me until I had finished the job, knowing I would probably make a bit of money out of the daily digs allowance too, so in reality, working 12 hour shifts, I would still have the best part of £300-350 per week for spends!

The job in Aberdeen breathed new life into me. For 3 months I worked 12 hour shifts in two-week stints, flying home every other Friday and then catching the return flight early on the following Monday morning. How quickly our fortunes can change. Now I'm getting a plane to work!

As I had hoped, I behaved myself (mostly). There was the odd night of drunkenness, but this was somewhat offset and 'quelled' by the fact I had struck up a 'friendship' with a local girl. So, I spent a lot of my evenings at her flat, enjoying what you might describe as a 'Highland fling' or 'flung', if you wish to be pedantic, either way, it was an awful lot of fun.

At the end of the 3-month stint and with the job complete, I had saved £3000! I had also been lifted out of my melancholy. I couldn't help feeling like I was 'back', my social standing somewhat restored! I was keen to live life again. So keen in fact that I booked a trip to Canada!

None of my friends were in a position to join me on my Canadian jaunt. So, I would be going to Canada alone. I would be lying if I said there wasn't a slight feeling of trepidation, but I was also aware that I would not be held back or have my adventure dictated to by the wants of others. So, in that respect, it was incredibly exciting and freeing! Needless to say, the intended trip had lifted my spirits, having something to aim for and look forward to also meant that by the time I was due to leave, I had stayed off the drink for two whole months. (although I had smoked a boat load of weed!). Still, I was very proud of this miraculous achievement, and as a result I was brimming with confidence. As far as I was concerned, I had fucking 'cracked' it!

As I boarded the flight for Toronto, I was naturally full of excitement. I felt invigorated. I felt alive! It was onwards and upwards from now on. I was truly looking forward to a proper adventure, and without tainting it, or ruining it with drink. The second day I was in Canada.... I got drunk and ruined it!

Canada is a beautiful country; I was taken aback by how clean it was! I was also impressed with how incredibly polite the Canadians were. During the flight I had imagined rugged mountains, moose and grizzly bears. I remember half worrying that perhaps I should have packed hiking boots, crampons and ropes.... and bear spray! So, I was 'just' a little disappointed when the plane began its descent into Toronto airport and I saw before me a sprawling metropolis of skyscrapers and the iconic CN tower. I remember thinking, 'it's just like America', ...the only difference being, I'm actually allowed in'!!

Being an 'experienced' traveller, I knew the drill and headed for the nearest youth hostel. Checking in brought back a lot of memories, especially when I got up the next morning and poured myself a cup of strong bitter tasting coffee, the smell and the taste snapping me back to a time past. With a new day ahead of me, I stepped out of the hostel and onto Yonge street, said to be the longest street in the world, a thousand miles end to end! Although I only saw about a mile and a half of it; the mile and a half that contained all the pubs and clubs of downtown Toronto. Funny, because when I had booked my flight, I honestly believed I was in for pups and cubs!

I sort of did the touristy thing! I went up the CN tower and stood on the glass floor, looking straight down, 1,135ft to the street below! I took the ferry over to Toronto island and hired a push bike to cycle around on, I stopped and sat for a while on, Echo Beach (far away in time?)! I even went to a baseball game at the Sky Dome. The Toronto Blue Jays vs The New York Yankees. But I didn't have a clue as to what was going on!

I decided to explore the city, so I got on the metro system and saw a place at the end of the line called, WOODBINE. So in homage to the brand of cigarettes my mother smoked, I went along hoping I might be able to buy a tea-towel or something similar with the word 'woodbine' emblazoned across it, but it turned out, it wasn't that sort of place.

Near the end of my second day, I found myself sat at a bar drinking a diet cola, I was quite happy! Then the barmaid seeing my glass nearly empty, gestured towards it and said, 'nother'? Without hesitation and with a broad smile I said, 'No I will have a beer please'! Two months without a drink, that first pint was golden, it was also the true starting point of my Canadian adventure!

That evening I took taxi cabs all over the city going from bar to bar (making up for lost time!). I felt alive with excitement as I mixed and mingled with the throng of night-time revellers. I had a great time before eventually making my way back to the youth hostel, where I found a party in full swing around the bar. My true character now fully animated by the drinks I had consumed, I instantly hit it off with a skater chick from London, Ontario! I forget her name, but I vividly remember she was an awful lot of fun, as we engaged in some extremely heavy petting in a secluded part of the hostel. Thankfully however, she was 'leaving' the next day, I say this because prior to this liaison, another girl had actually caught my eye!

Her name was Avril, and she was from Vancouver. There was something about her which I instantly liked! The next evening and with the skater chick now nothing more than a happy memory, I began chatting to Avril. As I did so, I innocently mentioned a few of us 'backpackers' were going out for a drink, and would she like to join us (me!)? I was delighted when she agreed. That night I never left her side as we sat in the bar, the two of us enjoying the mild flirting which was clearly taking place. I employed all my charm and wit in my attempt to win her round! I regaled her with my stories and watched as her face lit up with delight in the warm glow of the bar! She nearly fell off her stool when I told her the story about Neil Duncan and the Vic's inhaler!

This is the story: A bunch of us were sitting round smoking pot and listening to music in a friend's living room. Neil at the time had a head cold, so every few minutes or so Neil would take the Vic's inhaler, inserting it into each nostril in turn and then sniff with all his might at the decongestant! This went on for about an hour or so, before Neil announced he was going to the bathroom. He stood up from his chair and placed the Vic's inhaler in the middle of the coffee table and then left the room! As soon as Neil was out of sight our good friend Simón Pompidou, jumped to his feet, dropped his underpants, grabbed the inhaler from the centre of the coffee table and much to everyone's amusement rubbed the nib of the inhaler around his 'balls', before quickly replacing it in the centre of the table, pulling up his pants and sitting back down as though nothing had happened! Neil returned to the living room and everyone just carried on as normal! Then... SNIFF, SNIFF!! And everyone burst out laughing! Neil didn't understand and simply said, 'What are you all 'sniff', laughing, 'sniff' about'?! Everyone was in convulsions, 'sniff'! Avril was in hysterics and couldn't stop laughing at poor Neil's misfortune! (I've never told him!).

I really enjoyed Avril's company that night. She seemed a little bit special, I was truly smitten! That night in the bar the 'others' had decided to organise a trip to Niagara Falls for the next day, 'Do you fancy it'? I asked, 'Sure why not', she smiled!

The next morning bright eyed and bushy tailed, eight of us, (the same group as the night before), boarded the coach for the two hour journey down to Niagara. Having offered Avril the window seat, I sat down next to her, enjoying the closeness. At one point she laid her head on my shoulder, I instinctively put my arm around her now feeling the warmth of her body next to mine. I wanted more. I wanted to kiss her. But scared of a rebuff and potentially ruining the magical moment, I was too shy (sober!) to chance my arm!

I'm sure you don't need me to tell you just how breathtakingly beautiful Niagara Falls are! Once there we walked alongside the falls, at one point just a few metres from the water's edge, watching as it rushed over the top of the falls. I could feel the magnetic pull of the water, daring me close! We all stood in complete awe. 'Anyone got a barrel handy' I joked to the group, but it was really for the benefit of Avril!

We wasted no time in taking a trip on the 'Maid of the Mist', the little paddle steamer that takes tourists up as close as you can get to base of the 187ft drop of the Horse Shoe Falls. The deafening thunder of the water as it crashes into the gorge, creating a swirling mist of steam interspersed with rainbows was truly magical. There was something kind of romantic about it all! So, it was here that I chanced my arm and stole a kiss from Avril's cheek! She smiled! Feeling a little smug and somewhat pleased with myself, I triumphantly announced, 'There you go ...our first ever kiss'! She looked at me with a puzzled expression and said, 'But you kissed me last night in the pub'! Astounded, I couldn't help myself and all but shouted, 'Fucking .... DID I'!! I had no recollection; I had thought I had been the perfect gentlemen!

You can only stare at a waterfall for so long, before (A), it becomes boring, or (B), you need to use the bathroom!, even if it is one of the natural wonders of the world! Anyway, Avril was wonder enough for me; the day had been amazing simply because of her! When we arrived back in Toronto that evening, I asked her if she fancied going for a drink with me around town. Avril happily agreed, it was now clear that she liked me 'perhaps' as much as I liked her!

As night time fell on Toronto, we found we were both a bit 'squiffy' from all the drinks! We were young and we were both aware that soon we would be going our separate ways, our 'brief encounter' all but past, would soon be but a distant (albeit fond) memory! I think it's fair to say we were both caught up in the moment. So romantic was the day and the city at night, that we cemented our affections by way of an moonlight 'tryst' in a park in the centre of Toronto!! Only for the young at heart ...eh!!

A perfect day, we took our time as we strolled through the dark city streets back towards the youth Hostel, hand in hand. I woke up smiling. Truth be known I had gone to sleep smiling too. Me and Avril enjoyed each other's company for two more days before she packed her bags and caught her bus, as was always her intention, heading west to Calgary to spend time with some family. I never saw or heard from Avril again. Not that I had expected to. It's true, I was sorry to see her go, maybe it's also true that there's a part of me that's just an old romantic at heart, but I am not silly! The time we had spent together was perfect!

As I write this, I can't help but wonder where she is right now? How did her life turn out? Perhaps she's a devoted wife and mother, perhaps from time to time over the years, Niagara Falls has come up harmlessly in conversations or images have been flashed up on a TV screen. Perhaps she might inwardly smile at a fond distant memory, a secret, private time that her family are blissfully unaware of. A moment in her youth! Perhaps she smiles and thinks of a bloke called Pat! As I say, it was ...perfect!

****

Alone again! Me? Well, I just hit the pubs of Toronto with a massive grin on my face! I ended up in a district of the city called the Elephant and Castle and was sitting in a bar when I got chatting to a man mountain of a Canadian who said his name was Emmett. He was a larger than life character with a ginger beard and wild hair; he was also very good company. It wasn't long before we were both doing a lot of laughing. Then he said, 'Hey, Pat' 'Do you like to...', he tapped the side of his nose before adding 'pardy'! I gave him the old, 'Does a bear shit in the woods' look, before saying, 'Well, yes Emmett, my good man I 'doo' believe, I fucking do like to pard....A'! He actually chuckled like a little kid at my response, before he slapped the bar with a giant paw like hand and announced, 'Well it's all good then, eh'! I then watched as the hulk of a man disappeared into the gents. He returned a few moments later wild eyed and seemingly trying to swallow, as if he might have a gigantic aspirin stuck to his tongue! He sat down and discretely passed me the small bag of white powder under the bar before adding, 'Wait a minute don't make it to obvious'!

Ten seconds later I was in the cubical of the gents snorting a huge line of coke! I emerged from the toilets, wild eyed and seemingly trying to swallow a gigantic fucking aspirin lodged in my throat. Fuck me, it was good coke! Emmett nodded his approval as I passed the bag back under the counter. It was only two o'clock in the afternoon and I was flying!!!

The day took on a level of wild that I had not been expecting. Being from the city, Emmett knew all the best bars and hangouts, at some point we both chipped in $100 bucks each for more cocaine, which was soon delivered to the bar we were in. When it arrived, it looked like a bag of sugar, I had never seen so much coke! Emmett must have upped the ante, without telling me! He seemed very fond of the stuff, not that I was complaining!

I may have been in the Canadian equivalent of Soho, because I ended up in a 'titty' bar! A strip joint during the day (like dirt under your skin), has a level of sleaze that's simply uncomfortable. I actually took a little convincing! So, in an attempt to sell the idea to me, Emmett said 'No, it's cool, you can get a beer and a meal for ten bucks'! I looked at him disgusted and said, 'A meal ...a fucking ...meal! Who the fuck eats a meal in a Poontang parlour ...if the fucking meal ain't Poontang'?!

Emmett nearly choked as he shot beer out of his nostrils and guffawed into the pint at his lips! I think it was my British accent, the speed with which I delivered the statement, and the use of the word Poontang twice in one sentence, that made him involuntarily burst out laughing. 'You got a point there brother' 'shall we not go'? said Emmett. 'No... of course were fucking going, I just ain't ordering fucking fries'!

The rest of the day is somewhat of a blur, as we trail blazed our way around the city, I lost track of time, as we drank, snorted and belly-laughed our way into the evening. Now dark we had ended up back on Yonge street and quite near the hostel, I was running low on funds, so told Emmett I was going to dash off back to the hostel to cash some traveller's checks! After I explained what they were, he said 'Okay buddy, no problemo'! 'See you soon'! boomed the hulk of a Canadian! As I walked along Yonge street and as the fresh air hit my face, only then did I realise just how fucking wired I was! There was no way I wasn't going back! I cashed up $200 dollars and again made my way back up Yonge street towards the bar I had just left.

As I snaked my way through the throng, I passed a homeless man sitting on the side of the pavement, as I glanced in his direction he said, 'Hey, are you Pat'? Startled shocked and astounded I stammered 'Yeah... how the fuck did you know that'? The homeless man smiled and pointed to the bar opposite and said, 'Your buddy told me to tell you he's in there'! Still slightly taken aback I said, 'But how did you know it was me'?! The homeless man smiled, 'He told me to look out for a guy with a shaved head and a grey sweatshirt'! 'That's fucking amazing'! I said in disbelief, before the homeless man added, 'Yeah, he also said you would give me five dollars'! And held his hand out! The smile on both our faces was worth every cent!

I walked in the bar, as instructed by my homeless mate, but couldn't see Emmett, then I heard, 'Over here you crazy English fuck'! Emmett was sitting at a table with a bevy of hot looking Canadian women! Grinning from ear to ear he said, 'Ladies I would like to introduce to you, my very good friend... Pay ...trick'! I remember drinking a lot, I remember doing coke and eating the face off one of the blonde birds, I think she was quite taken with my accent. I remember flashing lights and being sandwiched between two of them on the dance floor! After that nothing!

I woke up at around 11 the next day. My head hurt, and I had no recollection of getting 'home'. I checked my pockets, I had sixty bucks in one pocket and a white skimpy thong in the other, urgh!? The blonde bird perhaps! I wondered what had happened to Emmett?

My hangover lasted all day, I think I may have been on a bit of a come down too, because I felt a little depressed! What goes up, must come down right! I fancied a joint, but not having any I decided to go for a walk instead. 'They' say it's good for the head, it clears the mind but I didn't have any energy either, so I didn't get very far. Probably because I was a physical wreck, no doubt from spending most of the night on the dance floor! So, it turned into a fairly uneventful day. I was glad, because the 'rest' done me good! I woke up early the next day, fully recovered and firing on all cylinders.

Not wanting to waste another day I decided to hop on one of the cities iconic red and white trams and take a trip to north America's busiest shopping centre! Eaton's! I don't know why because I hate shopping, but I had heard if you're in Toronto, then you have to go, it's a must! So, I did. I spent half a day aimlessly walking around the vast shopping centre. I had something to eat in a huge, worlds food hall, after spending half an hour deliberating what to eat as the choice on offer was mind boggling, (I had burger and fries!).

I brought my mum a 14 inch stuffed moose dressed in a Canadian Mounty's uniform and a fridge magnet depicting the CN tower! And then I left! On the way back I jumped off the tram here and there for a nose about and a pint before getting back to the hostel at around 9pm still clutching my moose and to find yet another party in full swing around the bar! I only had 3 days left in Canada!

****

The next day I found myself in a quiet little back street pub in a comparatively rundown part of town, not too far from the hostel, but just far enough to be off the beaten track. As such, it was frequented by locals rather than tourists, so it was my kind of place! It just so happened that there was an England v. Portugal game showing on the television in the bar. My accent had been noted by all when I had walked in and had asked for a beer, so every time England took possession of the ball, all the Canadians turned and looked in my direction, (seemingly) hoping for a reaction of some kind or a running commentary! Unfortunately, I have never been into football, to be honest I don't like it. Now I felt uncomfortable, because I didn't know what was going on in the game, but as a 'Brit' (and a bloke!) I felt like I should!

In an attempt to ease my discomfort, I began to confide in the bloke standing next to me at the bar, about how I wasn't into football. The man seemed friendly enough and agreed in a voice that reminded me of Joe Pesci, that I didn't have to!! He introduced himself as Leo, I shook his hand saying, 'I'm Pat'. We began having a good old chat about this and that, he mentioned he had 'seen' Coronation Street. He sort of shook his head apologetically and said, 'but I didn't really like it'. To which I helpfully explained, 'That's because it's shit mate'!

A couple of hours passed, the football was over, the pub had all but emptied and I was still sitting at the bar chatting with my new friend. I told him about my life back home, I talked of my adventures in the states and how I had always fancied coming to Canada. I explained how I was in Canada alone and that I was staying in the youth hostel up the road. He seemed interested enough, smiling and nodding in all the right places. The beers had certainly loosened me up, I began to tell Leo how during all my time in the states and now here in Canada I had never been offered any Hash! (solid/cannabis). Plenty of weed, but never any hash! 'can you actually get 'solid' in north America or is it only weed'? I had asked out of curiosity more than anything else. 'Yeah, of course.

Sure, no problem you can get it'! 'I could have some for you with in the.... I don't know... an hour'! He shrugged his shoulders as if to suggest it was no big deal. Then added, 'I can give my buddy a call, and get it now, if you want'?

I lent in close, lowering my voice and said, 'Yeah, that would be great.... you know, if you don't mind.... how much'? Leo shrugged his shoulders again and became (now I think about it!) a bit shifty, he was looking at the floor when he said, 'erm, 20, 20 bucks... yeah give me 20 bucks'! Delighted, I discreetly handed the money over, before adding, ...'You sure that's enough'? He momentarily hesitated, as if he were weighing up his options before saying, 'actually make it forty'! I slipped him the extra $20, then he whispered, 'Okay, I'll go and sort it and I will see you in a bit'! And with that he sneaked out the back door of the pub. Delighted that I was getting some HASH! I sat patiently at the bar drinking my beer and waiting for my friend to come back.

I would say it took about an hour, before I realised, I had very probably been had! I was so annoyed, that I continued to wait, refusing to accept the inevitable. It is fair to say I was fucking livid! Over two hours after he had left with my money, I spotted Leo sneaking in the back door of the pub. I assume he had wrongly thought I would have given up and left by now, but he was mistaken! He looked 'startled' when he saw me bowling towards him. 'You got my stuff' I demanded! I already knew, because his face said he didn't. 'Outside, I want a word'! He didn't attempt to argue. Once outside I let him have it!

In full rage I seemed to grow in size, I stood so close, that I knew it was intimidating and uncomfortable, 'Do you think I'm some sort of cunt?' I hissed! 'Give me my fucking money'! Wincing he said, 'I ain't got it, I gave it to the guy'! At the realisation I had well and truly been mugged off, I totally lost it. I roared at him, calling him every name under the sun. I also spat something fairly pathetic, but full of suggestion and in a menacing tone, that he was lucky, 'I was on fucking holiday'! And how he wasn't the first cunt to confuse niceness for weakness! It was only then that I realised that in my blind rage, I had in fact had hold of him by the scruff of his neck and had been shaking him and throwing him about a bit! His T-shirt was all but ripped from him, it was in shreds! Only strands of cloth were left along the neck line, it was then that Leo looked at me pleadingly and in his distinct Joe Pesci accent whimpered, 'What you doing man?, you're making me feel like ...I'm gonna cry'!!

'CRY'! 'Fucking cry', I roared. 'I'll fucking kill ya, you cunt'! I was so angry I wanted to hit him, but all the adrenalin that was now coursing its way through my body had sobered me up a bit. I started thinking, I'm in the city alone! This fucker knows where I'm staying, and I don't know who he knows! Slightly more guarded and suddenly aware of my surroundings, but still very angry, I had no intention of letting it go! I marched him (virtually shirtless) back into the pub, 'My money or my fucking hash'!

The few customers that remained all looked in his direction as he flopped his way back through the pub looking extremely distressed. I resumed my place at the bar and to my surprise watched as he disappeared into the kitchen? Why has he gone in there? Is he connected to the pub? Seconds later I heard shouting in a foreign tongue, Greek or maybe Italian, coming from the kitchen. I could hardly believe my eyes when I saw an old white-haired woman (mid-sixties?), shouting at, and slapping Leo, while he (pathetically) raised his arms in an attempt to protect himself! .... is this 'really' happening?!

A few moments later the old lady came and stood behind the bar, quite close to where I stood, she glanced at me a couple of times as if trying to size me up, before asking, 'How you know Leo'? Without smiling I stayed firm and simply said, 'the pub'! She looked me up and down and said, 'You shouldn't get involved with Leo'. 'You seem like a good boy'! I had just started to say, 'You don't need to worry about me...', when I saw it!! My heart fucking sank! I couldn't believe I hadn't noticed it before. Behind the optics, on the wall of the bar hung a sign which read,

'Beware of Leo'
The management has no affiliation with,
nor accepts responsibility or liability for,
the actions of Leo Theadopolis!

I didn't care about the money or the pot, he had mugged me off and I didn't like it! It was the principal. Of course, it was my own fault! I had asked somebody I didn't know, in a pub I was not familiar with, in a foreign city to buy me drugs. What had I expected! In the grand scheme of things, I had lost £20 quid (40 Canadian dollars). He hadn't made a fool out of me, I had! I was never getting my money back and I wasn't getting any hash! Leo was a hopeless 'wrong'un' and I had been a complete dick! Funny but no one ever ripped me off when I was travelling with the Geordie!

Eventually I gave up! I cut my loses, I left the pub and walked back to the hostel feeling like a right mug (and occasionally glancing over my shoulder, just in case!). However, I couldn't help but smile when I thought to myself, 'What you doing man, you're making me feel like I gonna cry'! That night I brought a bag of weed from a bloke I sort of knew in the hostel. It was good stuff!

Two days later I left Canada. It had been a roller-coaster! I thought about all I had done and all I had seen on my 'mini' adventure! As I settled into my seat on the plane, an idea occurred to me. 'I will only drink when I am out of the country'! I was sure this was an excellent idea! Rock solid in fact! When I got home, I gave my mum her moose. My mates phoned to see how I had got on.... so, I went down the pub to tell em!!!

Chapter Eighteen

I was 28yrs old when finally, it happened, ... I fell in love! After the furore and excitement of Aberdeen and Canada it didn't take me long to slip back into my old habits of heavy drinking. I knew I had been through a very difficult time of late, but I was convinced the worst was behind me. The attempts to stay sober were now all but forgotten. As restricting and as stifling as it was at my mother's I had during my time there, regained a bit of strength both emotionally and physically. I no longer felt like the loser I had imagined myself to be. I accepted I was a drinker and I silently accepted that on occasions I would let myself down with humiliating consequences. In short, I decided to go with the flow. I also accepted that my mother would always nag and moan regardless and due to my recent successes, I was almost hopeful concerning my future.

It was an ordinary Friday just like any other. The bloke I was working for had visited site early in the morning and had paid me in cash. With the money burning a hole in my pocket, I had finished work at around lunch time, jumped in the car and headed for the town centre to meet up with my mates for a few beers. After a couple of hours or so, I decided it might be wise to head for my local estate pub, so I could ditch the car and carry on drinking. Little did I know that a chance meeting that night would change my life for ever. It was to signal the beginning of the end ...of my youth!

I was still in my work clothes as I pushed the heavy door open and stepped inside. Being a Friday, the place was packed. I scanned the bar in search of familiar faces, when my eyes fell upon a girl standing at the bar with a group of her friends. There is nothing more intoxicating than the female form! She was tall and slim with short cropped blonde hair, cut close to her face. She wore a figure-hugging white blouse and a pair of skin tight snakeskin trousers that emphasised her long legs, on her feet she wore black strapped high heels. She was stunning! In that exact moment it was if the bar and everyone in it had just melted away into the background, leaving just her and her alone. An apparition! The embodiment of pure loveliness!

It was love at first sight! Until that moment, I had never really believed such a thing existed. I had always thought it was something 'made up' for telly programmes and films. I didn't even hesitate and made a bee line straight for her, I all but barged my way into the middle of the group and introduced myself with a brazen confidence one acquires after six pints of Kronenbourg! She said her name was Louise.

It was obvious to her friends that I only had eyes for her. I assume they sensed that she liked me too, because they backed away and left us to it. I brought her a drink and we made our way to a table in the corner of the pub. From the moment we sat down we didn't stop talking and laughing, although we had to shout most of the time to be heard over the music! Every now and again I would catch her friends looking over, checking that she was okay, which I found rather endearing. I also noticed that after she had had a couple of drinks her cheeks flushed a little red, I found this to be endearing too. In fact, I found everything about her endearing. I couldn't help myself, I liked her... a lot.

When the lights in the bar eventually came on at the end of the evening, indicating that the pub was closing I asked her for her phone number, confident that she would give it. As people started to mill their way out of the bar, her friends began to coral around her indicating she would be leaving with them. As she stood up and began to turn to leave, I moved in close and placed a tender kiss to her lips. It was a bold move. It is also not an exaggeration to describe it as electric! It is not a lie when I say we both heard the snap of the spark as our lips met. Nor is it untrue that we heard a whoop of delight rise up in a 'Woooo'! From her friends. I knew there and then, in that moment, that she was the one! I had never displayed tender affection in my local pub before (not that I am aware of any way!). That evening I all but 'skipped' home, in my car!

I couldn't believe my luck, nor could I stop thinking about her. I kept looking, longingly at the piece of paper with her phone number on it. It wasn't easy, but the next day, I held out until lunchtime before I finally buckled and picked up the phone, (please don't let it be a false number)! 'Hello, is that Louise'? 'Yes, speaking'. 'It's, Pat, I'm sure you remember me, I'm the devilishly good-looking bloke who spent the entirety of last night doing his best to charm his way into your Allan wickers, but sadly to no avail. Any-who I was just wondering ...if you fancied coming out and watching me get drunk'? ...you know ...that is if you're not washing your hair or something'? I could hear her grinning on the other end of the phone, there was a slight pause (about a nano second) and then to my utter delight she said, 'Yeah okay then'!

From that moment on the two of us were inseparable. We went everywhere and did everything together. I had scoffed at friends who had 'gotten all loved up', yet here I was carrying on like a lovesick teenager. She was everything I wanted! She was special. She was the one! She was so special that I don't wish to share with you the details of our intimacy, all I will say is this. The first time we made love, it was more than a mere physical act, it was more than just the mere meeting of two bodies! In the past whenever I had taken a woman to bed, it was all 'wahey'! 'Look at me, ain't I clever'! This was different. For the first time in my life, it meant something real, something deep. It took on a level of seriousness and meaning that was new to me. As such I felt a vulnerability I had not experienced before. Which I was both exhilarated and frightened by. It was such an intimate experience I had the strange desire to divulge my innermost secrets, to tell her everything. I wished to discard the front that I had built around myself and which I presented to the world. I only hoped that she felt the same.

There must have been something in the air, because I wasn't the only one who was loved up! My sister Bridie had met a bloke who in my opinion looked a lot like Robert Redford. I mentioned it to him once and he looked as pleased as punch! Bridie decided she was going to live with Mr Redford, so asked if me and Louise would like to rent her flat. There was no deposit or month upfront, we could even have it at cost. It was also fully furnished, so all we had to do was remember to bring our toothbrushes. We (perhaps I) jumped at the chance! So after only six or so months of dating, we moved in together. I couldn't have been happier. Having privacy, having a place of our own was wonderful. We were both enjoying life, living together certainly changed things, it made it more official, more serious. And I liked it, because I loved her! I don't wish to appear chauvinistic but, I was proud to call her my girl!

I realised It was now time for me to settle down and she was the one I wanted to settle down with. I dreamt of us buying our own home, of marriage, of kids and of growing old together. I was hopeful for the future. I was so caught up in the moment, so carried away with all the possibilities, that I had unfortunately forgotten to counter 'me' into the equation. Although it was indeed the right time for me to settle down, I found that try as I might, I just couldn't. I was full of good intentions, but rarely delivered the goods! Despite getting off to a great start and despite Louise being the love of my life, about 12 months in, our relationship began to falter.

Work had become a bit sketchy which didn't help, (secretly I felt embarrassed of my profession, as Louise's 'man'. I felt as though I should be something more! Not that she ever indicated this was the case). Louise wasn't currently working either as she was between jobs, which unfairly raised a few eyebrows where my sisters were concerned. So, things were a little difficult. It didn't help that I was frittering away most of the money we did have on necessities like drink and drugs! We were living together as a couple and I was desperately trying to be the man that I 'thought' she wanted me to be (although I never actually asked!). Perhaps I began to, unwittingly, put myself under a lot of pressure. I was 28yrs old, Louise was 24. When I look back to that time in our lives, I think things might have happened all a bit too quick. I think maybe I put too much pressure on her and perhaps she felt, 'suddenly' trapped? Perhaps I loved her so much I was smothering her? I don't suppose it helped that I was somewhat (emotionally) immature and also a hopeless fucking drunk! As much as I loved her and despite wanting to spend all my time with her, I didn't want to look like a mug in front of my mates either. I didn't want to appear under the thumb!

Just like in any new relationship, Louise had, at first met my representative! As the months unfolded, she began to see the (true) real me. She had been witness to the odd embarrassing episode where my drinking was concerned, however the number of embarrassing episodes were beginning to stack up. It was becoming increasingly difficult to dismiss or play them down. We had gone to the pub for a drink one evening and I had become so drunk that I had fallen asleep. I vaguely remember someone commenting, '...good boyfriend'!

On another occasion I had embarrassingly wet the bed, with 'her' in it (something I had not done since I had moved out of the house I had once shared with M, (and in my 'defence' it was only a little bit!!). Needless to say, she was not impressed! On other occasions I had gone out with Jim or Neil... or Paul...or all three, telling her I was only going for a couple; only for me to come home some hours later, unable to stand and with a trademark bead of snot hanging from my nostril! And if that wasn't bad enough and unbeknown to me, around about this time, Louise had spent an afternoon at my mother's house taking part in the age old tradition of sitting around the kitchen table, drinking tea with my mum and my sisters and slagging everybody off! My mother and sisters had laid bare the family history and had informed Louise all about my father's drinking and his violent ways. I think it's fair to say.... they had not done me any favours!

It was no surprise then that she began to blow hot and cold. It was also no surprise that I began to feel like I was losing her. Internally, I felt like I would never be good enough, not for her, not for anyone. I was annoyed with my mum and my sisters, I wished they hadn't said anything about my father. Did she now think I was the same? I hadn't deceived Louise about my past, I had been fairly open and honest about everything, except my father's behaviour towards my mother that is. Because that was his past, not mine!

Louise and I had talked openly about our lives and the different relationships we'd, had before we met. She had a past, which she was entitled to, and which needed no explanation. It certainly needed no apology! The truth is however, that I was so in love with her, that I didn't like the idea of her having a past with anyone else, even if it was long before I was on the scene! I didn't say anything! I knew it was wrong of me and I hate to admit it, but deep down I felt it reflected badly on me!! Had I absorbed some supposed set of outdated morals and a code of conduct from my parents? A set of morals that applied to 'my' woman, but not to me? Perhaps I had! I am not from the stone age, I live in the modern world, I knew I had no right to judge: especially me! But still, the truth was, I didn't like it. As a result, I began to feel insecure. Was her last lover better in bed than me? Was he better endowed? I sometimes felt like I was in a 'competition' of my own making, but I did not expect to win any prizes.

Louise was unhappy. Our relationship was on rocky ground and to make matters worse, my sister split up with Robert Redford and now needed her flat back, pronto! I was gutted. It was bad timing. I did not want this to be the end. Yet again I was embarrassed by my failings. I had little choice, but to move back to my mum's (again)! In an attempt to salvage our relationship and in a bid to keep us together, I asked (begged) my mum if Louise could move in with me, my mother reluctantly agreed. However, It was a fucking disaster. Louise left me and I was heartbroken.

Moving back to my mum's had been the final nail in the coffin. It was too much for her at my mums, it was so stifling you could almost feel the weight of the oppression hanging over you. I had endured it all my life and even I found it hard to bare. Just like every other girl I had ever been out with, she was not used to the harshness of my existence, the life I had come accustomed to. When Louise left, I was distraught, I was devastated, but I understood. I struggled on without her.

I cursed my parents and my upbringing. Every time I took a drink, I got drunk. Every time I got drunk, I ended up sobbing my heart out. I was inconsolable. I didn't cry in public of course, instead I would wait until I was alone and then take comfort in my melancholy. It was all that I had left. My mother found me sitting behind the bins in the back garden, (I had hidden myself away from prying eyes!). Horrified she had barked, 'What are you crying for'?! It was as if she was annoyed with me. I recall being embarrassed by my tears, by my loss. I felt embarrassed by my humanity. Not all the tears were for Louise.

It felt as though I had never gotten anything I had ever truly wanted out of life and now it seemed as though I never would. I felt like a complete fool for even thinking that I had ever had a chance. For weeks I wallowed in self-pity, lamenting at my lot. But then I became defiant! I decided this was a cause worth fighting for, she was worth fighting for! Why shouldn't I be happy! Somehow, I managed to get a grip on things and half sorted myself out. I also managed to convince Louise to give it another go! I was happy again! But It was short lived.

For the next twelve months we were off and on like a pikey collecting money on a fairground Waltzer. Each time I would ask for another chance, and each time I would inevitably get drunk and ruin it. During one occasion where we had separated for a week or so and had then got back together, I had an uncomfortable feeling that I couldn't quite shake off. I knew something wasn't right because the unease just wouldn't go away. I pressed her on what had happened while we were apart and discovered to my horror that she had betrayed me. I felt physically sick, I can remember the moment my worst fear was confirmed, and my stomach churned. But then who could blame her! I couldn't! She was young and beautiful. Why would she want to waste her time on a drunk? She had just done to me what I had done to every girlfriend I had ever had, ...'Ouch'!

Despite the fact I was totally gutted, I also understood. Why would she have any loyalty to me when every time I picked up a drink I 'betrayed' her! How could she picture a future together with me? How do you love a man who spends his evenings lying on the sofa, snoring and farting? It's quite simple! You don't. I took full responsibility for her betrayal, although technically we weren't together at the time. It was my fault she had no respect for me, because I didn't have any respect for myself. It was during a heart to heart that she told me the only problem with our relationship was my drinking! I was at a loss as what to do. I didn't want to lose her, but I strongly suspected I was fighting a losing battle!

Something had to give! Me and Louise were on yet another break. Secretly I was struggling with an inner turmoil I didn't understand. Whilst outwardly I kept up the pretence that everything was fine and that I didn't care! I had spent the entire weekend (doing just that!), out on the town with my mates. Like a dog off a lead! Pubs, clubs, drink and drugs. My appetite for anything that would ease my discomfort was insatiable. Through pure greed (and perhaps need) I did three days straight, before finally falling in the door in the early hours of Monday morning.

I can only assume I had collapsed on the bed and passed out. However, a few hours later my eyes snapped open as I shot bolt upright in the bed and drew in a big gulp of air, like I had just been resuscitated with a shot of adrenalin. My whole body glistened with sweat as it tried to rid itself of the 'badness' circulating around my system. I felt panicked, my body ached, and I felt battered, as if I had been in a car crash. I remembered nothing of the weekend that had just passed. I felt worried and anxious as if something really bad was going to happen! I inched my way out of bed, whilst thinking I have to go to work! Although I kept thinking it over and over in my head, I knew I wasn't going anywhere! What's the point? I work, I get paid, I blow all my wages on drink and drugs and then I am disgusted with myself and repulsed by my behaviour. Everyone gets upset, I hate me and then the whole sorry process starts again. I can’t carry on like this I have to do something.

It was 6.30am, I got dressed and went downstairs, my mum was already up and sitting in the kitchen drinking tea. As I entered, she shot me a look of disgust which was nothing to the look I got when I told her I wasn't going to work! 'Whaa...t'!! The unwritten rule, an absolute no, no! She wasn't impressed. Not that I really cared, because it was probably one of the best decisions I have ever made.

I took the telling off from my mum and then went back up to my room where I sat in silence on the edge of my bed. I knew I had to do something, but what? It took a few hours before I finally conceded to what I had known all along! I picked up the yellow pages and thumbed through until I found the number. At the forefront of my mind, I kept asking myself, 'Are you really going to do this?' But deep down I knew I had to!

From the privacy of my room and out of sheer desperation (and fear) I phoned Alcoholics Anonymous. My hands were trembling, and my heart was beating as fast as my mind was racing as it tried to catch up with what was happening! After a couple of rings, a lady answered the phone. If it hadn't been for the seriousness of my situation, when she had asked where I was ringing from, I might have been tempted to say, 'The waist down'! But I didn't! Despite the fact she was a stranger, she was very kind, reassuring and sympathetic. I told her that I thought, I 'might' have a drink problem! Sensing my embarrassment, she said, 'It's okay, I used to be like you'. And with that, the floodgates opened at her kind words, I began to sob. The tears just wouldn't stop coming. A lifetime's worth of bottled up emotions and hurt just spilled out of me. It was an overwhelming relief.... yet at the same time I felt like a complete and utter wanker!

She told me her name was Lynn, and that there was a 'meeting' near to where I lived on the coming Wednesday evening at 8 o'clock. She suggested that I should go and that she would be there to meet me. Apart from Louise and my mum, I didn't tell another living soul that I was going to an AA meeting, I couldn't, I was too embarrassed! Plus, I wasn't sure if I was making a huge mistake. Going to an AA meeting did seem a bit drastic. What would people think if they found out? Would they laugh at me for being a fucking

Jessy? Would they be thinking. 'Get a fucking grip mate! Worse, would they think I had lost the plot? So, I thought it best I keep it to myself!

When the Wednesday evening finally rolled around, I was understandably nervous. I had for a long time felt like I was damaged goods, going to the meeting almost confirmed it, yet at the same time I knew it was a positive step, so it was hard 'not' to feel quite optimistic! The meeting was held in a little hut at the side of a health care centre on the opposite side of town. It was dark when I pulled into the car park, I was glad because this meant there was less chance of me being spotted by someone I knew! The car park was quite full and there seemed to be a lot of people milling around the entrance to the hut, smoking and drinking (I guessed) tea! I stayed in my van for a while and smoked a cigarette while plucking up the nerve to go in. At ten to eight, I got out of my van and made my way to the front door. As I approached and made my way in, people said 'Hello' to me and some shock my hand as they introduced themselves (first names only!).

I had expected it to be dark and dingy inside with people hiding in the shadows, but it wasn't. Instead it was bright and cheerful. In the middle of the hall two rows of chairs (not a circle as I had expected!) were set out in front of a table, behind which hung two large banners, one said The twelve Steps, the other said The Twelve Traditions, neither of which meant anything to me. As I stood taking in my surroundings a lady approached and asked, 'Are you Pat'? She held out her hand and said her name was Lynn! She told me she was pleased I had decided to come along and that she hoped I would find what I was looking for. Then Lynn explained the format of the meeting; it would be in two halves. First there would be a speaker, who would talk about their experience. What it was like, what they did and what it is like now. Then there would be a break, for tea and cigarettes. After which the room would be open for 'sharing'! I think she sensed my trepidation and said, 'You don't have to say anything, ...unless you want to'. 'No-one here will ask anything of you. If you decide not to come back... no one will be phoning you to see where you are. Everyone in this room has been where you are now. We know it's not easy, but there is a solution! Take my advice, get a cup of tea, take a seat and just listen. After all, what have you got to lose'!

I did as Lynn suggested and took a seat (at the back, near the door!) in the, by now, packed hall. I did a quick head count, there were about 30 alkies', mostly smartly dressed, mostly smiling and most importantly of all ...sober! A hush fell over the room indicating that the meeting was now starting. A woman and a man sat at the main table in front of the rows of chairs. The woman said her name before adding she was an alcoholic. She welcomed everyone to the meeting and then some literature regarding the AA programme and ethos was read aloud before she introduced the speaker. He too said his name, before adding, 'and I am an alcoholic'!

I got lucky that night, I recognised the speaker. Although I didn't know him personally I knew he was about my age (30), I had seen him many times as I had made my rounds about the town centre pubs, but it had never occurred to me that he might be the same as me! As I listened to him talk, I was shocked to discover that he had done the same embarrassing things that I had, that he had experienced the same feelings of shame and remorse, the same sense of worthlessness and impending doom that had blighted my entire existence. He, too, had felt like a second-class citizen and, like me, had kept it a personal secret. For the first time in my life, I did not feel alone with my problem. Up until that point I had always thought it was just me who behaved like that. As the evening went on, I heard people (from all walks of life) who had been sober, 10, 20 even 30yrs, discuss how they had dragged themselves out of the gutter and were now living decent worthwhile lives. For the first time in my adult life it began to dawn on me that a life without alcohol was possible and what's more I could be happy. It was like a weight had been lifted from my shoulders. I felt unburdened!

I believe I changed that night, I was definitely different. It wasn't anything spiritual, the clouds hadn't suddenly parted as I was touched by the hand of God. I don't think I believe in God anyway, well not in the traditional sense. I don't believe there's some bloke with a beard sitting on a cloud waiting to smite me down if I get it wrong! If it were to be suggested to me that 'God' was an internal dynamic force of 'good' present in all of humankind, then I think I could go for that! Anyway, I was different, nonetheless. Perhaps it was hope! For not only did I feel different, but I truly believe I looked different too! A sadness that I had not been aware of, had been lifted from my face and the dullness had gone from my eyes. People noticed!

When I got home, my mum was still up and waiting in the living room, keen to know how it went. As I entered the room, she turned in her chair (my dad's chair!), and said, 'How did you get on'? I replied with a smile, 'It was really good mum, I'm glad that I went. I'm going to go next week as well. I feel much better for it.... I am definitely an alcoholic mum'!

A worried look of concern washed over her. Her words stumbled a bit as she said, 'Well... I don't know if you're.... actually... an alcoholic'! She looked frightened. The woman who had spent the last 14yrs telling me I was a useless cunt just like my father! The woman who had constantly berated me about my drinking, was now having doubts. As I, for the first time in my life, had never been more certain. I smiled at her reassuringly, 'Its okay mum'. 'You don't have to worry about anything, this is a good thing, I am going to get the help I need and everything's going to be all right'.

If my mum's response was not what I had expected, then Louise's response to my new found belief was not only surprising, but also disturbing! It totally threw me. When I had told her the 'good news', she began to cry! I asked her why she was crying? Louise said, 'If you stop drinking then you might not love me anymore'! What the fuck does that mean? I had thought, I had hoped, she would be happy that I had stopped drinking. She had maintained it was the only thing wrong with our relationship. I found her statement very confusing.

I had never really believed that I could live a life without alcohol, but now I was excited by the very prospect of it. True to my word I kept going to the meetings and was surprised to find I had not taken a drink since that very first Wednesday. It was nothing short of a miracle, (that is, if you're the sort that believes in such things?). I started to enjoy going to the meetings. Although I strongly sensed that they weren't really my 'type' of people, however I still had a healthy respect and admiration for each and every one of them. As the weeks passed, I began to experience a new sense of freedom that I had not previously known. I had done the impossible! I had done what my father had not! A new world was opening itself up to me. No more Mondays missed off work. No more blowing all my wages in the pub. I could start up my own business, I might become a property developer! Fuck me, I'm going to become a 'Millionaire'!

They were early days and I was naïve! Clearly it was fantastic that I had stopped drinking, in fact I felt quite the hero. However, I was still smoking pot (on a daily basis) and snorting coke with my mates at weekends. I decided this was a fair compromise because I didn't have a problem with drugs, it was just drink that was the issue. In fact, I could use drugs just like the next man, no problem! As I say I was naïve! Despite my 'recreational' drug use, I hit the ground running. My life vastly improved, going from strength to strength in leaps and bounds!

I think it's a fair assumption that most people drink in order to change the way they feel. They drink to celebrate, commiserate or console. They drink to be happy or to be sad. Some drink to numb out the pain of their existence, or the shame of their failings. Of course, some drink just to be sociable and no harm done! They have a saying in AA, 'The best thing about getting sober is you get your feelings back. The worst thing about getting sober is... you get your feelings back'! I found that stopping drinking was the 'first' step in sorting out the mess I had left in my wake as I had crashed my way through life!

Guilt, loss, despair, blame, resentment, anger and even rage are emotions all attributed to the bereavement process. Bereavement doesn't just apply to the death of someone you have loved. You can go through the same set of emotions when you lose your car keys; you can be bereft. Which I suppose is how I was after I had stopped drinking. A bit like a child who has had his favourite toy confiscated. I was bereft at losing my comforter! I was okay at first, because I was on cloud nine for weeks, but then the bubble burst and the 'feelings' started to kick in!

I couldn't believe what a fool I had been. How I had let people take advantage of my good nature. I got angry, perhaps rage would be a better description. In fact, I was full of rage for months! I was angry with my dad; he had been my male role model, so it was his fault I was an alcoholic. I was angry with my mum, her constant nagging had soured any fun that could be had by a young man. If it wasn't for her, I would be alright, I would be like my friends. I decided my mum had not so much given me the wings to fly, as clipped them! I was angry with Louise. Why couldn't she just accept me for who I was? Why did she have to hurt me? The last one was the most painful of all: I was angry with myself, for allowing it all to happen. I felt like the world's biggest mug! I couldn't have been easy to be around at that time.

Louise had just started a new job working for a large hotel chain. She was busy with her work and seemed to be happy in her new role. I didn't notice at the time but a 'new' distance between us, had emerged from the rubble that was our relationship! However, despite this we had begun looking for a new home, I was excited by the prospect and looked forward to the day we could truly be together. We couldn't afford (probably wouldn't get!) a mortgage, so we settled on renting, until hopefully our situation improved. Louise was so busy with her new job that I found myself viewing properties on my own. I accepted this, because I loved her, however it didn't go unnoticed with family and friends. The truth was, I felt a little bit embarrassed by it.

One evening we were sitting on the sofa at my mum's house watching the TV. We were alone as my mum had gone to bingo when out of the blue Louise turned to me and said, 'Oh, I brought a house today'! She said it very casually as if it were totally normal. Confused I said, 'What the fuck are you talking about'? 'What do you mean you brought a house'?! 'With my mum'! She said matter of factly. She continued to explain that as we had no chance of getting on the property ladder, her and her mum had decided to buy one together. I was now even more confused, and I was also insulted. When did they fucking decide that! Did she not think it worth her while mentioning it to the man she is supposedly going to spend the rest of her life with! Where the fuck do 'I' fit into the equation!

I was so hopelessly in love it was unbelievable, I still felt as if everything that was wrong with the relationship was my fault, I took sole responsibility for the direction and consequences on our relationship as a result of my drinking! If I had been more of a man in the first place, then this situation would not have arisen. Therefore, it's my own fault. I tried to justify and make sense of what I was hearing, I concluded, and I'm sure she indicated I was correct in thinking, that her mother was in fact.... giving us a helping hand onto the property ladder as a result of 'my' being useless! We would move into the property, we would pay the mortgage and renovate the house... thus adding value... sell the house... pay her mum back her stake, plus some on top and hence, we are established property owners! It's a win, win situation for everyone! Having calmed down and having convinced myself that this was indeed the case, I innocently asked 'So how much are the mortgage repayments'? To which she replied in an offhand way, 'Oh, ...I don't know'. I never did find out!

Things went from bad to worse for Louise and me, not only was the distance between us growing, but I was also kept in the dark and out of any dealings concerning the new house. I don't know what she wants from me anymore, I have desperately tried to be the man 'I think' she wants me to be, but it seems I keep coming up short. She even hinted that she likes taller men! Shall I get a pair of stilts? Or perhaps some platform shoes? I'm 5ft 7in, I'm not a dwarf! She is actually starting to get on my fucking nerves!

****

Our relationship did not survive the changes. For the first time ever, I finished with her. I didn't want to, but as a man I felt had to! I had been sober for a couple of months when one day we were talking and a serious discrepancy emerged. It was, for me, the final straw. When I questioned her about it, she stood in front of me in a very self-righteous manner and wagged her finger in my face telling me I was wrong. I was out of order and that it was all in my head! I almost believed her, but then she said something, (I can't remember exactly what it was), but I knew it was a lie, and a terrible lie at that. It was at that precise moment my head lowered and I felt my heart break. Not for the first time I felt my stomach churn and roll over. I was so gutted; in fact, I was devastated. I knew in my heart she was lying. It had never before crossed my mind that she would lie to me or have any need to. My mind began to race as she continued to wag her finger, what else has she lied about? I wasn't a drunk anymore! I remember what happened last week and the week before that, I remember who said what and when. There were no longer any blank pages in my memory for her to fill in on my behalf. I didn't get angry, I didn't call her any names, I just got up and left.

The truth was I wasn't angry, not anymore. I was just sorry. I had fought hard to save our relationship. Now I wasn't sure if there had ever been a relationship to save. It was a bitter pill to swallow. It's not uncommon in a relationship to have one party that cares more than the other. It's now my experience that if you don't want to get hurt you're better off being the one that doesn't give a fuck! It was strange being without her, I missed her. But what could I do? I moped about quite a bit. Work wasn't the same. Yes it was easier, because I wasn't hungover all the time, but I had started to question my direction in life, my work was not fulfilling. I continued to go to my AA meeting every Wednesday night and I continued to stay sober. I liked the fact I no longer drank; I just felt a little lost.

After a month or two things began to settle, and I started to feel happy. I was getting use to my new life without alcohol and without Louise. I was even toying with the idea of going travelling again. I had always quite liked the idea of Brazil. Then out of the blue and quite unexpected I received a phone call. Louise phoned with the ruse of wanting some pot. I knew this wasn't the real reason. I knew that the fact that I had finished the relationship had ruffled her feathers somewhat. After all, that's not how it works is it! I hadn't come running, I hadn't picked up the phone begging for forgiveness. I was clearly moving on. I was torn, one part of me desperately wanted to see her and the other wanted to just forget all about her. I couldn't help it, I arranged to meet her for a drink in a nearby pub!

When she walked in, I couldn't help feeling that it was nice to see her. She had a vodka and orange and I had a cola. I watched her cheeks flush as she drank her drink, I thought of the night we had met 3yrs earlier. I gave her the pot, that I knew she didn't really want and then we chatted about how things had panned out. We agreed we had both made mistakes. Needless to say, It was inevitable that we decided to give it another go. Of course, I had been hurt by her actions, she had clearly been hurt by mine, but I loved her. I had to concede my part in it; after all, I had hardly been Mr perfect. We decided to draw a line under the past and let bygones be bygones. However, it did not go unnoticed by me that there had been a power shift in our relationship. Not that I was trying to control anything, I was just aware that the ball was no longer 'fully' in her court. Not for now anyway! No more back and forth, no more silliness, I'm serious about making the relationship work, So much so, that I was planning to ask Louise to marry me! But Louise gets in first and trumps me! 'I'm pregnant' she whispers!

31yrs old and I couldn't wipe the stupid grin off my face! I hugged her, I kissed her, I reassured her, I told her I loved her and that I had never been happier! I was over the fucking moon! The only woman I have ever loved is carrying my baby! And the icing on the cake? Louise agrees to marry me! I'm so excited I want everyone to know, so we rush round to my mum's house to tell her that 'we' have good news!

My god I've never been so embarrassed, it was brutal! She is clearly not in favour and instead of 'congratulations', she just gives us both a dirty look and leaves the room! Mortified, I'm left standing looking at the floor, hurt, angry and deflated in front of Louise! My mum has always been like this, I shouldn't have expected anything else. Worst of all, I feel weak, for not pulling her up and letting her know just how fucking rude and insulting she has just been! It really didn't help matters.

CHAPTER NINETEEN

I THOUGHT IT WAS GOING TO BE DIFFERENT! I thought we were moving on. I thought we had put the past behind us. I thought we were going to be happy. I thought wrong!

Nothing I did seemed to please her. She seemed dismissive of everything I said and did. If I asked her if she wanted a cup of tea, she would stare off into the distance, with me teetering on the side-line, whilst awaiting her decision. She seemed bored. She seemed disinterested.

Louise had always blown a bit hot and cold, but now it was just an icy chill. Her and her mum had brought the house, but no date had been set for moving in. We had been round and had a look and I had become excited by the possibilities of refurbishing the place; re-plaster, new bathroom and kitchen, a loft conversion perhaps! Now with a baby on the way and a perceived mortgage to pay, I threw myself into my work and after a particularly good week on site I had arrived at Louise's house, all excited, because I had cleared £1300 take home!

'I think we've got enough to do the bathroom up'! I had announced triumphantly and very pleased with myself. But Louise shrugged her shoulders and scrunched her face saying, 'Yeah I wouldn't worry about it for now'. I would have thought most women would have been delighted! How am I supposed to respond to that? I felt utterly deflated, to be honest I was starting to feel like the biggest mug god had ever put into two shoes.

Louise moved into the house she had brought with her mother, I didn't!

****

She is three months pregnant when I end the relationship. I say the words, 'It's over'. It's not what I want, but I feel I have been backed into a corner. I feel I have no choice. After all I 'have' changed, I can't allow myself to be mistreated in this way. I remember thinking 'Am I going to let my child watch me get mugged off by their mother'! Her bump is beginning to show, our child is growing inside of her. I love our baby.

Things have not turned out how I had envisaged, but there is no point flogging a dead horse! I accept our relationship is over for good, but we can still work together to be good parents. I am truly naïve; I still haven't yet realised that I will only be a Sunday daddy. Nor have I yet realised that she is now holding all the cards! I put a brave face on it all, and when I meet up with my friends in the pub, I joke that Louise has reached the end of her first trimester. They all look at me with blank expressions and I just grin! Because life is good! I don't drink! And I am going to be a dad!

I try to discuss matters with Louise over the phone concerning our baby, however every time we agree on something, she later backtracks and tells me its not correct or that she didn't say it. It's frustrating, so I turn up at her/mother's house with a notebook and pen. Which really pisses her off! I am excluded from all matters baby. I know it's a very special time for any woman having her first child. I am not trying to intrude; I am not trying to take over or get in the way. I just want to show my support, I want to be involved, but I am left out in the cold and I am kept in the dark about everything.
I'm working as hard as I can, trying to get as much money together as possible for obvious reasons. One afternoon while on site I receive a text message from Louise, it reads, 'it's real I have heard the heartbeat'! I stare at my phone in disbelief and re-read the message again and again, and then I phone her, 'What do you mean it's real, have you been to the doctors'? She tells me she has been

that morning and had a scan. I'm gob-smacked and hurt, '...Why didn't you tell me, I would have come'! As usual I didn't get a straight answer, nor did I earn any more money that day. In fact, I was finding it increasingly difficult to stay focused and concentrate at work, which meant my earnings plummeted. It was becoming perfectly clear that Louise wasn't going to make things easy for me. I couldn't understand how she failed to see that although I understood our relationship was over, I still intended and desperately wanted to be a good father. I wasn't walking away from our child. (I'm still sober!).

I became defiant. I decided that if this is how she wants to play it, she can crack on. She can do what she likes. I will be a good dad regardless and I will have a great relationship with my child. I will love my child and my child will love me. A few months passed with virtually no contact between us, there was 'really' no point! But as the time neared, I went to see her. I have to say it was a pleasant shock when she opened the door and stood before me holding her by now large bump. I detected a vulnerability about her that had not been there before. I sensed a softening towards me. My visit was civil and matter of fact, I told her I wanted to be at the birth. It was not the first time I had asked, but I got the same non-committal and dismissive response I always got. 'Can I, or can't I'? By the time I left I was still none the wiser!

CHAPTER TWENTY

IT WAS 6AM ON A THURSDAY MORNING, I was getting ready to leave for work, when my phone rang. Looking at the screen I saw it was Louise's number. Immediately panic stricken and flustered I all but shrieked down the phone, 'What's happening, are you okay'?! Louise said, 'It's started'! 'Can you take me to the hospital'!? As I stood in the hallway, my mind began to race as the enormity of the situation hit home. I was momentarily at a loss; I didn't know whether to turn left or turn right! Then I roared into the phone, the immortal line 'Hold on, I'm coming'!

The drive to her house was hurried to say the least, every light seemed to be on red and despite it being early in the morning every car seemed to be in my way and blocking my path. Once there and having helped her from the house and into the car I drove her to the hospital, Louise's mother (who was down as her birthing partner), arrived shortly afterwards. Once in the delivery room Louise lay on the bed with her mother stood at her side, while I positioned myself standing in the corner of the room, well out of the way and feeling every bit the spare part. I wasn't sure what to do or what was expected.

The midwife and a nurse were (as far as I could tell) examining Louise. Then I heard one of them say something about her 'contraptions', being close? Then the midwife gave me a quizzical look, 'You daddy', she enquired. 'Yep that's me'! I replied with a forced smile. I was aware that I must have looked like a bewildered child. 'Don't worry, we take care of daddy too', she said with a reassuring smile! It was the nicest anyone had been to me since we had arrived and the first time I had been acknowledged as having

a n y
legitimacy in being there. It may sound silly, but I felt like I finally had a friend, someone on my side! And then it all happened very quick!

The midwife announced that the baby was coming and with that everyone sprung into action, including me! Without thinking I all but shouldered Louise's mum out of the way and claimed my rightful place beside the mother of my child. I took Louise's hand in mine and like a man 'out of his depth', with my free hand I began (probably annoyingly), patting her on the head whilst encouraging her to push, ...push! However, being the gentleman that I am, I stayed away from the business end of things!

On the 24th of January 2005, at 1.40pm our beautiful little boy was delivered unto the world, weighing in at a respectable 6lb 8 ounces. My first glimpse of him was of a flash of grey, a hand and then a foot as the midwife passed him to the nurse. There followed a brief commotion concerning Louise, a slight (non-life threatening) complication, although I was never told what it was. As a result, Louise was immediately whisked out of the room still on her bed and quickly followed by her mother. The nurse handed me the baby and a split second later the room was empty. I was literally left holding the baby!

I had a brief moment of panic. A feeling of real concern and disbelief washed over me because I had been left on my own and I wasn't sure what to do. I slowly moved to a chair in the corner of the empty room and sat down blown away by all that had just happened. I had not been prepared; I didn't even know I was going to be there! I held my newborn son in the palm of my hands and marvelled at his perfect little face. I whispered, 'Hello son, I'm your dad'. I was overwhelmed by the love I felt for this tiny little mite and I felt a strong desire to protect and nurture my newborn son. I couldn't help myself and tears of pure joy rolled down my face. For the first time ever, I felt like I had some purpose in life. The birth of my son had given my life meaning and worth. As I gazed at him through tear-filled eyes, I knew I would never drink again. I didn't need god to tell me, I didn't need AA to tell me. I just knew. I felt it in my bones, I would not put this child through what my father had put me and my siblings through. I was the happiest man alive! Just me and him, sitting in an 'empty' room 'full' of love!

That evening I drove the 'three' of us home (to Louise's). It was a very special time. I kept picking him up and cuddling him and planting little kisses on his forehead and when I did put him down in his moses basket, I kept walking over, stopping short, a foot or so away so as not to disturb him and leaning forward staring in at him in total awe. For the next three weeks I was in my element. I stayed with them both in her house for the first few nights, doing the night time shift so as to allow her some much-needed rest. Every time he stirred, I was there at his side, picking him up and gently rocking him and placing tender little kisses on the crown of his head. I changed his nappies and bathed him (I couldn't feed him!). I cooked her dinners, to help build her strength up, I remember making her chicken soup because I reasoned that's what you give people when they are ill! I was happy; it was all I ever wanted. I also knew it was only temporary, we were just playing happy families. We were not a couple and I would not be staying! Eventually I had to go back to work, it was a retch, I didn't want to leave him. So, every evening I went straight from work to see my son.

****

I knew I was fucked as soon as she opened the front door. She didn't even have to say anything. She'd, had her hair done and she was back in her skinny jeans. She was no longer vulnerable. The softness towards me had been replaced with a harsh familiar coldness. It was evident that the truce was now over, and the war was back on! I understood! And I accepted that she would not want me in her life, or her home, on a daily basis. Realistically, it made sense! With that in mind I knew it was time to broach the subject of access!

'I think we need to discuss what we are going to do about access Louise'. She looked appalled! She looked at me like I had just lost my fucking mind! And then with a look of total disgust and horror stated, as a finality and in a mocking tone, 'You're not having him'! There was no doubt in my mind that she was serious. The look on her face told me she meant every word. With the realisation came the feeling like I had just been stabbed in the heart! At no point during the last nine months had it ever occurred to me that Louise would not want me to be a part of our sons' life! 'What the fuck do you mean, I am not having him? He is 'my' son, of course I'm having him. What! Do you think I'm just going to walk away? Are 'you' fucking mental?!! She was angry! I had never seen her like this before, she said it again with venom, 'You're not having him'! I was angry, hurt and flustered. I didn't mean it; it just came out as I tried to make my point! I said, 'Yeah, I tell you what Louise, how about 'I' just take him, and you will never see either of us again.... how does that sound'?!!

Of course, I didn't mean it! It was a ridiculous comment, it had been said in the heat of the moment. I had just meant to prove a point. Not in a million years would I be capable, nor want, to take my son away from his mother! I'm not an idiot, I'm not a monster, I was just angry! Needless to say, my comment was like a red rag to a bull! Louise countered, 'If you don't leave.... I'm ringing the police'! Flabbergasted by her threat, I shook my head with pretend fear and mock disbelieve and said, 'Oh, you fucking mug'! 'Go on then ring em, I don't give a fuck 'who' you ring, I ain't going anywhere, until you tell me when I can have my son'! and with that I sat down on the settee. Louise phoned the police. 'It's my ex, he won't leave, and he's threatened to take my son'! Louise sounded scared, which made me feel very uncomfortable, but still at the same time I couldn't believe what I was hearing. 'I'm alone in the house and he won't go'!

I couldn't believe how pathetic it all was, is this what the police do all day, attend fucking squabbles and disagreements? She was still on the phone when I shouted out, 'And don't forget to tell them what a fucking gimp you are'! The police arrived about ten minutes later. They were actually quite nice!

Two police officers, one male and one female. Louise said her piece, and then I explained what had happened, how I had been there every day for three weeks, but when I had turned up today from work she had made it clear I would no longer be welcome! The two police officers were actually pretty good about it all, I got the impression that they dealt with this kind of thing a lot. The female officer began discussing things with Louise, while the male officer took me to one side and explained that as it was not my house, then obviously I would have to leave. He also suggested I do myself a favour and seek legal advice from a solicitor regarding access for my son. He said, 'Look mate every time we get called out it will just go against you, take my advice, I've been in a similar situation'! I was gutted it had come to this, but at the same time I knew the police officer was right.

I stood in the living room flanked by two officers, while the only woman I had ever loved sat on the settee holding our baby son. She looked every bit the victim, which without her actually saying anything implied I was therefore the nasty bullying brute in all this! Knowing I was about to leave I gestured towards my son, but Louise flinched and pulled away. 'I just want to give him a kiss goodbye'?! Louise refused and held our son close to her chest. 'Why can't I give him a kiss goodbye'?! I asked. She hesitated, while it seemed she tried to come up with something legitimate to say in front of the two officers. Then she mumbled a low barely audible, 'Your hands are dirty'! in reference to the fact I had been working on a building site all day. I was surprised when the female officer chipped in and said helpfully, 'Why don't you go and wash your hands mate'! 'That's an excellent idea', I replied appreciatively! When I returned from the bathroom (that Louise tiled!), she very reluctantly allowed me to hold our son and give him a kiss goodbye, and then I left.

I didn't see my son again for three months.

CHAPTER TWENTY-ONE

THERE'S HURT.... AND THEN THERE'S.... HURT! It felt like life had just turned around and kicked me straight in the bollocks! The pain was crushing. I thought my head might implode!

If a man had evoked the feelings and emotions that she had evoked in me, then I am certain I would have served a prison sentence. I apologise If that sounds like macho bravado bullshit, but it isn't! I am a human being, I have feelings! The message is clear, I'm not good enough to be his dad. I feel like I am being punished but I am not sure what for. Is it because she believes I abandoned her when she was 3 months pregnant? I may be wrong, but I thought I had done all I could to make the relationship work, I really didn't know what else I was supposed to do, she just wasn't interested. She wasn't interested in me! And now this! Why?

I was upset, I was angry, and I felt worthless. My dad was allowed to see his kids! Why can't I see my son, I don't even drink! I wasn't violent, I wasn't cruel! I wasn't a cheat! I admit (reluctantly), that I had been verbally abusive once or twice, but only regarding affairs of the heart! I don't think that qualifies me as a tyrant or a bully, just a human being. I think any 'man' would have responded in the same way! So, what's my crime, that I was a hopeless drunk. Well I'm not a drunk anymore, I've given it up, I've sorted it out, and this is my reward! I am really struggling to cope with it all.

Unbeknown to me at this time, my mum and Bridie were worried about me. They were concerned I might do something stupid. Not to Louise! But to myself! Nothing could have been further from my mind, and they needn't have worried. I was 15 months sober the day my son was born. I had no such intentions. However, I did have every intention of fighting Louise every step of the way concerning our son Jack! It was to be a very tough time for 'all' involved! I found it almost impossible to concentrate. Sad confused and angry, I was on an emotional roller coaster, so much so that I flipped one day at work with a couple of surly cockney chippies who tried to mug me off.

A right pair of bastards who thought they were a bit tasty and a bit special! They strutted about the job as if they owned the place. They were dismissive of and spoke down to everyone. Woe betide anyone who showed weakness! These pair of cocks obviously thought they could bully their way to a fortune! Unfortunately, they tried it on with me, when due to all that was going on in my life, I was just about ready to explode! I just wasn't in the mood for their silliness! I was on my own loading out a house with all the materials that I needed (a day's work in itself!), when the two bully boys menacingly appeared, sneering in the doorway. They both had smug stupid looks on their faces when the bigger one of the two said, 'Yea... h, were working in here now mate'! And then just left it hanging there like I was backward or something! .... In other words, 'Fuck off you mug'!

Like a volcanic eruption of pure rage, I exploded! I lost control. How dare they think they can take fucking liberties with 'ME'! I got right up in their faces and all but frothing at the mouth, I roared obscenities at them both! I told them exactly what they could do and exactly what I thought of them as they both shrank and backed their way out of the front door. I was so angry and so full of rage that I actually scared them! I think it's rare to see two grown men actually 'look' frightened, but that's what happened! The bigger one of the two realised I wasn't messing about, to the point that out of sheer terror, he made a grab for the hammer in the side of his tool belt. It was like a red rag to a bull, I flew at him, knocking him flying backwards. The audacity of the man, who the fuck did he think he was! As we sailed through the air I managed to get a couple of rabbit punches in and still had hold of him as we both ended up rolling around and grappling in the mud outside the house, (in front of forty cheering blokes!). His bully boy mate froze! He didn't know what to do, so he did nothing!!

It ended in a stand-off, before the two surly chippies, having received a taste of their own medicine 'chipped'! Neither showed up for work the next day! But I did! 'Fuck em'! 'Fuck the lot of em'! The truth of the matter is this, as much as I had frightened the two men. I had also frightened myself! The incident shook me up a bit, it could have been really nasty, it could have been a lot worse! It made me consider what 'I' am capable of! It made me consider the fact, that I may be destined for a lifetime of shit!

Kramer vs Waste of Space! I had never been so angry, so outraged or so saddened. I had hoped me, and Louise could sort things out amicably (like adults!) but in my heart I knew this was not going to happen. Like it or not I was going to have to get the ball rolling, but like a man about to leap from a bridge, I was hesitant to do so! It was with a heavy heart that I contacted a solicitor.

****

Mr Foley was every bit the stereotype! He had grey swept back hair, a grey beard and a grey 'crumpled' suit to match. He wore spectacles and spoke with an educated accent. I don't mind telling you as I sat in his office during our first consultation I felt (in comparison) like a total Oik, as I delicately explained the difficult set of circumstances, I now found myself in! I explained how I felt I was being punished for ending the relationship and how I just wanted to fulfil my obligations as a father and wanted to play an active part in my sons' life. He informed me that taking Louise to court would be a very expensive process and could take years to reach a suitable outcome! He said quite often 'these' matters could be resolved via mediation, if Ms Peterson, were amenable, 'obviously' I protested that it would be a waste of time. He concluded that it may well be the case, but if it came to it, it would show the court I was willing to try and resolve the matter. As futile as I knew it was, a date was set for mediation! And so, it began!

When the day arrived for Louise and me, to attend the mediation session, I was surprised to see she had actually turned up! What's more she was early! I had never known her to be early for anything. As I entered the office where it was to be held, a female mediation solicitor was already talking with Louise. She carried on talking and did not acknowledge the fact that I had just entered the room. I stood just inside the doorway for what seemed like an age, as I continued to be ignored!

'Excuse me, I'm Mr Delaney, I am here for the mediation session'. She looked me up and down, giving me the once over and said, 'Okay, take a seat and we will make a start'. I couldn't help but think she had already made her mind up about me. She stated her name and told us why we were there. She was talking directly at me, I was looking directly at her and appearing like I was giving her my full attention, but I wasn't even listening! The words that were coming out of her mouth were not making any sense, they all seemed to form together into one big babble of noise. How had it come to this? Louise was 'genuinely' the only woman I had ever truly loved. I would have done anything for her. I had given up the drink, I was over the moon we had a child. I even respected her for 'not' wanting to be with 'me'!! Why then are we sitting in a solicitor's office!

As I sat in the chair trying to make sense of it all and taking in my surroundings, I looked first at Louise and then back at the solicitor, who was still directing babble at me. It was at this precise moment that I was overcome with a very strong and very real urge to get up out of the chair, walk over to the corner of the room and crouch down with my hands over my head and curl up into a ball! It was a very real urge, one that I had to actually fight! Am I going insane? I think my mental health is beginning to deteriorate! I feel like damaged goods! It was the first time me and Louise had been in the same room together since the incident with the police. I was still angry and defensive; the truth is I felt uncomfortable being around her.

I snapped back out of it, just in time to hear the solicitor who was still talking at me say, 'So if you had your son, say, for a Saturday afternoon, where would you take him'? And then just left it hanging there, while she gave me a long patronising look! It just came out! Sarcastically I said, 'Drag racing and then down the pub with all my mates'! 'Where do you think I would take a 5-month-old baby'?!

Obviously, my sarcasm didn't help matters, the solicitor was only trying to help. The outcome of the mediation was that I was allowed 2 to 4 hours access every Saturday at my mothers' house. The 'condition' being that there was to be 'no' contact between Louise and myself! She would bring our son to my mothers' house, but I was not allowed to answer the door. My mother would receive and return our son to Louise, without any interaction between us. Pathetic! But at least I was going to spend time with my son, I was actually 'quite' happy! I was looking forward to seeing my kid! As I left the solicitors office, I saw Louise across the car park, I couldn't help myself and said (pleadingly), 'Can't we just be friends'?, 'No we can't', came the reply and with that she got in her car and drove away.

I looked forward to and enjoyed my son's visits. We had both been truly blessed with a beautiful little boy, who seemed to have been born with a naturally cheery disposition! He was a proper little smiler; it was easy to make him laugh (which in turn made me laugh!). The family would all descend on my mothers' house every Saturday and make a huge fuss of my son. I was glad, I had worried that due to Louise's reluctance to allow me to play a part in his life, that he would grow up not knowing or being part of my family.

My mother doted on Jack, but seemed a bit put out when I insisted on feeding him and changing his nappies. I think she thought I was being a bit of a Maggie! (a Maggie is a man, who engages in the woman's jobs and tasks, so is therefore 'no' man at all! It's an Irish thing!). She failed to see the importance in what I was doing. I knew that if my son was hungry or unhappy or if he needed changing, then I needed to be his first port of call, not my mother! While I'm sure it was always well intentioned my mother had a habit of being overpowering and controlling, I had seen what she had been like with my sister's kids and was mindful not to allow it to be the case with mine!

Things ran smoothly for a while and I was happy. Each Saturday I enjoyed the time I had with my young son and when Jack was collected by his mother, I would immediately begin to look forward to the next Saturday visit. One Saturday as I waited for my son to arrive, there was a knock at the front door. Without thinking I answered it. It was Louise and Jack, she was 'early'!

'Hello son', I beamed, with outstretched arms to take him. Jack smiled and lent forward in his mother's arms, as babies do, indicating he was happy to come to me. Louise said or rather stated the word 'No' and backed away clutching Jack tightly to her chest. She sounded the 'No' like she had just been confronted with a real-life monster. I couldn't help myself and guffawed and said, 'What are you doing! Just let me take him'! But she refused! I had broken the 'rules' by answering the front door in the house that I had both been born in and had lived in all my life! I flayed my hands in the air in frustrated disbelief!

As I did this my mum was making her way down the hall, realising that something was up, she said, 'What's going on'? To which I replied, 'She won't let me have him.... because I am not supposed to answer the fucking door'! I actually 'chuckled' at the absurdity of it all, however my 'chuckle' was short lived, because upon reaching the open door, my (very Irish) mother, called Louise, 'a stupid looking cunt'! Frustrated I let out a sigh and put my head in my hands! There was no visit!

The very next day! I received a rather harshly written letter from Louise's solicitor stating that Ms Peterson, was no longer prepared to carry on with the arrangement due to my breach of conditions and also the vile abuse she had suffered at the hands of my 73yr old mother. Apparently, she had feared for herself and 'her' son's safety! To be fair, I'm a man and I'm as tough as old boots, but my mum can still put the fear of God in me! So, it was back to the solicitors!

I explained to Mr Foley what had happened on my mother's doorstep, I also explained some new developments, how Louise, had in fact moved house, without telling me, so I currently did 'not' know where my son lived. She had also refused to tell me when she was registering the birth, as a result my name was not on the birth certificate. This meant 'to my absolute horror', that I had no legal rights or legal recognition concerning my son. I was also extremely hurt to discover that my son would not have my surname! On top of all this, I had developed a fear that Louise was planning to abscond with my son! I had really hoped we could sort things out between us, but it was clear this would never be the case. Lastly, I stated that I could not rely on Louise's 'good will', or word alone, with regards to our son and the role that I would play in his future. My solicitor agreed that the only viable option was to begin court proceedings to obtain a section 8 court order which would give me the legal rights I needed.

Rather embarrassingly I broached the subject of how I was going to afford a lengthy and expensive court case. I didn't have 'any' money! Mr Foley explained that the rules concerning legal aid had changed, however there was a provision of £2500 pounds put aside for cases such as mine, but it would not last long in a case that could go on for years, if Ms Peterson was to prove difficult. The only way I could qualify for 'full' legal aid would be if I was in receipt of some form of benefits. I had to fight this! If I walked away now, then I would never be a part of my son's life, I could not let that happen. I had no choice but to sign on!

I explained to Mr Foley that I was self-employed. I explained how my work had suffered and I was not earning very much. I was genuinely embarrassed, I actually apologised to him! I apologised to him on mine and Louise's behalf, I told him I was pained and embarrassed that we (Louise and I) could not come to an amicable arrangement, I was sorry for all the unnecessary time it would take up and for the unnecessary cost to the taxpayer, I meant it too! Mr Foley sensed my shame and rather gallantly said, 'Not at all, Mr Delaney. Think of the cost to the taxpayer if the boy grows up without a father'!

While I awaited the first court hearing, Mr Foley negotiated on my behalf and I was allowed one hour a week with my son at Louise's mothers house, (not the house they brought together, her actual house). As much as I enjoyed seeing my son, I was uncomfortable in these oppressive surroundings. I felt like I was being monitored (and judged!). The day I went to the job centre, I felt like the world's biggest loser, a total fucking scumbag. I was 32yrs old, I lived with mum, I'm an alkie, I have no money and I'm not allowed 'unsupervised' access with my son! How the fuck did it come to this!

The job centre immediately started trying to get me to take shit jobs, to get me off their books, but I couldn't take the 'shit' jobs, because then I would not be in receipt of benefits and would no longer qualify for the legal aid I needed.

I was explaining my dilemma (or lamenting to be precise), to my friend Simón Pompidou and his wife, Hazel. She was in the final year of her midwifery degree, 'Why don't you go to college'? she suggested, 'You could train as a counsellor or a social worker; you're on the dole, so it won't cost you anything and it will get them off your back. Plus, I think you would make a really good social worker! You should seriously consider it'! All work is honourable, but I had grown tired of humping plasterboards about all day. I couldn't help but think I was selling myself short. And I had long since held the believe that given the opportunity I could do better. I could achieve more!

Now that I was a dad, now that I was sober, I wanted (needed) a better life, different from the old one. I was sick of the feast and famine culture of site work, nor did I believe site was a particularly good environment for me anymore. I wanted a career, I wanted security, above all else I wanted to be taken seriously! It's not uncommon for someone 'like' me to feel like they want to give something back. Perhaps my experiences maybe of help to others who are struggling. Men who are suffering in silence! Men who put a brave face on it all, to keep up the pretence that everything is hunky dory, when it clearly isn't! Just like I had!

I pondered Hazel's suggestion; she may have a point! And now would definitely be the perfect time to do it. Half-heartedly, not really believing and more out of curiosity than anything else, I picked up a prospectus from the local college, (which just so happened to be at my old high school). I began to consider my options.

As well as daydreaming about my future, I kept myself busy by doing odd (cash in hand) jobs for family and friends. I was doing a little plastering job for Jim's mum in the accommodation above her newly acquired pub, The 'Fiddlers Elbow'! We were discussing the plastering, when she asked if I would be interested in moving in above the pub? The rent being so cheap, it was virtually free! It was a tempting offer! I was seriously thinking about going to college, and I knew I could barely get peace enough to read a newspaper at my mums, let alone study, so I quickly agreed.

Jim, however, being a good friend, pulled me to one side and said, 'you sure it's a good idea Pat, you know with your drinking and that'? He had a point, but I had long since had any interest in drink and assured him that seeing all the long face paddys sitting at the bar every night would actually be good therapy! So, I moved in, confident it would not pose a threat to my sobriety.

As much as I loved my mum it was good to be out of her house. In fact, it was a breath of fresh air, I liked living above the pub because it was the best of both worlds! It was quiet during the week, most evenings the bar would be practically empty by 9.00pm, so it was fairly peaceful upstairs in the flat. The weekends however were fucking mental!!

Even though I wasn't drinking the 'lock ins' were legendary. When the pub closed for the night (Fri/Sat), it was as if somebody flicked a switch and the place magically transformed into Jim's play-ground! (Like Fat Sam's 'speak easy' in Buggsy Malone!). More often than not there would be more people in the pub after it 'shut' than when it was open! And as soon as Jim's mum had left, the music got turned up and all the 'recreational' drugs came out! I (we) loved it! Not drinking really wasn't a problem, I was still one of the boys and I could still 'pardy'! It wasn't unusual for me to be up all night and snorting (very long!) lines of cocaine of the bar!

Life's funny, you can be having the time of your life and not know it! They really were good times, non-stop laughter with good friends. Despite the fact we all engaged in drug taking it was all relatively harmless, there wasn't one bit of badness in any of us (we were just a bit wild!). It was just pure fun! There was always plenty of women around too! Which was nice. Excluding Louise, (and my mum!), and for reasons unbeknown to me, I just couldn't (at that time in my life) put a foot wrong as far as women were concerned! I vividly remember late one evening, having just said goodbye to Jessica, I closed the door, turned around, smiled and said, 'Hello Nicole'!!!

Was it merely because I was sober? Or was it something more like 'women's intuition', were 'they' picking up on the very real and profound change in me? The truth of the matter is this, living above the pub, having fun and getting lots of attention was the perfect escape I desperately needed from the very serious 'realities' of my personal affairs! In many ways it was like I was living a double life!

****

Mr Foley contacted me concerning the court case. He informed that the court had insisted that Louise and I would attend a meeting with a CAFCASS officer (children and family court advisory and support service), in the hope that we could reach an amicable agreement thus avoiding an unnecessary court case! 'You know it will be a waste of time, Mr Foley' 'I still wish to pursue the matter through the courts. I need legal recognition as my son's father, not just her word that I will be able to see him'! He agreed but said, 'I strongly suggest you attend as the court has requested Mr Delaney'.

The meeting was scheduled for 10am in the same building as the family courts but on a different floor. On arrival I was ushered into a very small consultation room which contained a small table and three chairs, and nothing else, except Louise. I was shown the seat next to her and told the Cafcass officer would be along shortly.

Together we sat in stony silence, each wearing a stern expression and looking at opposite ends of the room. Eventually the door to the small room opened and an official looking woman wearing a business suit and clutching a pile of papers under her arm walked in and took the chair opposite us. She didn't introduce herself, instead she said, 'Now, the great thing about a contact centre is....' At this point with my hands held up in front of me, I jumped straight in, 'Whoa! what you talking about, what do you mean, contact centre! Nah... nah, you can forget your contact centres, because it ain't happening, over my dead body am I going to a fucking church hall to see my kid'! It was the first time anyone had mentioned contact centres. I was fucking livid!

The Cafcass officer immediately became flustered, stood up, snatched her pile of papers from the table and very abruptly said, 'Well, there's obviously no point talking to you'! And started to leave! I was astonished, 'Where are you going' I demanded 'You haven't even listened to my main points'! With this she spun round towards me and with real menace and a snarl on her face, tapped the side of her temple and all but spat, 'Your main points are in your head'! And then stormed out of the room. I could not believe what had just happened. How is that professional? Louise could not wipe the smirk off her face. At that exact point, my only ambition in life was to outlive Louise, just so I could go '...Haa'!!!

When I left, I headed straight for Mr Foley's office on the other side of town. Still 'reeling', I told him all that had happened. Mr Foley said it was very unfortunate that she had chosen to go down this route and if she was to insist for the contact centre then I had little or no choice but to concede. To make matters worse the contact centre was to be for 6 months! 6 months before I could get her into court. I didn't like it, but Mr Foley was right, I had no choice! As I sat opposite him in his office I stared at the floor, deep in thought.

When I lifted my head, I looked at Mr Foley and said, 'You know... when she was pregnant, ...I had hoped and prayed for a boy'. He knowingly, from one man to another, nodded his head and in his posh accent said, 'Of course, of course'. I looked at him quizzically for a moment, before saying, 'Err-mm, no... I don't think you understand Mr Foley! I hoped and prayed for a boy, because I thought if we had a girl, it would grow up to be like her and then I wouldn't be able to love it'! Mr Foley couldn't help himself and burst out laughing!

****

I applied for and was accepted on a full-time access to social studies course at the local college. At the initial interview I explained to the lecturer, that the last time I had written anything it was 4ft high, on a breeze block wall and it was 'spelt' wrong! I added that I had spent my working carer in the construction industry which had incorporated many roles (mainly bacon ones!)! I informed the lecturer that I had dutifully followed my father into the industry, as this was what was expected of me (a bit of a fib?). I went on to briefly tell him some of the family history concerning my father and sister and the impact it had on the immediate family, and how as a result, I realised at a young age the difficulties and challenges some people face throughout their lives. I didn't mention any of the difficulties or challenges I had faced! I concluded the time was right to fulfil my potential to work for and with, people in crisis. I was delighted to be accepted and couldn't wait to get started in the coming September.

I told my mum the good news! 'YOU'. 'College, huh... who the fuck do you think you are'?! It was not the response I had hoped for. But I should have known better! Hurt and confused I left. My sister Bridie was more supportive, I think secretly she would have liked to have done the same, but like me she had never been encouraged or supported to invest in bettering herself. I considered it might be fear on my mum's part; was she frightened that if I educated myself, I might question! Perhaps.

On the way out of the house I passed my brother on his way in, 'Connor, do you think I'm being selfish going to college'? His response startled me even more than my mum's, 'well, an hour a week ain't enough is it'! What the fuck is that supposed to mean?! Obviously, he was referring to the one hour I spent with my son! I was gob smacked. Did he think I was happy with the arrangement?

It was clear the family were talking about me behind my back. I became (justifiably) paranoid. 'They' must think this is all my fault. Do they not see that I am trying to secure a decent future for me and my son? Do they not understand that it concerns me that I have wages one week and not the next (construction). I am the youngest in the family, I am also the only one who has a child who they do not live with. This is not an easy situation for me to deal with.

Ironically, since I have had to start court proceedings my mum has not stopped going on about what a wonderful father my brother is to his three kids! Which he is! In fact, if I could be half the father he is, my boy would do all right! It just seems a bit insensitive of my mum, (when I'm fighting to see mine), as every time she says he is a wonderful father, it has the implication that I'm not! And it hurts!

I conclude 'fuck the lot of them'! I know what I am doing and why I am doing it. By the time my son is four years old, I will have finished my studies and I will be established in my new career. My son will have a father who is dependable, who does not drink and who has a worthwhile job. The boy will want for nothing! What's more I will have broken the cycle of shit!

Chapter Twenty-Two

The contact centre was situated on the outskirts and in a rundown part of town and held in an equally neglected and drab looking church hall. I was to attend once a fortnight, every other Saturday from 10am till 12. It was suggested that I arrive at least 10 minutes early to avoid the possibility of contact with Ms Peterson, (as she was now referred to). Our son would be handed over to one of the centres volunteers who would then bring my son in to the hall and hand him over to me for our two-hour visit.

I arrived for the first visit early as instructed and gave my name at the front desk. I was then led into the hall and shown a chair against the wall next to an old-fashioned steel radiator under a huge window. At the far end of the hall was a mountain of well-used toys (which brought back memories of me having my tonsils out!) and at the other end of the hall, was a stall set out, selling sweets and drinks, which was manned by another volunteer who could, presumably, keep an eye on things. I looked around the hall at the other men who were also waiting to see their kids, I couldn't help wondering why they were here?

As children started to arrive in the hall, one man in particular stood out from the rest, he was an Asian man with three kids. I recall him standing at one end of a football table, while his children stood huddled together at the other. They looked frightened and made no attempt to go near him, in fact, they cowered away each time he gestured towards them. I didn't like it! Because I didn't know why?

Another man who was with his mother and had decided 'we' were mates, began talking to me. 'I've just got out'a prison and the bitch won't let me see em'! His mother looked embarrassed on his behalf. A few moments later my face lit up when the door opened and a WRVS (women's royal voluntary services) woman entered with my son. Such a happy little boy. It was lovely spending time with him, but the two hours went too quick, again the WRVS woman appeared and took Jack from me and returned him to his mother. She reminded me to wait for a few moments to avoid contact with Louise.

As the weeks rolled past, I noticed that each Saturday I was due to see Jack, I felt sickly, ill almost, as if I had butterflies in my stomach. Slightly worried, I mentioned it to a friend of mine. 'Excitement', he exclaimed! And it was! Sometimes we need to have the obvious pointed out to us!

It was Father's Day at the contact centre. The door opened and in toddled Jack with a huge infectious grin on his face. He looked as pleased as punch as he marched towards me with an outstretched arm, with which he was holding a bag aloft in front of him. The bag contained a Father's Day card which he had scribbled and dribbled on! and an individually wrapped small square of fruit cake with icing on the top! I beamed with delight! I thanked him and hugged him and smothered him in kisses, while noticing he hadn't taken his eyes of the little cake! I opened it and offered it to him and watched in awe as his little hand reached out and completely removed the top halve that contained all the icing, I laughed at his innocence.

When it was time for Jack to go, the WRVS woman commented, that I was the only dad who had received something for Father's Day. To which I replied, 'That's because I'm the only dad who shouldn't be here'! She gave me a little smile and then took Jack back to his mum, while I hung back and waited.

****

September, and I was back at school, literally! Rotherham High was now the local college. It was a strange yet pleasant experience full of nostalgia as I walked around the school that I had left 17yrs earlier! I half wondered if I would stumble across any old school desks with, 'I love Pat Delaney', scrawled across them, something 'I' use to write regularly in an attempt to 'drum up' a bit of interest! But alas... I didn't!

I started the access course fully expecting to be sat at the back of the classroom clueless as to what was going on and feeling out of my depth, but the opposite was true. I was totally engaged from the outset. I loved it. It was refreshing to be using my brain as opposed to my brawn. We did all the core subjects, (Maths, English, etc.), but I particularly enjoyed sociology and psychology. I enjoyed getting stuck into the lively debates, I came alive during these discussions.

There was a disproportionate number of women on the course and it would seem I had caught the eye of one woman in particular. Rachel was tall and slim, attractive, intelligent and had an excellent sense of humour. I remember when she had said, 'Blokes don't like it if you're funnier than them', to which I replied with a smile, 'Shut up and make my dinner'!

I liked Rachel. I enjoyed her company. She always made a point of sitting next to me in class and if someone else had taken 'her' seat, I would catch her giving them dirty looks. I was enjoying the attention but resisted the temptation of taking things any further than friendship. I felt that a relationship, would amount to being disloyal to my son and his mother, it didn't sit right! But still, the flirting continued!

As part of our course work, we studied the human life cycle, and child development. We discussed and studied how children can form secure attachments and bonds with one or more primary care giver! I thought of my mum being annoyed that I had insisted on feeding and changing Jack, and just smiled. In psychology we studied, operant conditioning, punishment and reward, Pavlov's dogs, Skinner's pigeons and Carl Rogers' client centered therapy. I found it interesting, and particularly liked, Rogers' suggestion that for a human being to be truly happy, they needed only two things. Firstly, unconditional love, from a parent or a child perhaps (I have that!) and secondly, they must strive to fulfill their true potential (that's what I'm doing!). He didn't say they had to succeed, they just had to try! I absolutely loved these subjects. It all seemed relevant!

I was enjoying being a student, but I was struggling financially. I had been allowed to keep most of my benefits while studying, which also entitled me to qualify for full legal aid concerning Jack. Plus, I was allowed to work part time (we truly do live in a remarkable country). As a way to compliment my studies and also as a way of earning some much-needed cash I applied for a job as a support worker at a residential care home for adults with learning disabilities. I was interviewed and once all the relevant CRB checks were complete I began working at Bluebell Court. The wages were nothing short of insulting, but for the first time in my life I had taken a job which wasn't all about the money!

Being the only male employed by the care home, I was at first regarded with a 'splash' of suspicion by my predominantly West Indian female co-workers and, as the latter might imply, also as somewhat of a novelty! However, it didn't take long before my warm personality shone through and I was readily accepted as just 'one of the girls'!!!

I loved my new role, it turned out to be the most 'eye opening' and rewarding work I have ever undertaken. I learned about the delicate balance between care and control. I saw at first hand the theory of my studies being implemented into the practicalities of real-life situations.

The residents that made up Bluebell court were all real characters in their own right. They came from all walks of life and were of all different age groups, male and female, and with varying conditions and needs. Each new day, I was surprised by the individual resilience and personality traits displayed in the struggles and victories of each resident.

I knew I wasn't supposed to have favourites, but I couldn't help it! Keiron was 20yrs old and had Autism. He also had an excellent personality. He loved his music and would 'strut' around the house with his headphones on, giving me the thumbs up whenever he saw me and would shout 'Good man Patrick', above the level of his music! He was a good-looking lad and I knew that if he didn't have his difficulties, then he would be the sort of bloke that would probably beat you up and nick your girlfriend! I couldn't help but love him for it!

Sadly, not everyone in Bluebell Court was joyous and free like Keiron. Some were, and I think it's hard to put it any other way, tragic! But even in the most harrowing of cases there is joy, as much as my role would permit, I made it my business to be considerate, kind and caring. I was also mindful that at times I needed to be fair but firm, ...just because you have a disability doesn't mean you can take the piss!

It was during a meeting with the care home manager that I was told of Lorna's story. Lorna was a 31yr old woman with a severe learning disability and a resident at Bluebell Court. She had lived with her doting mother (a single parent) who had brought her up in a safe and loving household environment. Everyone had thought it was cute, when aged sixteen Lorna, announced she had a boyfriend. He too had learning disabilities and some health problems connected to his condition. Everyone cooed when they saw the two love birds together.

At the age of seventeen Lorna's mother took her to the doctors because she was complaining of feeling unwell. The doctor confirmed that Lorna was 6 months pregnant! It had been a shock to all, but, obviously just because Lorna and her boyfriend both had learning disabilities did not mean they were 'void' of the same feelings and desires as any other loved up teenagers. 3 months later, Lorna gave birth to a perfectly healthy little boy. Four months later and while undergoing routine surgery related to his condition, the father of the child died at the age of 19. Lorna's mother continued to care for her and now, her young son, until she too passed away when Lorna was 21yrs old and the boy was only 4.

Social services became involved as there was no one to care for them. As Lorna was not capable of providing the care her son needed, the boy was placed into foster care while she was removed from the only home she had ever known and placed in Bluebell Court. As the boy grew, he also became aware! And as is sometimes the case with the awkwardness of youth, he was embarrassed of his mother! Now aged 14, he would promise to visit and then like most teenage boys, fail to turn up! Leaving Lorna confused, upset and alone whilst trying to deal with feelings and emotions she barely understood! I had a lump in my throat! Walking away from Bluebell Court at the end of an 8 hr shift, it was hard to feel sorry for yourself!

****

Jack, my perfect little boy! Jack's first birthday had come and gone. I had not been allowed to attend his party. Instead my sister had delivered his gifts on my behalf. I had been sober now for more than two years and I liked it. I was enjoying college and my time at

Bluebell Court; it was helping to put things into perspective for me. I was also enjoying the attention I was getting from Rachel, it was very flattering, but still I held firm (although I wasn't sure for how much longer). More importantly my 6-month stint at the contact centre had come to an end, I was relieved. It was now back to court! However, the first port of call was an 'informal' 'chat' with the dreaded Cafcass officer. I was not looking forward to it.

I arrived for the meeting and was relieved to find it was not the horrible woman from before, instead I was 'treated' to a very condescending man dressed in a smart suit. Right from the off, he spoke down to me! 'Now, obviously, 'we' all want to avoid a lengthy and expensive court case'! Well no, actually I don't! 'Right. Now, it says here that you weren't all together happy about attending the contact centre were you, but I think you will agree it was very worthwhile, don't you?'! And then looked directly at me to confirm that he was right! At this point I jumped in and said, 'No, actually I do 'not' agree, it was completely unnecessary and was anything but worthwhile! I am still annoyed that me and my young son had to meet in a fucking church hall, all just to satisfy Ms Peterson's whim! All this has achieved is to stall the process of me gaining the legal recognition and status I need to ensure I am allowed to play an active role in my sons upbringing by six months, because it has become painfully obvious to me that I cannot rely on Miss Peterson's word alone. I was 100% against the contact centre. In fact I only agreed because having studied Bowlby's and Mary Ainsworth's theory's on attachment, I knew that if a strong paternal bond is not formed with in the first two years of the child's life then there is a possibility, it will never form. So where would that leave me? ...Like a long-lost uncle? Well that was a chance I was not willing to take... because I'm his father'!!

The Cafcass officer was shocked and stunned into silence. He looked out of his depth! And then stuttered, '...Did you study

Bowlby, for this case'? His whole demeanour had changed, he was suddenly convinced that I knew more than he and it unsettled him. So I stated, 'Partly for this case, but also as part of my ongoing studies', and then I sat silent and offered no more!

He shifted uncomfortably in his chair and began fidgeting with his tie, it was like he had forgotten Louise was in the room and talked directly and only to me for the rest of the meeting. He was no longer condescending. He stared down at his papers and gently offered, '....and how often would you want to see your son'? 'well obviously I would love it if he lived with me, but that isn't the case. Logic says I would like to have him for 50% of the time but that isn't realistic is it? He will have school and stuff. So, what I would like, ...all I'm asking, is to have my son as much as possible, but without disrupting his day to day living'!

The meeting ended with the Cafcass officer agreeing that I had done all that I could and that the next natural step needed to be a court hearing. Louise never said a word, she did not look happy. As we left, I couldn't wipe the smirk of my face! My college course was really paying dividends! What's more, me and Rachel were going on a date!

Rachel was a breath of fresh air. It was a total contrast to the relationship I had with Louise. For a start it was the first time I had ever meet someone whilst sober! I had not wanted to enter into a relationship with Rachel, due to my belief that it was somehow a betrayal to my little boy; would it imply I didn't care about my son if I embarked on a new relationship? My dilemma was that I felt at ease and comfortable in Rachel's company, I liked her! She wasn't just some bird from the pub! Rachel had picked me up one morning to give me a lift to college. As we drove along chatting about our course work, there was a pause and I asked, 'Will you come out for dinner with me Rachel?' She smiled and said, 'You took your time didn't you, I thought you would never ask'! 'Yes, I would love to come for dinner with you Pat, as you well know'! I placed my hand on her knee and smiled and thought to myself, 'my god she is beautiful'.

The months of flirting, the casual glances across the classroom and the humorous innuendo, that and the simple fact we had actually taken the time to get to know each other, created a super-charged sense of yearning in us both! It was, on my part anyway, a real desire to unravel the shroud of mystery surrounding her. Without intending to, I had in an old-fashioned sense being courting her! As a result, it had made it all the more special, all the more intense. I found her looks, her intellect and her body incredibly alluring. I wanted her. Despite my urgency I remained gentlemanly and respectful, something that would not have happened had I been drinking. Who am I kidding. 'None' of this would have happened if I had been drinking.

We went out for dinner. Sitting opposite her in the restaurant, I could see she had made a real effort. She looked absolutely stunning and seemed to shimmer in the soft candlelight of the restaurant. She was fun to be with. I realised she made me feel good about myself. I felt human again. I had about me a sense of pride that she was sitting in a restaurant with me! Small talk and polite flirtation, neither of us was interested in the meal. We could both feel the tension between us as our hands occasionally brushed each other's across the table, we both knew where the evening was headed.

Our first night together was incredible. She was everything I had hoped for. The first time we embraced and kissed, it was heavenly (divine). We had both waited a long time for it, both imagining what it would be like. She had about her the amazing ability to make me feel incredibly masculine! That night she gave herself to me, allowing me to take charge, her femininity, her vulnerability, heightening the already electric atmosphere in the room. All through the night we explored each other's bodies, all the pent-up desires released without fear of retribution or rebuff. It was spontaneous, it was incredibly passionate, and it was unbelievably hot! At one point during our love-making we were clinched in a passionate embrace, when we both stopped for the briefest of moments and stared directly into each other's eyes, ...and then ...I winked at her!! I will never forget the shear look of delight that washed over her face as she turned her head away and we resumed our frantic endeavours. And so began the best relationship I have ever had! Well ...for the first 12 months anyway.

College was going better than ever, for obvious reasons! We (students) only had a few months left on the course. I was amazed at how much I had learned and how much it had already changed me. Everyone including me was busy agonising over their (university) UCAS application forms. I had decided to do a degree! I had only applied to my local university, being 33yrs old and having a young son, I had no desire for the Uni 'experience' or for living away from home, so I was pinning my hopes (bit of a gamble) on being accepted in the university in my home town. My first choice was the 3yr BSc Hons Social work degree, I would have actually liked to have studied Psychology, but I felt I had more of a realistic chance of finding paid employment, within social work. When I had begun college, I had thought I would like to work with people with alcohol and drug misuse issues, but I had now changed my mind and had set my heart on working in child protection. I was going to be the hero and save all the kids, all the kids, accept my kid that is!

I had surprised myself by doing exceptionally well in my studies. Unlike my family, Rachel saw the worth and recognised the merits in what I was trying to achieve, and so was supportive and encouraged me every step of the way. It was reassuring (and refreshing) to have someone believe in me! I needed someone to believe in me. It was a huge boost for my morale and self-esteem.

Because of all that was going on I decided it was time to leave Bluebell Court. I had mixed feelings. On the one hand it would free up a lot of my time which I could use for studying. On the other hand, I genuinely enjoyed it! It really was the most rewarding work I had ever done. It certainly gave my life and my 'difficulties', perspective. I don't think it was a total coincidence that I had taken a job in a 'caring' capacity when at the same time I had been denied the opportunity (right) to care for my own son! I remember mentioning this to McGillicuddy's brother, Andy, in the pub one night. His eyes became glassy as I spoke about the hurt of being denied, ...and then, I saw that he was crying! It was a bit awkward, but to be fair, he was ...really, ...really ...pissed'!

During my time at Bluebell court I had gained certificates in lifting and handling, non-violent crisis prevention and medicine administration. (I scored 96% on the exam), not bad for a hairy-arsed builder! More importantly I had learned valuable lessons regarding the interaction between service user and service provider. It allowed me the opportunity to apply the theory of the classroom to the practicalities of real life. It truly complimented my studies and put me in good stead for the workplace. On top of this I had met people I would never have had the opportunity to meet, if I had stayed in construction. The whole experience had changed my view of the world I live in, and the part I play in it. I was going to miss Keiron! He was a real star and a joy to be around. A pretty cool geezer! (I must remember to keep him away from Rachel?!).

There was a certain sadness at leaving, too. I was aware that if I was to go back a year later or even ten years later, their lives would not have changed! I realised that in Britain we get the best care available. Not the best care possible! The two being miles apart, but that's just how it is. I was saying my goodbyes to the residents and staff and had popped into Claudia's office (one of the west Indian women) to say 'cheerio'! Claudia was a big, big woman! She was sat in her swivel chair and turned towards me as I entered the room. 'Just wanted to say goodbye Claudia', I said cheerfully. She tilted her head back and looked at me down the length of her nose and said, 'It's a shame you're leaving, you're alright you are Patrick. You know them black girls all like you, you know.... ' She shook her head before adding '....and they don't normally like white blokes'! 'What you leaving for'? I was momentarily lost for words! Claudia, then took on a more serious expression before sucking her teeth and saying, ...'Man if I weren't married, I would wipe the floor with you Patrick'. At a loss as what to do, I smiled and said, 'Well, thank you very much, you're too kind'! I was shocked, I was stunned, was I 'insulted'? (maybe?), I was also a little bit frightened. But most of all, I was 'chuffed'! I couldn't stop grinning! Jesus Christ she would eat me alive!

****

I received a letter from Mr Foley, informing me a date has been set for the first court hearing. The letter warns me not to expect too much from the hearing as it is unlikely to be resolved in one sitting. Despite this I am relieved the ball is finally rolling. The day of the hearing I am dressed smartly in a dark blue suit, shirt and tie. I have polished my shoes and as I check my reflection in the bedroom mirror, I can't help but think of my dad. I arrive at Mr Foley's office prior to the court, so as to go over the details of the hearing.

As I stood in his office I felt 'naturally' nervous! I also felt incredibly embarrassed. Unbelievably I have not yet told, Mr Foley that I am a 'recovering' alcoholic! Until now the subject has not 'really' come up. To make matters worse, I feel I have developed a rapport with Mr Foley and now have the added pressure of not wanting him to think I am a tramp! As Mr Foley prepares some documents to photocopy, I steal myself and say, 'Mr Foley'! 'I think there is something you should know before we arrive at the court. I'm sorry I haven't mentioned it before, but to be honest I'm quite embarrassed about it'. Then, taking a deep breath, I blurt out, ... 'I'm actually a recovering alcoholic. I attend AA meetings (fib), but I have not taken a drink now for over two years (not a fib!). So, she is definitely going to throw it at me, when we get in the court room!' I felt like such a scumbag stood in front of the eloquently spoken and well-educated solicitor. So much so that I could barely meet his eyes! So, it was somewhat of a surprise when Mr Foley said, 'It's quite alright Mr Delaney, I fully understand as 'I' am a recovering alcoholic myself'! And with that he left the room! Well fuck me sideways! What are the chances! I was totally shocked; I can't begin to tell you how much his honesty meant to me. It lifted me beyond belief. I instantly had the utmost respect and admiration for the man. He didn't have to tell me! But he did, and I will never forget him for that! I walked into the court room brimming with a new-found confidence. Louise was already there seated next to her solicitor. I felt nothing when I saw here. I took my place next to Mr Foley (my main man!) and waited for the judge.

When the judge entered the room, we all stood, until he was seated. He was a tall thin man and completely bald. It sounds strange, but he had a heart shaped head which reminded me of an alien! He briefly went over the particulars of the whys and the what fors, as I sat confidently next to Mr Foley. The judge then asked why was the 'absent parent', being denied access. The term 'absent parent' really pissed me off. I had pointed out at every opportunity that I was 'not' absent; I was denied! But no one was interested in what I thought! He directed the question again but this time at Louise. I thought here we go! She didn't even hesitate as she pointed directly at me and in a loud clear voice for all to hear said, ...'he takes drugs'! I was dumbfounded! And before I realised it, I had shouted out, 'No I fucking don't'!

My words 'rang' around the wood panelling of the court room like someone shouting 'hello' into an enormous cave! Everyone knew I was lying, including E.T. Sitting up the front. Which is probably why he banged his gavel at my lewd outburst and said, 'now... now... Mr Delaney'! I saw Mr Foley wince as he looked at the floor. Louise's solicitor told the court I took cocaine and smoked marijuana and as a result, Miss Peterson, did not feel confident that I was responsible enough to have unsupervised access with 'her' son. Mr Foley went to speak, ...but I spoke over him! He was not impressed. I got into a heated debate with the judge, I strongly denied taking cocaine and pointed out, that I was in fact 'teetotal', I asked that he ignore her spiteful comments as there was no truth in them! The judge however pointed out that unfortunately, there was now, an element of 'doubt', so her 'concerns' could not be ignored. He then said, 'So what about the marijuana'? I told him that I did not smoke marijuana, adding, ‘I'm a 33yr old man, I am not saying I have never had a drag on a joint, at say a party for instance. But I am not 'A', ...hippie' (good one?), before adding 'do you ever have a class of wine with your evening meal'? I was going to continue, 'Does that make you an unfit parent'? But the judge shot me down and said, 'Yes... yes... alright Mr Delaney'. He looked pained as he said, 'would you be willing to undergo a drugs test to alleviate miss Peterson's concerns surrounding the allegations of cocaine and marijuana use'? I didn't skip a beat as I said, 'It’s unnecessary, but yes of course, I will do it right now if you like'? Knowing it would never happen like that, you understand!

Then the judge frowned at me, 'Mr Delaney, if I were to order visitation rights at....' he glanced at his papers, '...your mother’s house until such a time as we receive the results from your drug tests... do you promise, 'not' to smoke marijuana for 72 hours before you have your son'? Was I hearing right? Did a judge just ask me to 'promise' not to take illegal drugs! It was my turn to frown at him! However, I instantly recognised the man was trying to do me a favour, so I simply said, 'err... yeah... okay'!

I was pleased I was going to have my son at my mother's house, it was brutal at 'her' mothers house. I didn't feel comfortable, so in turn it did not feel natural. I was also glad Jack was going to be part of my family again, something that was very important to me in light of what had happened to my sister Kathleen.

Once I was back at Mr Foley's office, I apologised for speaking over him in the court room, I hadn't intended to! I just couldn't help myself. He didn't let me off lightly, I knew it had pissed him off, but he was professional enough to let it go.

'So how do I go about taking and... passing a drugs test'? 'well Mr Delaney, it is normally done via a hair sample which is sent for analysis'. 'what drugs, if indeed any, have you taken in the last six months'? I felt a little uncomfortable when I said, 'cocaine and marijuana'! '...and ecstasy'! Mr Foley sat forward in his chair and said, 'I see', before letting out a big sigh, and adding, 'I hear cocaine is very cheap these days'! It sounded almost comical in his posh accent. I slightly grimaced, 'Yeah, about £40 quid a gram!'. There was a pause before I (jokingly) mumbled, 'do you wanna go halves'? There followed an awkward silence as we both pretended, I hadn't said it!

Mr Foley said that due to my short hair style (almost a skin head) if I were to get it cut, it would take three months before I would pass a test. As my birthday was on the horizon, I quickly did the maths and scheduled the drugs test for three months after my blow out! I had my blow out! I smoked as much weed as I could without passing out or being violently sick. I snorted as much cocaine as I could without my eyes popping out and stopped just shy of my head actually imploding! I actually snorted a fair amount of Rachel's arse (legend!), but that's probably a story for another time! I also consumed as much MDMA as I could without either bursting into flames, hugging myself to death or winning the world Gurning championships! Then on the 8th of April, I stopped! Nothing passed my lips or was consumed by me for the next three months which could jeopardise the drugs test. It was a painful, long, drawn out three months.

Although I had long-since had or even wanted an alcoholic drink, I hadn't actually had a sober day in my life. One way or another I had always had something, usually a joint of an evening, or of a morning if I didn't have Jack or college. So, this was new territory for me! Stone cold sober!! it was difficult. The hardest thing for me to deal with was my resentment towards Louise. I wasn't even with her. I didn't live with my son, but I am not 'allowed' to share a joint in the privacy of my own home with my new girlfriend, because my new relationship has conditions imposed on it, by my old one! I remember a dangerous thought entering my head. 'Alcohol is not illegal'! I quickly quashed the idea, acknowledging it for what it was, 'ridiculous', but not illegal. The truth was I liked not drinking!

I continued to see my son at my mother's house every Saturday. I love that little boy so much. He was an absolute joy. He had a wonderful temperament and a confident ease about him, plus he was always smiling. I was never happier than when I was with Jack. It didn't matter how my day or week had been or how I was feeling, as soon as I saw him, I was immediately lifted. Watching him toddling around the place and noticing the little character developing within him, I was thankful to be a part of it!

****

My college course was coming to an end, and almost everyone had attended interviews for their respective universities, except me! I hadn't even heard anything back! I was becoming increasingly worried; what if I don't get offered a place? I had worked hard and had given it my all, especially in light of all that was going on in my personal life. Rachel had her interview and had received an offer for a place on the social work degree course. I was really pleased for her, she was a bright girl, she too had worked hard and deserved it. She assured me not to worry, 'You will be alright, I'm sure you will get in, there is still plenty of time'. Her facial expression said otherwise; she was just as concerned as I was! I had all but given up hope when finally, I received a letter from the university inviting me to attend an interview day!

On the day, I had to write an 800-word essay on a well-documented child protection case. I had to take part in a group discussion with 14 other, potential candidates, and I was also interviewed by two senior social workers. It was all so important to me that I had prepared well for the interview process. When it was all over, I felt as though I had done all that I could, and I would now just have to wait and see! It is no surprise then that I was over the moon to receive a letter the 'very next day' from the university. It read: 'Due to your strong performance at interview yesterday we are taking the unusual step of making you an unconditional offer, regardless of the outcome of your current studies. We therefore hope you accept our offer and look forward to seeing you in the coming September'! I couldn't have been happier, Rachel was quick to point out that nobody else had been made an 'unconditional' offer!

My three-month forced abstinence from everything 'good' was up. The drugs test was conducted in Mr Foley office by a representative from the drug testing company. Due to the legality of the test, the representative informed me of every obvious step of the process. He put on a pair of white gloves and said, 'I will now extract a single strand of hair from your scalp using these scissors', he showed me the scissors! 'I will then place that single strand of hair into this small envelope, before sealing the envelope and sending it off for analysis. Do you agree to continue'? 'I do'. He then said, 'Okay, can you now confirm that the envelope is empty'. With this, he held the envelope aloft with his white gloved hand, between his thumb and finger and gently squeezed, so the envelope opened, allowing me to see inside. 'Yes, I confirm the envelope is empty', with this I let out a little sigh and looking at Mr Foley said, 'He thinks he's fucking Paul Daniels'! Mr Foley burst out laughing! And in his posh accent said, 'yes, it is quite like a magic trick isn't it'! No sooner had the hair been plucked from my head and sealed in the little envelope, I stood up and said, 'Are we done'? When it was agreed that we were, I legged it out of Mr Foley's office and back to my room above the pub. On arrival, Rachel was there to meet me. 'How did it go'? She enquired. 'No time Rachel', I said grinning, as I brushed passed her and made my way into the room. She followed me in and closed the door, as she observed me making my way to the mirror on the mantlepiece. I placed my hand behind the mirror and extracted a bag of cocaine, a bag of weed and a joint that I had pre-rolled that morning! I sat down in the office chair in front of my computer table, opened the bag of cocaine and set out two fat lines of coke, one for me and one for Rachel, and then snorted them both! Arghhh! 'Sorry Rachel' I said grinning and rubbing my nose before setting out two more. I felt an instant buzz as the cocaine entered my system. It was probably the best line of coke I have ever had. I sat back and picked up the joint, stuck it between my lips and as I lit it, inhaled, taking deep long drawn out puffs. I felt my whole body begin to melt as I relaxed for the first time in three months! As I smoked the rest of the joint, Rachel performed a sex act on me, I wished I could have stayed in that moment forever! I contemplated just how utterly amazing she was, before smiling to myself and thinking, I'm none too shabby 'meself'!!

It had been a crazy few months, a lot of amazing things were happening to me. Not least, that I had decided to forgive Louise! I know that sounds incredibly lofty of me, almost pious, 'I forgive you'! But it was true! I didn't just think it, I meant it! In fact, I felt it with every fibre of my being, it was like I had shed something. I was tired of carrying around all that hate and anger, it was starting to do me in. Perhaps I had simply ran out of steam! All I know is, it was real and I felt lighter for it, unburdened!

Perhaps I had never 'really' hated her at all, it is after all a very strong word. I think I may have had hate and anger confused. I still didn't believe I had deserved the treatment I had been given, but nor did I believe she had ever intentionally set out to hurt me, not really. We were just two people caught up in something that was extremely difficult to handle. I have my issues just like she has hers. I sometimes think my alcoholism has been a convenient smoke screen for her own shortcomings! This may sound like I have an unbelievable cheek, especially in light of all that 'I' have been! But she was a shit girlfriend. However, it is becoming perfectly clear that she 'is' a fantastic mother. For that I count my lucky stars.

I passed the drugs test. Mr Foley scheduled the next court date. A little over a month after having the hair pulled out of my head I was back in the court room. This time I was calmer, I was more composed, I did not speak over Mr Foley, instead I allowed him to do his job. The judge summed up; I had done all that had been required of me. The contact centre had reported that I had not missed any of the scheduled appointments, I had been persistently punctual, and I had adhered to all conditions imposed at the centre. My drug test results showed no evidence of any drug use whatsoever! Mr Foley told the court that I was in fact teetotal and was currently studying for a social work degree at the local university. He therefore saw no reason why I should not be granted a section eight court order, which would grant me the same level of parental responsibility as the child's mother, he also added that I only wished to play an active part in my sons upbringing and did not wish to disrupt or infringe on the loving relationship the child already enjoyed with his mother.

The judge awarded me the section 8 court order! It had taken almost two years of stress and heart ache to get the legal recognition that I believed had been mine all along! I now had parental responsibility! I was also now allowed to have unsupervised access, including overnight stays and a provision was also made so that I could attend the local registrar's office (on my own!) and have my name added to my son's birth certificate.

This did not change the fact that my son did not have my surname, something that had pained me very much when I first realised this was to be the case. However, it didn't really matter to me anymore. His name had no bearing on how I felt about him, he was my son and I loved him regardless of what ever title he had. I was glad it was finally over. It had been a very difficult time (for all involved!), at a time when, having addressed my alcohol problem, I had hoped life was going to be all rosy and nice! I had hoped my life would be easy now alcohol was out of the equation. It wasn't easier, but it was a whole lot better, I was a proud father, and now I had the same rights as any other dad! I now looked forward to having my son for the whole weekend, not just a limiting couple of hours! I was looking forward to putting him to bed and reading him a bedtime story, and checking on him throughout the night, and being there when he woke up to make him his breakfast in the morning. I was looking forward to all the normal stuff that fathers and sons do.

My family and friends and of course Rachel who had supported me all the way, were pleased for me. My mother hugged me, and said, 'You won'! I smiled politely, as at the same time, my heart sank. Yes, it was a good outcome, it was the rightful outcome. But I was painfully aware that there were no winners!

The first full weekend with my son was a very special occasion for me. For the first time since he had been born, I had felt like a proper dad! No conditions, just me and my boy. My mum being old Irish and well meaning, did her best to take over. After all I had been through there was no way I was going to let that happen, even if she did think me ...a bit of a Maggie!

****

Do you want my egg? I think most families have silly little traditions that are perhaps exclusive to that family and are passed down through the generations! Nearly every child that has ever stayed at my mother's house has enjoyed the morning ritual of the boiled egg and toast for breakfast! Each child, including me, has had the age-old trick, 'Do you want my egg', played on them.

Having eaten your boiled egg, you turn the empty shell upside down and place it back in the egg cup, then you offer it to the adult next to you, they say 'thank you' and then tap the top of the empty shell with their spoon and feign surprise when it is discovered the egg is empty, 'wh.....at'! much to the delight of the young child!

I played the same age-old trick with Jack, as my mother played along. He thought it was hysterical! Me and my mum both smiled at his innocence! I was happy. I was glad. My mum told me her father use to play the same trick on her! In turn she had played it on me when I was a child and now, I was passing it on to Jack, aware that one day he would do the same with his kids! I wondered for how long in our family, had the egg joke been runny, (ha-ha!). For years to come at breakfast, Jack would always offer me his egg! It may seem silly. But it's the little things that matter.

When a child is conceived, technically you become a parent! But the truth is you know nothing about parenting! Instead the child guides you, you learn to respond to the child's needs and wants, the child teaches you to be a parent! Jack taught me so much, so many lessons. I learned (or maybe it just came naturally) to love unconditionally. I have been for ever grateful. I feel truly blessed.

CHAPTER TWENTY-THREE

I PASSED MY COLLEGE COURSE WITH FLYING COLOURS; it would seem I was not the 'fuck wit' dinosaur I had imagined myself to be! They were exciting times indeed. I know it wasn't Oxford or Cambridge, but for someone like me to be going to university felt like a momentous achievement. I was the only one in my family to do so and, after all I had been through, I was quite proud of myself. I had even brought myself a little satchel for my books (bless!). I now knew with the utmost conviction that my future was bright; everything was suddenly within reach. There was great change afoot.

It had been all over the news that America was set to get its first black president, some Irish bloke called, Ba, rock Obe-ma-he, or was it, Ba-rick 0-bar-he. I'm not sure, because no one could yet, pronounce his name properly! And if that wasn't exciting enough, the town I grew up in was set to get its first, pot smoking, cocaine snorting, recovering alcoholic social worker! Now a full time 'mature' student, I was no longer on benefits. Instead I had bursaries and student loans to live on, plus occasionally I got cash in hand (building) work during the 'school holidays'! Everything seemed to be falling into place. My life wasn't just good, it was fucking excellent! So much so I think it scared me a little!

I noticed my friends were treating me differently too, with a newfound respect that had been missing when I was a hopeless drunk! I enjoyed my new status. Rachel was still treating me like a king, and I loved it.

Did I love her? I think I did. I was just perhaps a little reluctant to drop my guard and show it. Once bitten, twice shy or so they say! I think Rachel thought she had hit the relationship jackpot! I was (for once) a proper man! Someone she could count on. I was thoughtful, I was caring and attentive. I was dependable! I think the fact that I didn't drink was refreshing for her, too. There was no, 'I was just out with the lads' or 'I will be home in a minute'. I was her man! And she adored me for it. She was happy! I truly felt comfortable around her; there was no pretence. I began to spend a lot of time at her house, almost but not quite moving in! The wildness of living above the pub had been curtailed by my true admiration and unfaltering respect for Rachel. We had a great relationship! I had been honest with Rachel from the beginning, I had held nothing back. I felt like there was a real connection between us.

I wasn't smoking as much pot as I use to, but we both enjoyed our weekend coke sessions! We would talk and fool around, laughing non-stop into the early hours. Cocaine also made us incredibly rampant and horny and became a regular and integral part of our love making, which I have to say was 'fucking' great, ...in the beginning at least! As time passed, I became aware that she was a bit more into the cocaine than I was! It was still good, ...but It changed things!

Almost overnight, Louise stopped being awkward! It was a noticeable, welcome, and instant difference. Silently, I wondered if she had conceded some newfound respect for me as Jack's father. Had she come to realise that there was no ulterior motive, I just wanted to see my son? I don't know!

All I know is, it registered that she was being different. I never once questioned it! I just went with it. It was, after all, all I had ever wanted! It would seem the fight was over.

The good life! I had a great relationship with Jack. Louise had 'softened'. Rachel adored me, and my mother was struggling to pick fault! I had fought for my rights and for those of my son, and they had been upheld. My successes, my studies and my work placements were changing me. I was fast becoming a new (professional) person. I certainly hadn't turned my back on any of my good friends or old work mates, but I now spent most of my days mixing with academics and intellectuals. Now 'a respectable man', I became guarded about the 'ugliness' of my past and wished to leave it exactly where it was.

I had completed my first year of university. It had been hard work; we had been warned that the course content had been designed to be thought provoking and challenging and would no doubt lead to a fair amount of introspection (soul searching!). As a result, not only had I learned a lot about social work practice, but I had also learned a lot about self! I was finding answers to questions I hadn't even thought to ask! To enhance our understanding, there was often suggested reading titles. One such book (which I loved!), forced me to consider my own childhood and subsequent transition into 'troubled' adulthood! The book was called *Counselling for Toads,* by Robert de Board (a pastiche of *The Wind in the Willows* by Kenneth Graeme). The author explained the process of transactional counselling and explored the theory of 'The Actual Child and The Adjusted Child'!

The adjusted child (toddler?) would perhaps like to run around whopping, shouting and creating havoc, but can't. It must adhere to the conditions imposed by its care giver/s! The 'actual' child is subdued and shrinks back, all but losing its voice, into the 'adjusted' child, who in turn learns to quash and quell its wants and needs, so it no longer develops (grows) as it 'naturally' might!

I couldn't help thinking of my younger years as a small boy, my own wants and needs were often overshadowed by the chaos and drama of my parents' relationship. Hadn't I quickly learned to 'accept' and be quiet! Don't make a fuss, because mum is upset, keep quite because dad is hungover! Be a good boy and play quietly! Hadn't I learned at a young age to internalise my own feelings so as not to offend my dad or upset my mum? A happy and contented child who is always smiling, in the midst of violence and chaos! A house full of angry adults. What of my own anger? Stifled, hushed and internalised to the point I can barely acknowledge it. Sulking is a form of anger! 'Fuck this, I'm off to the pub, that'll show em'! Isn't that silent anger / resentment?

Of course, like any form of study, you must try and remain objective. The temptation to (seek) pick out the bits that fit, can be overwhelming! However, it made sense to me! The author also discussed the three states of being (mind), Parent, Adult and Child! All human beings (except maybe psychopaths!), share the same set of emotions and feelings. And whilst experiencing these emotions / feelings we can 'flit' between, Parent, Adult and child (sometimes within seconds we can be all three).

The child state: this is perhaps when we feel sorry for ourselves: 'It's so unfair?' We maybe stroppy; we may sulk. Equally we may be playful! Parent: this is when we are critical of others, we can be righteous; perhaps telling others what they should or shouldn't do. The Adult state: is the only one, where we can grow, evolve and learn. It is the state of 'being' where we are practical, methodical and reasonable. I think my mum (quite naturally) spends most of her 'being' in parent state. She is always critical of others, especially me (isn't that so unfair!?). Continually telling me what I should or shouldn't do! 'If only you did this or that, 'then' you would be okay'! I have (secretly) long-since harboured the idea that my own alcohol problems, my addiction, is in fact a childlike response to issues I either do not fully understand or cannot fully control. That isn't to dismiss 'mine' or anybody else's addictions as 'silliness', because it's not! It's the opposite, it's very serious and its real. However, I can only deal with my issues when I remove myself from the parent or child state of being and endeavour to remain in the adult state, of clear thinking, practicality, reasonability and methodical problem solving. Which is easier said than done! Its no-good feeling sorry for myself and sulking!

Although I have long since stopped going to AA meetings, mainly because I decided 'they' weren't really my type of people, I am reminded of something from the AA literature:

'Self-knowledge prevailed us nothing'!

CHAPTER TWENTY-FOUR

I HAD EVERYTHING I WANTED, THERE WERE NO PROBLEMS, there were no issues. In fact, life could not have been better. It was a Saturday morning and I had just woken up in Rachel's bed, I looked over at her side of the bed and saw that she was already up, I could now hear her pottering about downstairs in the kitchen. Sitting up I swung my legs over the side of the bed and sat motionless for a moment, staring at my feet, and then I decided I was going to do it!

I had been sober for three years, three months, two weeks and so many days! In a few moments of waking up I had reasoned that if I could go that long without a drink, then surely, I could have a few pints on a Saturday and then leave it alone for another three years. After all I have just proved I could do it. I got dressed, headed downstairs and told Rachel I was going out! 'Where you going'? She asked. 'The pub'! I announced over my shoulder.

I walked to the nearest pub and once inside ordered myself a pint of Guinness! Like an out of body experience, it was surreal! That morning as I had sat on the edge of the bed, I did not once consider the consequences of my actions. Nor, I am ashamed to admit, did I consider the impact it would have on my son. It would seem the desire to take a drink had come from nowhere, straight out of the blue. If you had asked me why I did it, I would have been unable to tell you. I took my pint of Guinness over to a secluded table in the corner of the bar and sat staring at it for what seemed like an eternity, but in reality, was probably no more than a couple of seconds. What was I thinking? The truth is I wasn't! I wouldn't allow myself too! I picked up the pint glass and held it to my lips,

I then took a big gulp, draining a third of the glass before smacking my lips. I instantly felt a dull like ache across my shoulders as the alcohol entered my body. If it took me 10 minutes to drink that first pint, then I would say that's how long it took to completely destroy everything I had and all I had worked for. I drank two more pints and by then I had stopped caring! I made my way into the town centre, going from pub to pub, drinking like a mad man. I just couldn't get it down me quick enough. After all I had three years to make up for! Within two hours I was so drunk I could barely stand up, nor could I stop smiling and that's because I am an alcoholic!

I stayed out all day. What I did and were I went I have no idea. Late that night I returned to Rachel's house completely wasted. To make matters worse I wrongfully thought I was in the bathroom and took a piss standing in the middle of her living room! 'mum...., mum... he's pissing'! shouted Rachel's teenage son.

Remarkably I was not in trouble with Rachel, in fact she found the whole episode hilarious. She had never known, or seen, 'her Pat', drunk before. And despite my admissions, despite my honesty, she didn't really believe I was an alcoholic! The next morning, I woke up in Rachel's bed. I had an overwhelming feeling of dread come over me. I knew I had spectacularly fucked up! I also had a rip-roaring hang over. News travels fast! Word had quickly gotten around that 'Pat' was back on the drink. So fast in fact that I was barely out of bed when my phone rang. It was Jim, I could hear the excitement in his voice, 'You been on the beer, Pat? Is it alright if I come round'?

The whole thing was bizarre, it was like I had woken up famous! (or infamous!). Rachel couldn't stop smiling and saying how funny I had been the night before and when Jim arrived, he was grinning from ear to ear. I told him I had a bad head and wouldn't mind going for a couple, 'You know just hair of the dog'! 'Of course, Pat, why wouldn't ya'! agreed Jim happily. Was I being praised? My God they haven't got a clue! In the pub Jim told me how he was glad I had taken a drink, because he never thought I was an alcoholic anyway. He seemed pleased with me, like he had got his old friend back. Before adding, 'You were alright until you meet 'her' Pat. She fucked you up'!

I couldn't look at him. He was obviously referring to Louise. He was also totally wrong. Louise had not been the cause of my problems. It's true my attempt to settle down with Louise had brought 'my' problems to the surface, ...and for all to see. I stayed quiet, I let it slide and I said nothing! Why would Jim, Rachel or anybody else for that matter understand. I was the one with the problem and I didn't understand! But what I did know, what I did understand perfectly well, was that this was serious, this was bad. I am fucked!

Jim was never much of a drinker. After two pints he made it clear that it was time for him to go. During his company I had pretended to be a bit blasé about the drinks in front of me. Just a couple I had said. I already knew it wasn't enough. 'You might as well drop me off in town Jim', I said nonchalantly as we were leaving. He looked at me a little miffed. 'Fuck it, I'm out now', I smiled.

I don't recall much of the rest of that day. Again, I drank like a mad man, hitting the top shelf quite early! I got insanely drunk, and arrived at Rachel's house late that night, again barely able to stand. I don't think she found it quite as funny as she had the previous evening! And the next night, well that just wasn't funny at all. It wasn't fair on her. It would seem I was now a binge drinker! 3 days (and nights) seemed to be the standard length of a session or spree, although there were occasions when it stretched to as many as 8 days straight. When I was on it, I would wake up, drink, pass out, wake up and drink. I would do this until I could physically take no more, or I had run out of funds.

Hindsight is indeed a wonderful thing, whenever I think back to that time in my life, I whole heartedly wish, that after I had taken that first drink I had done the decent thing and phoned Rachel, ...to tell her how truly sorry I was. To tell her that I had made a terrible mistake and I wouldn't be able to see her any more, its over! That's what a man would have done, but I didn't. Instead I clung onto her apron strings for the next two years and very nearly pulled the poor girl down with me.

And what of Louise and Jack? Had Louise been right all along, was this what she had expected? Was this what she had been waiting for? Had she been right to try and prevent me from being a part of 'her' sons' life? Had I mis-judged her? The truth was I just didn't know any more. True to form I said nothing. I did what I had always done. I put a brave face on it and kept my thoughts and feelings to myself.

I no longer had work to contend with, all I had to do, was make it to class and sit upright and I struggled with even that. Poor Rachel was blissfully unaware of how bad things really were. I started spending less time at her house and more time above the pub in an attempt to hide the amount I was drinking. As for Louise, I told her nothing of my relapse. I couldn't, I was scared she might stop me seeing Jack. I was already in a very delicate state. I would not have been able to cope with losing my son. Because I was binge drinking, I managed to stay sober when it was my weekend to have Jack. I did my best to protect him from my alcoholism, and always tried to create a happy and welcoming environment during his visits. However, it didn't stop the feelings of guilt and remorse. I could barely look Louise in the eye, in fact I struggled to look anyone in the eye; I felt like a total loser. I thought, if someone were to look into my eyes.... then they would see 'it' in me! I would be found out.

****

One Friday afternoon after lectures, me and Rachel were having a drink together in a pub across from the university, when my phone started ringing, when I looked at the screen I saw Louise's number. I immediately panicked, as I didn't want her knowing I was in the pub so I ran outside before answering. Louise was very matter of fact, as she said, 'I'm having a party for Jack's 2nd birthday tomorrow in St Anne's church hall, you can come if you like'. I was momentarily stunned. I was also over the moon. I had not been welcome at his first party and had assumed I would not be welcome at his second. I immediately got excited and started saying, 'Yeah, of course I would love to! Look I will pay for the hall and the cake and th....'. Louise cut across me, stopping me dead, and said 'No'! 'I don't want you to, we will be cutting the cake at four, you can come then'. And hung up!

Confused. I stood in the street outside the pub trying to understand what had just happened. I had gone from being really excited to totally deflated. It was like someone had held their arms out, open wide and with a big smile on their face, suggesting I was about to get a big hug. But when I step forward, instead of a hug I get an almighty slap around the face! I was hurt. I walked back inside the pub and told Rachel what had just happened. 'Fuck that! Get there at two, all kids parties start at two'! That's what I loved about Rachel!

The phone call had changed my mood. Of course, I was glad I was going to the party. Although it stung a bit that I wasn't good enough to go to all of it, still I wasn't truly welcome, still I was being kept on the side lines. I was 'quietly' very angry about it. Louise had really pissed me off! Rachel sensed I was upset about it, although I had not said as much, so she decided to go home. I on the other hand decided to stay out and drown my sorrows. Needless to say, I was out for the rest of the day. And of course, I got paralytic drunk. I remember going from pub to pub, telling anyone who would listen, just how hard done by I was and generally misunderstood.

It must have been around about closing time that I found myself on the opposite side of town in a particularly rough boozer. An altercation had occurred between two men outside the pub leaving one man with a broken jaw. Within minutes there were police crawling all over the place! It had absolutely 'nothing' to do with me but being very drunk and still angry from Louise's phone call earlier, I decided to tell the police 'I' was not happy with 'their' poor handling of the situation. Adding that as professionals they should know better! It is no surprise then, that they told me to shut up and fuck off! I cringe now just thinking about it. It was the red rag I had obviously been looking for. I became aggressive and verbally abusive and have a vague recollection of whipping a police car door open and telling the driver he was a 'fucking cunt'!

As you would expect, I was promptly and rightfully arrested, bundled into the back of a van and driven to the station. I must have been a bit of a handful, because the next thing I remember is standing with my hands cuffed behind my back outside a police cell, whilst surrounded by five police officers. I was still being abusive when one of the officers said, 'Right, we need to take your jacket. Okay, we are going to take your jacket ...now'. To which I replied, 'No', '.... you're fucking not'. I was being incredibly cantankerous and hostile, and for no reason at all, ... I decided to do a 'runner'!

Where I thought I might have been going, I have no idea! I must have taken all of half a step, before being pounced on by five very pissed off coppers. I rather embarrassingly, remember putting up an almighty struggle before landing face down on the concrete floor of the police cell, my main concern being my 'bubble of snot' might burst. One of the officers then applied a pressure point behind my ear with a single finger! It hurt like fuck, and what's more I deserved it. Had it been the seventies! Pat Delaney would have got a kicking for sure! 'Alright... alright, I fucking give up... you cunts', I snarled in defeat. Within a split second the handcuffs were off, I heard the cell door slammed shut behind me, leaving me alone, laying face down on the floor like a demented animal! At some point I must have fallen asleep.

I awoke the next morning totally ashamed, full of remorse and sober as a judge. I could not have been more apologetic as I was charged with drunken/disorderly and abusive and threatening language (I didn't know the last bit was actually a criminal offence, I thought it was, well ..just out of order!) and to make matters worse (and probably because I had been such an arsehole!), they didn't let me out until 11 am, and I had to be at Jack's party for two!

I had brought Jack a 'shake 'n' Go' Scalextric for his birthday. I was still severely hungover and full of remorse when I arrived at the little church hall for his party. Would everyone know what I had done? Would everyone know that I had just got out of the police station? Apart from a few members of Louise's immediate family, I did not know anyone at the party. Feeling completely dishevelled, but hoping no one had noticed, I stood alone in the corner of the hall. I was a stranger at my own son's birthday party. I felt like all the mums were looking at me and thinking, 'Who's he! Jack was oblivious to me being there; he was dressed as a pirate and had a drawn-on pencil moustache! I watched him, excitedly running around with all the other kids and felt a pang of overwhelming pride followed by an even more overwhelming feeling of loss! I didn't feel a part of anything. In fact, I had never felt so removed, so detached. I had never felt so worthless and low in all my life. I have always loved my son. I love him more than life itself. From the moment Louise told me she was pregnant, I loved him. I love him with all my heart, I knew he deserved better. Despite this I couldn't wait for the party to be over. I desperately wanted (needed) to leave. I needed another drink.

****

I had a bad dream. There was total silence. I was standing on the middle of a frozen white pond. I was perfectly still, and then I heard a faint noise from beneath my feet and then total silence again. The same silence you get after a particularly heavy snow fall. I didn't move a muscle, and then I heard it again, 'crack'. I looked down, just under my foot, a small black line appeared. Motionless, I watched in bewilderment, as it started to grow, moving away from me! Then again there was the complete silence. I looked about me with only my eyes, scared that if I moved my head I might.... Another crack appears and then another! Still more appear accompanied by the same familiar 'crack...crack.... crack! All of them begin to speed up, as they grow faster and faster away from me. I brace myself knowing it is only a matter of time. I am full of fear!

****

I asked Rachel to take my cash point card as I didn't feel I could be trusted. Her response crushed me. 'I don't want to be with a man who can't look after his own money'. She looked horrified that I had even asked. I was immediately embarrassed, I remember thinking to myself, 'For God's sake... help me', but I didn't say it, I didn't want to look that weak, instead I turned, walked out of the room, slammed the front door behind me and headed to the nearest pub. Fuck em all!

I was surprised by how quickly my drinking had gotten out of hand. It was not so much the amount I was drinking, rather what happened 'when' I was drinking that was the problem! Every time I took a drink it was pure potluck how it ended up. I was arrested a couple of more times in quick succession. I was worried the university would find out. One of the arrests resulted in a caution for battery and possession of a class C drug. Not really the end of the world! Unless you're a student social worker! It sounded much worse than it actually was, I looked up the definition of battery in the dictionary it means 'menacing touch'! I was losing control and I was devastated! I told Pompidou and his wife Hazel, about my latest arrest and subsequent caution. Simón said that he had heard that around 10% of law students, do something stupid on a night out while at university resulting in an arrest and as a result cannot practice law! Simón's wife said I should say nothing to the Uni and get my degree! 'Once you have it, they can't take it back off you'!

It was very good advice! The trouble being it was also a total head fuck. Arghhhh!!! A struggling alcoholic, studying for something he will probably not be able to practice once he graduates! It was all too much! Four months after taking the first drink, university was over for me! I ran away, too ashamed to tell the lecturers why I would no longer be attending! It was a spectacular fall from grace. There was no doubt in my mind that I was in fact a complete failure. A loser of the highest order!

And on top of all this, me and Rachel were struggling, or rather Rachel was struggling to save our relationship. We were still doing a lot of cocaine, something that had started off as great fun, but had now become something else, resulting in 'no' fun and relentless arguments! Cocaine changed her, she seemed to like it a bit too much! I became worried about her, I felt responsible, but if I tried to talk to her she became defensive and hurtful with her remarks. And yet still she tried to save our relationship. The poor girl was fighting a losing battle because I had already given up. I was having an affair with alcohol! I was lying about it, I was staying out late and making excuses for it, I was covering my tracks concerning the amount of money I was spending on it, I even smartened myself up, if I was going out to indulge in it! It was nothing short of a full-blown love affair. I put alcohol above all else.

Now that university was over, I needed to pay my way. I had a word with Jim, and it was agreed I could work back out on site with him and another lad called Lance, what's more I could start on the Monday. I was pleased I had good news and told Rachel of my plans, 'realistically, I can earn about £400 a week', I beamed, whilst feeling very pleased with myself! However, I felt chided when she said, 'That's not enough! You would need to earn double that'!

On the Monday morning, Jim and Lance, picked me up as promised and from the moment I got in the car we didn't stop laughing, all day the jokes and gags flowed! It actually done me the world of good, I was on familiar ground, it was nice not to have to mind my P's & Q,s, and it was a relief not to have the pressures of studying weighing heavy on my mind. It was good to be one of the 'boys' again! I realised I hadn't laughed so much in years. Unfortunately, due to all the clowning around, on average I only earned about £400 per week! 'Fuck you Rachel'!

On the plus side I think (secretly) Rachel, liked seeing me in my work boots and ripped jeans!! Working was doing me good, my head started to clear, I began to think straight, I felt better, things were actually starting to look up! And then Rachel dropped the bomb shell.... 'She's pregnant'! I wish I could say I was pleased. I wish I could say poor Rachel received the same big grin that Louise had got when she had told me her good news. The truth was it frightened me! I was already struggling with all that was going on. I wasn't sure how 'I' would cope! I am not a heartless man, I hugged Rachel and told her everything would be alright. The truth being she was just as worried as I was! Rachel was not a fool; she knew I was struggling too!

I wondered what affect it would have on Jack. So far, he had me all to himself. Is it better that his father is single, or is it healthier that his father is part of a family unit and Jack becomes part of that unit too? I didn't know! It took a while for the realisation that I was to be a father again to sink in. But I soon came around, I even began to like the idea. It was also the first time that I had truly considered that I was going to spend the rest of my life with Rachel. We would get married and make a proper go of things, no more silliness! I actually began to feel quite optimistic about 'our' future. So, I decided I needed to reign myself in, lay off the recreational drugs and curb my drinking, just like I had at other crucial moments in my life, ... but I didn't! I tried, I tried really hard! But the more I tried, the more it seemed, I just couldn't do it!

I was on my way to work in the car with Jim and Lance, when I decided to tell them the good news, 'Guess what lads'? (I slightly paused for effect!), '...Rachel's pregnant'! It hung in the air for a second before Jim shot me a look of pleasant surprise as a massive schoolboy-like grin erupted across his face! 'Fucking hell' he sniggered, 'so is Nicola'!! It was my turn to look surprised as an equally massive grin manifested itself across my face! I couldn't believe it! Then Lance sitting in the back made some sort of involuntary gurgle, before he trumped us both as he roared, 'FUCKING HELL'!!, 'you ain't going to believe this, ... but so is Alice'!!! All three of us were stunned into a moment's silence, before we sent up a massive cheer in the car, 'Weh woohoo'!!! And then we all burst out laughing in childish disbelief! 'Fucking hell', I said, 'Have they all been working on checkout 9 in Asda or something'! What are the fucking chances of that!!!

****

Me and Rachel discovered we were having a boy! We decided we would call him, Thomas. 9 months later Jim and Nicola had a little girl, they called her Lilly Rose! Lance and Alice also had a little girl they called her Phoebe. Me and Rachel were no longer together, she had miscarried, I wasn't there when she lost the baby. I am ashamed to tell you I was drunk and laying in the gutter.

When it had mattered the most, I wasn't there. There were no comforting words, no shoulder to cry on and no offers of support! It was the ultimate betrayal. It was simply unforgivable. Rightfully, I hated myself! There were no words to express my shame and guilt. Still I desperately clung on for dear life, desperately trying to salvage something from the wreckage of my existence. I had not meant to betray Rachel! Despite my attempts to do the right thing, I could see everything disintegrating before my very eyes.... until I was left with nothing.

It didn't end with a bang. There was no blazing row. No fireworks. That's not how our relationship ended. Instead it was, on her part, the quiet realisation that 'I' was no longer worth fighting for. She had simply had enough. I had made it impossible for her to respect me as a man, let alone a man that she had once loved. Her 'Pat' was nothing more than a helpless child. In a last bid ditch attempt to be rid of me, she lent me the money for a deposit on a flat near the town centre! It was in a deprived area full of run-down bedsits, housing, down on their luck single men! It was excruciatingly embarrassing having to accept her offer of help, after everything I had put her through, but it was that or the street. I was so ashamed. Even though she had every right, she didn't hate me. In fact, she was very good about it all, albeit in a detached and matter of fact way.

She even helped me move. She helped me settle in, like I was an old friend and nothing more. An old friend that she would not be keeping in touch with! Once I was in and everything was done, I thanked her and feebly tried to offer some form of an apology. I can see her now, standing in the doorway. Her parting words could have been something along the lines of, 'You're a cunt and I fucking hate you'! 'You selfish prick; do you realise what you have put me through'? 'I hope you have a shit life'! Instead she said, 'I feel sorry for you Pat'! And walked out the front door and out of my life for ever.

As soon as the door shut, I felt the loneliness close in around me. Like a child sitting alone in the dark, it was more than I could bare! So, I marched to the nearest shop, brought a bottle of whisky and some cans and then sat drinking alone in an empty flat. That night I cried myself to sleep in wanton self-pity.

****

I sat motionless in the bath. Legs out straight, back arched and my head bowed forward. My hands clasped together just under the water line. I did not create a single ripple on the perfectly still water as I watched the swirls of steam rising. I was deep in thought. I was done for. There is no hope for a man like me! Louise and now Rachel! Three years of hard work, all that effort for nothing. What have I got to offer? I felt a tightness in my chest. What about my beautiful little boy, who deserves so much more than a father like me. Rachel's parting words raced around my mind, 'I feel sorry for you'. I would have preferred it if she had been angry, if she had been abusive and had screamed obscenities at me. The worst thing was, I knew she had meant it, she did feel sorry for me. Her pity was soul crushing, I don't want to be pitied! The bath water has gone cold.

All I had left was Jack! He was the only constant in my life, he was the only one in the world who was always happy to see me. An innocent! Blissfully unaware! I felt sorry for him ...having a father like me! I had ruined everything, and everything was gone! I was a loser and I was lonely. So, I did what I have always done, I put a brave face on it, which wasn't that difficult as I hardly saw anyone anymore. The lads I had grown up with had begun to shy away from me because I was a liability and a drunk. I was aware of this and so it was painful and excruciatingly embarrassing. As a result, I shied away from them even more. I had never experienced loneliness like it. It didn't help that I had put the weight back on, I was bloated and breathless from drinking and looked permanently tired. I looked like one of the great unwashed! A fucking tramp! I felt barely human. If I was talking to someone, I struggled to make or maintain eye contact, that is unless I was very drunk or very high and then I would be practically touching noses with the poor unfortunate. No more bursaries or student loans, and no work. I was back on the dole. I had no money and no car, so I had no chance of getting work either. Desperate, I briefly went back to the AA meetings, but they didn't really help, I did not want to hear about a higher power or turning my life over to a God of my understanding. I didn't believe in God! And why would I!

I carried on binge drinking. The only time I ever felt normal or happy was when I had Jack to stay, and that was tinged with guilt. I changed the weekends that I had him to coincide with when I got my dole money so I could ensure I would have food in the cupboard, nice biscuits and sweets and a couple of quid to try and make a fuss of him. In my defence I always made an effort for Jack's visits, I always made sure the flat was clean and tidy and most importantly that I was sober!

I remember having to sign on one day. I had no money whatsoever. I always liked to have at least enough for a couple of pints, just to make the whole ordeal bearable, to take the sting out of it! But on this occasion, I didn't have a bean. I was going to have to walk past every pub and off-licence, both in and out of the town centre and without so much as a sniff of a drink. To make matters worse I had a squeaky trainer, so every other step reminded me of just how shit my life had become! I could not carry on like this. I knew I had to do something.

****

The doctor prescribed a drug called anti-abuse. If you drink alcohol while taking anti-abuse it will make you violently ill! Thus, stopping you from picking up a drink in a moment of weakness. However, I soon realised (being a binge drinker), that if I wanted to drink, all I had to do was stop taking them, and 2-3 days later I was good to go! As I wasn't so much a daily drinker (due to lack of funds), their effect was limited. I also knew that I would not be prescribed the medication indefinitely as it can cause severe liver damage!

I might be a drunk, but I'm not an idiot! I knew enough to know that eventually I would have to stop taking them. Psychologically nothing would have changed, I would still be a drunk. The doctor, having listened to my concerns, referred me to a drug and alcohol service. Once there I explained my situation and helpfully suggested that perhaps I might need rehab! The drug and alcohol support worker all but laughed and said, 'No, ...no, I think you will be alright, I think you will do it'? I assume he meant give up the drink! So pleased was I with his 'diagnosis' and 'belief' in me, that when I left his office I headed straight for the nearest pub where I commenced to get completely shit faced and eventually arrested! I was not in a good place, it had not been easy for me to ask for help, and I felt like I had been laughed at.

I had now been living alone in my flat for about 8 months and I hadn't paid a single bill, I had even drank the rent money on more than one occasion, resulting in my family having to bail me out. It wasn't uncommon for my mum and Bridie to turn up at my flat with a bag or two of shopping.

I had brief moments of sobriety; times when I decided with a steely determination that enough was enough; but they were always short-lived. During one of these (steely) periods, I had received an unexpected tax rebate of £500, which for me, was like winning the lottery. Determined not to drink, I stayed in my flat and spent £250 pounds on cocaine. When I eventually came too, I was horrified and distraught. I reasoned, carrying on like that, then I might as well go and get pissed, so I did! 36yrs old and I was sinking like a stone. I was a fucking mess and I didn't like me at all!

Eventually the flat became too much to handle on my own. I was ducking and diving from everyone, I was scared to open the front door, that is on the rare occasion someone might actually knock on it! I would go days without talking to anyone (but myself!). I strongly sensed my mental health was deteriorating. I wasn't coping. So, like the pitiful child I was, I ashamedly asked my mum if I could move back home. She reluctantly agreed. My mum was 76 yrs old and did 'not' need the hassle, it was unfair of me to ask. She had lost her husband and her daughter to alcohol, she didn't want me back at home, but I think she was scared she was going to lose me too!

The moonlight flit. I did a bunk from the flat and moved out in the middle of the night, I left a note for the landlord (a lie) explaining I had moved to Ireland for work, I was sorry for the short notice and hoped the deposit would cover the months' rent! It was a cringe-worthy move! But I took some comfort in the fact I left the place spotless and as I had found it. To be honest it was a relief, there was a comfort in moving back to my mother's house. I suppose it was like moving into a 'safe' house, only the person 'I' feared, the person I needed protecting from ...was me! My mother made it clear there would be conditions! And I was glad, I welcomed them. I had to get myself sorted, for Jack's sake if nothing else. Unfortunately, I was so far gone, try as I might, I could not live up to my mother's demands.

****

I had the dream again. It left me feeling very disturbed. It is almost the same as before, only this time there is a crowd gathered around the edge of the pond. They are to far away for me to make out their faces. Are they jeering at me? Or are the concerned? I don't know. I feel foolish standing alone on the ice. I feel uncomfortable with them all watching, I feel as though I am naked, but I am not. Then one of them throws something, ...it's a cabbage! It lands close to me, I look down, but it is not a cabbage it's a dead fish and it winks at me! Then the ice beneath my feet gives way. I feel myself drop and then I wake up. I'm really worried.

Out of the frying pan and into the fire. I feel safer with people around but it's hard at my mum's! I feel like my family are all judging me, 'Why are you here'? I continue to struggle just like I always have. I'm embarrassed by the fact that I am in my late thirties and living with my mum. I can't even contemplate the idea of trying to meet a girl and then having to explain myself. I am permanently sorry. Sorry I came home drunk. Sorry I haven't given you your money. Sorry I called you that. Sorry I exist! In fact, my whole life is like one long drawn out episode of that 1980s Ronnie Corbet, sitcom, 'SORRY'. My life is unbearable! In fact, it is fucking awful! (Language, 'Timothy'! SORRY!). I couldn't stay in the flat, but I think I have made a mistake moving home!

I didn't think it would be possible, but living at my mum's I become even more isolated, I feel alone even when I'm with people. I begin to question the point of my existence and struggle to find a convincing answer. I am to scared to leave and stand on my own two feet; I don't trust myself. I know the dole would pay my rent somewhere, but I know my only option would be a dingy bedsit with 'shitty' carpets. I can't allow myself to bring Jack into an oppressive environment like that. As difficult as it is for me, at least its clean and safe here, I think it's better for Jack's sake if I stay at my mum's. That might sound like a convenient excuse, but I know in my heart that it isn't! And so, it continues.

CHAPTER TWENTY-FIVE

MY MUM BECAME ILL. SHE WAS 77YRS OLD and had begun acting strangely, we (the family) later discovered that she was repeatedly getting urine infections due to kidney failure.

Christmas 2009 my mum was taken into hospital, she was in a bad way, she looked awful and was rambling, talking absolute nonsense. I started to 'see' her as the little old lady that she was instead of just being my mum! The doctors said one of her kidneys had failed and was effectively poisoning her, so she needed to have it removed. He pointed out that due to her age it was a very risky procedure.

While on the operating table my mum suffered two heart attacks. She survived, but only just. She spent weeks in intensive care hooked up to various machines and tubes. The surgeon stated that she only had a 30% chance of surviving, but pointed out, she had been starved of oxygen on the operating table and if she did manage to pull through, then there was a chance she might have brain damage. Things did not look good for my poor old mum. She deteriorated even further and was given the last rights by a priest. None of us knew what to do. I didn't want to lose her. I couldn't lose her. I needed my mum. Apart from Jack, she was all I had. So, what do you do when all else fails?

I was in a world of my own as I made my way around the maze of hospital corridors, when I came across a door with a sign above it which read 'Chapel'. I couldn't help but feel slightly 'silly' as I checked both ways along the corridor to ensure the coast was clear before I pushed the door open and peeked inside. It was empty! For once I was glad to be alone! At the front of the chapel by the alter, stood a Christmas tree. It did not have any decorations on it, no black and gold beer cans!

Instead it was covered in prayer cards. So, I did the only thing I could, I prayed. I prayed to God that my mum would pull through. I asked God to give us our mum back. I asked that he let her live until she was 86. 86 seemed fair! I bargained, 86 was a long way off, I felt It was a good compromise. I put a donation in the little tin next to the prayer cards and wrote out a card and placed it on the tree amongst all the others, hoping 'He' might read mine first. I left the chapel as quietly as I had entered, but not feeling quite as silly. I then re-joined my distraught family at my mother's bedside.

Three days later, surrounded by her children, my mum opened her eyes, sat up in the bed, and with a look of total bewilderment, shook her head and said in her Irish accent, 'Jaysus, I can't believe it, 50 and I'm pregnant again'! It was such a relief we all burst out laughing. My nephew Dan, quipped, 'Who's the father'?!

After the initial furore and excitement at the realisation that we had our mum back, a thought occurred to me! When no one was looking I slipped back into the little chapel, got down on my knees and said a prayer of thanks, ... Just in case!

I really thought I had lost her. Twice I thought she was dead. Later, when she was back home and fully recovered and as we discussed how serious her situation had been, I joked and said, 'Well mum, you can't kill a bad thing'! She gave me a cursory look.... and then grinned! My mum made a full recovery, there was no sign of any brain damage. In fact, she seemed stronger than ever. I however was not!

****

He didn't deserve me! And I didn't deserve him.

Like most little boys, Jack hero-worshipped his dad, which in turn broke my heart. His innocence, his unfaltering, unconditional love. Such a perfect little kid. How I wished I was a perfect dad.

Parenting my son in my mother's house was difficult, to say the least. She constantly interfered. She undermined everything I did and over-ruled me at every opportunity, while always reminding me I was just like my father, 'No good!'

It was as if she didn't want me to be his dad. It felt as though, in her eyes, I had lost the right to be a parent and she was happy to remind me of it. The strain of living under her rule was becoming unbearable. I wasn't sure for how much longer I could keep it up.

I sought escape at every opportunity. If I could afford to, I would spend my days in the pub getting drunk, but when funds were low, and I was reduced to counting pennies, then I could only buy cans from the corner shop. This caused a serious dilemma as I was not allowed alcohol in the house. But one way or another I had to have my drink. I needed to escape from self! So, I started to sneak 'it' into the house. Cans were difficult to slip past my eagle-eyed mother who even had a habit of checking the bins for empties. However, I soon realised a half bottle of whiskey was easy to conceal in my jacket. Neat whiskey in big gulps straight from the bottle and in secret became normal.

On a Thursday evening my mum still went to bingo round at the local church hall. This meant I could bring in cans of Kronenbourg or Stella and had a two and a half hour 'window' in which to get as much down me as I could, before she returned. Then when she came home, I would have to try and act normal and pretend to be sober.... which is easier said than done! Especially when you're three sheets to the wind. I often found the best course of action on such occasions was to… hide!

Sometimes, if I was desperate for a drink early in the morning, I would get myself a 'little' carry out from the shop and go for a walk over the fields, so I could drink uninterrupted and without being seen. I remember one morning I was sitting on a gravel path on the side of a hill that overlooked the town. It was around 7am and I was drinking cans of Kronenbourg, when a family friend who was out walking her dog, stumbled across me. I could see the genuine concern on her face, and I heard it in her voice too, when she asked, 'Alright Pat, you okay mate?' I was sat on the floor surrounded by empty beer cans, I had tears running down my face. I had held a hand up to shield my eyes from the early morning sun and quite matter-of-factly, said, 'Yep, having a beer, do you want one'?

Of course, I was embarrassed, but not as much as I should have been. I had crossed a new threshold; I had gone past an imaginary line in the sand. I just didn't care anymore, I had no more fight, there was nothing left to give.

I started to contemplate suicide. I contributed nothing to the world. In my mind I was the exact definition, the very epitome of, 'a waste of space'. Every morning I would wake up wishing I hadn't. I would lay there in my bed thinking about the blue rope that hung on the wall in my mum's shed. 30 minutes, that's all it would take. Then it would all be over. I wouldn't suffer any more. I would no longer be an embarrassment or a burden, no longer would I be a liability. I would no longer blight the life of my son. I was in constant psychological pain, just by 'being'!

Poor Jack. My beautiful innocent little boy. It was bad enough his dad was a hopeless drunk, how could I then heap the stigma upon him of having an alcoholic father who had killed himself. Would he grow up thinking I hadn't cared; would he grow up thinking I hadn't loved him? I couldn’t do it; I couldn't abandon him. I began to fantasize about being killed in a car crash or dying of some incurable disease, then I would be off the hook. I would be diminished of any responsibility. 'Did you hear about poor Pat, his poor son, isn’t it awful'! Instead of, 'What a selfish cunt'! 'he was just like his father.... no fucking good'! Every morning for months, I woke to the same set of thoughts and came to the same sorry conclusion, 'I am so pathetic, I don’t 'even' have the ‘luxury’ of killing myself'!

I told no one! I took the tellings-off from my mum. I accepted the disproving glances from the family, and I continued to drink at every opportunity. I continued to be an arse, and my mum continued to berate me for it. She had a habit (as do most people) of kicking me when I was down. Her verbal assaults were always worse when I was at my lowest.

I had the constant and very real threat of homelessness hanging over me. On more than one occasion, I was tempted to just walk out the door and go and live on the streets. I remember thinking, that I could grow a beard and then no one would know it was me. Then it would be final! Jack's dad’s a tramp, a proper down and out. Things were so bad, so oppressive, I once packed a little holdall and headed off to live in the nearby woods. Obviously, I was very drunk when I came to the decision to go native! I can recall hanging the holdall up on a tree to keep it off the damp floor (like I had seen in wildlife documentaries!) and then attempting to light a fire, but It was March and everything in the woods was soaking wet, so I couldn’t do it. I even tried using a sock and a letter concerning some debt or other, that for some reason I had put in the bag! But still I couldn't get a fire going! Having failed the very basics, I sat on a log in the middle of the damp woods and drank the contents of my holdall, when I finished the last can, I went 'home'. My mum hadn't even noticed I had been gone!

I became a stranger in the very house I had grown up in. If visitors called to the house, I would hide upstairs, too ashamed to come out of the bedroom. I became the bloke creeping about upstairs while guests drank tea and gossiped below.

It was harder when Jack came for the weekend because then I could not hide, I had no choice but to interact. I loved spending time with my son but hated having to endure the constant negativity from my mum. I developed the habit of taking a few drinks during the day before Jack arrived in the evening. I think it was the (sub-conscious) thought of having to deal with my mum for the whole weekend with no escape, while also putting on a brave face for Jack. Obviously, the daytime drinks were a bad move, it was only a matter of time before I fucked up, drank too much and brought the wrath of mum down on my head! 'Call yourself a father'! She would let me have both barrels just like she had with my dad and worse in front of my son.

It was an impossible situation to which there seemed no end. Jack has 'never' heard a bad word between me and ‘his’ mother; a fact that I am very proud of! In fact, the only times he has ever heard raised voices, concerning my drinking, was when my mum was attacking me. The worst one, the one that sticks out in my mind the most, was the time I had arrived 'home' 30 minutes after Jack had been dropped off by his mother. I thought I had been a 'good boy’. Knowing I had Jack, I had 'sensibly' only drank 5 or 6 pints of Fosters (piss water as far as I was concerned), but my mother was laying in wait! As soon as I walked through the door and into the kitchen, she started attacking me, calling me all the names under the sun. Jack was playing in the front room so I pleaded with my mum to keep her voice down as I didn't want Jack to hear! But she wouldn't! I stood in front of her totally demoralised, deflated and defeated as she screamed abuse at me, telling me I was no good, I would never be any good and she wished I was dead! Then she stormed out of the kitchen and into the front room.

I don't know how much longer I can bare it. I stood alone, I gathered and composed myself, I put on my brave face and then walked into the front room to pretend all was well. As I entered the room, I saw Jack's bewildered little face and heard the venom in my mother's voice as she told him, 'I don't know why you bother with him, he's a fucking waste of space,' and then she hissed, '.... and he takes drugs'! It was a step too far! Say what you like to me but don't you fucking dare say those things to my son! I was furious! I didn't care that 'she' was my mother! I told her in no uncertain terms to, 'Shut the fuck up'!

'Come on Jack, take no notice' I said gently as I led him into the kitchen, I told him she didn't mean it and there was nothing to worry about, she was just being silly. With little choice I phoned Louise. I apologised and asked her to come back and get Jack, bless him. When she returned, she made no remark, if anything she was very understanding. I think she pitied me too! Deep down she knew there was no badness, just hopelessness!

As soon as she and Jack had left, so did I.... I headed for the pub!

Things never stay the same. Jim phoned offering me work, I agreed even before he had said, where, what or how much! I just needed to get out of that house! I went from having virtually no money at all, to having between £400/500 per week.

Now you might think I seized this opportunity to improve my situation, perhaps get a place of my own, surely that's what any normal person would have done. But I'm not normal. I'm no good.

So instead, I hit the drink hard, I suppose I was making up for lost time. Every evening I headed straight for the pub and if I didn't have Jack then I spent the entirety of the weekend in the pub too. 'Strange', but I began to feel like a man again! I even managed to scrape enough money together to buy a cheap second-hand car!

Looking back, I'm not sure if this was a good move as I was coming home drunk every night and on more than one occasion, I was shown the front door. I knew I wasn't welcome with a drink in me! So there were times when I had no choice but to sleep in my car, which in turn meant I had to drink and drive (something I was guilty of anyway!), as I couldn't let the neighbours see me asleep in the car outside my mum's house. I just didn't care anymore. I knew it was irresponsible, but I was constantly drink-driving. It was pure luck that no one ever got hurt or worse killed, it's not an excuse, but I was no longer in the right frame of mind! I was losing the plot!

One Saturday lunch time I pulled up outside my local pub. Some of the regulars and the landlord were standing outside smoking, as I parked up, I nodded and smiled at them. They, in turn, nodded and gestured back. The next thing I knew the landlord was tapping on the driver's door window. 'Pat, give me the keys mate'! I had fallen asleep behind the wheel. I didn't argue, I just pulled the keys out of the ignition, handed them to him, and then walked straight past him, into his pub and ordered a double Jameson with ice! I had no shame! A week later I again pulled up outside the local pub, this time with the whole front wing missing and the right hand head lamp completely smashed in, I got out walked up to the bar and ordered my usual double Jameson with ice. To this day I still don't know what I hit.

Things got so bad that if the landlord saw me coming, he would take the Jameson's down off the optics and hide it! If I ever needed confirmation that I 'may' have a problem, then I think that was it. I was out of control, literally! I was a danger to myself and to others, I was full of bravado, but alone I was frightened! Something bad was coming my way, I could feel it in my bones.

I had always been a happy drunk; it was hard to accept, that I was changing. I was becoming cantankerous and narky! I was getting a bit 'switchy' in the drink! Now every time I took a drink, I drank to black out. I had always thought, 'blackout' was the same as 'passed out' but it isn't! I suppose alcohol-induced psychosis is as good a term as any. Talking, walking, going from pub to pub, but on a completely different planet. On autopilot, (only I didn't have a clue where I was going ...or what I was saying!). I continued to (occasionally) get arrested, once or twice the police were actually quite good and just gave me a lift home for my own safety, on other occasions, if I became aggressive and abusive, I would wake up in the cells starring up at the sign strategical placed on the ceiling above the mattress, 'Are you tired of drink and drugs?, are they costing you more than just money'? I had also begun to get barred from pubs. This was surprisingly a new phenomenon for me, because I am a happy drunk and a nice bloke, right!

****

Three-day sessions, where the norm! I recall one such memorable bender. I had gone straight to the pub from work on the Monday evening, I had got so drunk I could barely stand and as a result was unable to go to work the next day. Not wanting to put up with the wrath of mother, I left the house at 8am and took the bus into town. I was too early for the pub, so I brought a small bottle of whisky from a corner shop and sat in the square in the middle of town, smoking and taking sneaky sips from the bottle, as I watched the 'normal' world making its way to work. When the doors of the pub opened at 9 30am, I entered, ordered a pint of Stella and took my place amongst the rest of the town bums. I was by now on first name terms with the vast majority of them. By eleven o'clock I was paralytic, by eleven thirty I was barred.

I remember staggering around the town centre with an awareness that I had to be careful not to get accidentally arrested as this would seriously hamper my intended splurge! Everything is a bit hazy from that point on. I remember getting into a scuffle and getting thrown out of some bar, I remember waking up in some woman's bed! But not much else, and then two days later I came to! I was standing at a bar clutching a Jack Daniels. Where I had been, or what I had done, was a complete mystery to me. I was still drunk, but I was also aware that I was very hungry (as far as I knew I hadn't eaten since Monday!), so I left the pub and walked down the street to a Café and ordered a meal of mashed potatoes, sausages, onions and gravy. Ravenous, I cleared the plate and then left the Café. As I attempted to cross the street heading for the pub opposite, I collapsed on the pavement. (I knew I shouldn't have had that last sausage!). I am not sure how long I lay in the street, nor do I know how many people or cars must have passed me in complete disgust. It was 2 o'clock on a Thursday afternoon and I was laying on the pavement completely out of it, and on the main thoroughfare from the town centre to the motor way. At some point, I came round and managed to get to my feet and thus staggered into the pub I had been heading for. As always, I pretended to be more sober than I actually was, ordered a pint of Guinness and sat down at a table in the corner and promptly fell asleep.

'Pat, wake up, wake up'! Confused, I lifted my chin off my chest and found I was looking at my sister, Bridie? 'What are you doing here'? She said, 'Paul rang me', I looked to my right and saw my good friend, McGillicuddy, sitting opposite looking rather sheepish. 'Sorry Pat, I had to ring her, I didn't know what else to do'! I knew it was the truth, but I told him off anyway! I knew he was concerned about me, and I don't know who else he could have rung, because Bridie was the only one who hadn't given up on me. With a sadness in her eyes she said, 'Come on Pat, it's time to go'! Like a child I didn't argue, I didn't put up a fight. I rose from the table and was helped to the car, I let her drive me home to impending doom! As we passed our estate pub I 'demanded' she stop the car and let me out, naturally she refused! Once home she made me some strong coffee and told me to go to bed. I had no intention of going to bed, but I nodded my agreement, nonetheless. My mum didn't say a word to me, I think Bridie must have told her to lay off me for a bit.

10 minutes after my sister had left, so did I. I headed straight for the local pub. Remarkably, when I walked in, McGillicuddy was sitting at the bar. He did a double take in disbelief, it would seem I had found a second wind. I had not had my fill! And therein, laid my 'real' problem!

No amount of alcohol was ever enough. At no point during my drinking did I 'ever' think, 'That's it now, I have had enough, I will go home'! It just wasn't there. It was like it was missing! What about self-preservation! The truth was, every time I took a drink, I tried to achieve a level of drunkenness that does not exist. How then can I ever be happy or content if I can never achieve my goal?

The next morning, I awoke full of the usual remorse, guilt, shame and a reluctance to leave the sanctuary of the bedroom. It's difficult to convey how I truly felt on such occasions. I was suffering from more than a mere hangover or self-pity. I was too ill to eat, only managing to sip water as it was all I could keep down. It was the total demoralisation of self!

My stomach rolled with angst. My eyes, wide, dry, and aching, my head swirling with fear. Wave after wave of nausea hit me. Hot and cold sweats and feeling unclean as if my skin were covered in a fine film of scum. I had no worth. I had no point! Palpitations, like an irregular heartbeat! Where do I go from here? The blue rope? And I bet I have probably lost my job too! It was normal, all of it! It was what I was used to! I was also used to swearing an oath that it would never happen again.

A week later and fully recovered, my shame, my oath, all but forgotten 'I' made the 'decision' to go for 'a' drink! I returned to the scene of the crime!

I was only on my second pint when I went outside for a cigarette, I stood with my back to the road in exactly the same spot where I had collapsed the week previously. I was deep in thought, thinking how lucky I had been, when a wave of panic came over me. How long had I been lying on the pavement? How many people had seen me? What if it had been somebody I knew, that had seen me? My God! What if Louise had driven passed with Jack in the car with her! Just as I was thinking this, I heard a child's voice shout, 'dad'! I turned around and there was Jack smiling and waving from the passenger seat of Louise's car! They were stationary at the lights (almost exactly where I had been laying!). Startled, but doing my utmost to remain composed, I trotted over saying, 'Alright son, how are you'? Whilst adding, 'Don't worry, I'm not drunk'! Jack smiled and said, 'I know dad, I can tell by your eyes'!

With that the lights changed, and both my son and his mother waved and smiled as they drove away, leaving me standing alone on the side of the road outside the pub. 'I will ring you tomorrow' I shouted as I waved after my son. I was numb! I was aware, but could not quite process, what would have happened, if that had been a week earlier. I shuddered as I drained my glass and went back inside the pub!

My son was 7yrs old and I was 39. How much longer can I get away with my behaviour? How long before my son realises his dad is a waste of space? Does he already know?

****

Me and Jack were out in the back garden at my mum's house. Jack was in a world of his own busily playing make believe with his toys when he suddenly stopped as if he had just remembered something, turned to face me and said, 'Oh yeah dad, I nearly forgot …. mum's pregnant'!

Shocked, I think I must have said the word, 'REALLY', about three times! I didn't even know Louise was seeing anyone. I had to try and compose myself and hide my utter astonishment! I tried to make it sound totally natural when I said, 'That's excellent news son'. 'I'm pleased you are going to have a little brother or sister', (which I was)! Before adding, 'It's nice to have family around you, especially when you are older'. I smiled at him and ruffled his hair, and said, 'Remember it don't matter how many kids your mum's got, ...I've only got one'! He just grinned at me and carried on playing with his toys!

Perhaps it wasn't as much of a shock as I imagined. After all I had been expecting it ever since we had split up. I had assumed she would meet someone, settle down and start a family of her own. So, I suppose it had been a bonus that for the best part of 8yrs, I hadn't had to deal with some bloke muscling in and trying to be my son's dad! I decided to give her a quick call. I congratulated her on her good news, I didn't bother mentioning that it would have been nice if she had told me herself. I said 'Louise I don't wish to pry on your personal life, I know it's none of my business, but if there's going to be some bloke about... well, as Jack's father I would like to know who he is'!

I thought it was a reasonable and fair comment. Louise said, 'it's not anyone you know and there's no need to worry because he won't be involved'. I was surprised at what I was hearing, and just said, 'Oh... Okay... erm'. Louise continued, 'Yeah, he's doing a lot of huffing and puffing about it all at the moment, but to be honest, I am hoping he will just fuck off"! And he did! Selfishly I was glad. I felt like I had been let off the hook. I was happy to accept she was moving on; I didn't begrudge her anything, but to be honest I was glad I didn't have to worry about some 'dick' on the scene either!

We all have issues, of that I am certain. It's not for me to try and justify the actions of others. But eight years after my battle had started with her over Jack, it would appear she was now embroiled in a new battle with some other bloke. I couldn't help but wonder, has she just done to 'him', what she had tried to do to me?!

That's just one of the many problems; when you're an alcoholic, you believe 'everything' is your fault. If the Americans carry out an air strike on Bagdad, then it's my fault! I am certainly not trying to wriggle out of my responsibility or for my part in the break-up of mine and Louise's relationship, far from it. I don't blame her for running a mile (I would have!). But not wanting me to be a part of Jack's life, I don't believe it was ever just 'really' about me! I can't help but think I was somewhat irrelevant for reasons only known to her. She did not want a man in her life. No wonder I had been banging my head against a brick wall. However, this is not my fight. I am just grateful that I have a relationship and more importantly a bond with my son.

It was coming up to Jack's eighth birthday! Louise told me she was planning to take him to Disney Land (Paris) for his birthday weekend at the end of January and would I like to come! I was Stunned, shocked and delighted all at the same time! Firstly, because had it been the one in America, I would have had to say no!? Secondly because it would be the first time the three of us had ever been away anywhere together as a 'family'. I thought it would be nice for Jack (obviously she did to!) to have both his parents together on his birthday, something he might remember for the rest of his life.

Louise's invitation to join them had lifted me out of the darkness I had been wallowing in. Having something to look forward to and also to work for, had lifted my spirits. I was excited about the trip but being so soon after Christmas and with me being self-employed, I was also concerned about raising the money. Louise hadn't asked me to fund it (she has never asked me for anything!), but as a man, I felt it was my chance to shine!

As luck would have it me and Jim were starting on a job that promised to be a good earner, so I expected to earn well. The first week back on site after the holidays is always a bit slow due to management, materials and what not! So, by the second week and with only two weeks to go before I embarked on the 'family trip' I was chomping at the bit to earn some big money.

Even for January It was bitterly cold that second week back, so I was dressed accordingly! The first snow drops began to fall at around 8.30am. By 9 o'clock, a heavy blanket of snow had fallen and by 10.00am the site agent had shut the job. I could not fucking believe it! I was devastated. I desperately needed the money, but I was not 'allowed' to work.

I was in a foul mood as me and Jim inched our way home through the snow. 'Just my fucking luck' I ranted. 'I can't believe they've shut the fucking site Jim. Fucking snow'! I concluded that I had been wasting my time even trying to do the right thing, because nothing ever works out for me (it's so unfair!). I had been a good boy all over Christmas (in fact a lot of Alkies take their foot off the gas at Christmas!?). I'm trying to be decent and normal! And the fucking heavens open! It took Jim and me over two hours to travel the 17 miles back from work. Hard done by, I felt justified in asking Jim to drop me off at my local pub.

There were only a few 'hardy' regulars in the pub, the worsening weather conditions keeping most away. The snow was now falling heavier and faster and with no sign of letting up. As I gazed out of the pub window at the huge snowflakes and the deep blanket of snow, I was aware just how quite it all was, there were no cars on the road and no people. I briefly thought of the pond in my dream, but quickly pushed it out of my mind.

I resigned myself to the fact it was 'out of my hands'! There was nothing I could do about it. It was an act of God, a natural disaster! I 'fancied' it was like being snowed in, in a remote cabin, hoping the meagre provisions (money & beer!) would last until the big thaw! So, I might as well get drunk!

I stayed drinking all day and well into the evening, only when I left the pub, did I realised that day time had turned to night, the crisp white snow twinkled in the cold darkness and made a scrunching sound under my footsteps. My mood having been alleviated by all the alcohol, I decided in my drunken wisdom to pay a visit (booty call!) to a woman I had been seeing (on and off!), who lived on the far end of the estate, (definitely a good idea!). Ever the gentleman, I did not wish to turn up empty handed, so I stopped off at the local Co-op and brought a bottle of whisky! Then on the way out of the store and as an afterthought, I stole a bunch of flowers from a basket outside the shop. I remember thinking this was incredibly cheeky of me and hilarious, as I ran off down the road laughing.

It was now getting late and the streets were deserted as I turned the corner into a long tree-lined avenue. I noticed the snow on the path had been turned to sheer ice, probably by school kids earlier that day on their way home. As there was no one around, I found it impossible to resist!

I broke out into a run and then jumped into the stance of a surfer to see how far I could slide! What a sight I must have been, sliding down the road, arms outstretched, one hand clutching a bottle of whiskey the other a bunch of stolen flowers and me with a grin a mile wide!

It was a perilous journey, but I made it to her front door and rang the bell. When she opened the door, she was horrified to see me, swaying and grinning like a demented monkey while clutching gifts! She wasted no time in making it clear that I wasn't welcome and all but told me to do one! I didn't really blame her, I understood! I was also so drunk, that I didn't really care. I apologised for the intrusion and gave her the flowers, but not the whiskey. And then I left, staggering up the road in the dark and the snow, swigging from my bottle. I must have cut quite a pitiful solitary figure!

I made it about halfway home. I can only assume that I slipped on the ice and had landed spread-eagled and flat on my back in the snow and then passed out, still clutching the by now almost empty bottle. I have no idea how long I lay passed out in the snow.

Perhaps it was somebody looking out of a bedroom window or someone in a car that saw me and phoned an ambulance! To this day I do not know who made the call, but it is not an exaggeration to say they saved my life!

The paramedics said I was very lucky. If I had fallen over somewhere more secluded and had not been seen, then I would have undoubtedly died from hypothermia. My saving grace was the fact that I was dressed appropriately for the weather conditions due to the fact I had been to work: boots, gloves and a hat (which I had nicked from the pub!). The paramedics also said I was the politest drunk they had ever meet, but I had refused to tell them where I lived (even unconscious I feared the wrath of mother!). Eventually they went through my phone and rang the last number I had dialled, which was the woman I had gone to 'visit'. She, not knowing what to do, had in turn phoned the only person there was to phone, Bridie!

My poor sister, had to get out of bed at 1.30am and drive across town in treacherous weather conditions, no doubt panicking. On arrival the first thing she said was 'Where's your teeth'?! I had lost them in the snow!!!

When Jim picked me up for work on the following Monday, he couldn't stop laughing at my misfortune and my missing teeth. So, I told him to 'Thwuck white whoff'! To add insult to injury he then added, 'You know, it says a lot about a man, when he is prepared to go about with his two front teeth missing'. So, I said it again!

It was excruciatingly embarrassing in front of Louise and my son, when I turned up minus my nashers! Louise just shook her head in disbelief. Jack, being a child, was a bit more vocal. 'What you going to do about your teeth dad'! Like always, I tried to turn it into a joke and said, 'Don't worry son, as soon as we get to Disney land, I will get a photo of me and goofy'!! I put a brave (albeit toothless) face on it! But I was cringing on the inside.

I (just!) managed to get the money together for the trip. I had no choice but to go, I couldn't let Jack down (ouch!)!! What a sight! Me with no teeth and Louise sporting a large bump carrying somebody else's child. You couldn't make it up! (I suspect we would have been turned down for the Jeremy kyle show, for fear of lowering the tone!).

Despite mine and Louise's combined conditions, me and Jack had a whale of a time, I just wish you could see the photos! The shock of nearly dying, the shame of no front teeth and the realisation I had nearly ruined Jack's first (Griswold!?) family holiday, forced me to sit up and take notice, I had to sort myself out, once and for all, ...(again)!

I began to make some headway. I had a rather splendid set of dentures made, which were very convincing and afforded me a winning smile. When Louise saw them, she simply said, 'Well done'! Secretly I wondered how long until I 'lost' this set, everything was a worry, even teeth.

I also went back to the doctors and was again prescribed Anti-buse. I knew it was now a case of do this or give up on life entirely! For the first time since I had relapsed almost 6yrs earlier, I felt hopeful. I felt like I might have a chance! I was still smoking pot on a daily basis, but I hadn't had a drink for three months and cocaine seemed all but a distant memory!

Work had dried up to non-existent 'again', but that's the construction industry for you. I was actually okay with it all. I had come to the conclusion that I needed to get a 'real' job with a regular wage, something away from construction.

I had earned a little money doing a cash in hand job and with the proceeds had brought myself a second-hand laptop. The 'plan' being I would create a CV (I hadn't needed one before!) and start applying for 'proper' jobs online. I was feeling very positive as I explained my intentions to my mum, and as a gesture of good will, I also told her, 'And as of Monday, mum (today being Wednesday), I'm going to decorate the house for you, from top to bottom. That will keep me busy during the day and in the evenings, I can continue with my job search on the laptop'! 'Can't you start the decorating tomorrow'? 'err... no mum, like I said, I want to set up a CV and stuff like that, then I will be able to start the decorating on Monday'! 'Yeah but I want my kitchen done'!

My mum hadn't asked me to decorate, it had been my idea. I had offered without any prompting. I was supplying all the paint and did not expect (obviously!) any payment of any kind. She had lived in the house for 50yrs. I had just offered to redecorate the whole house for nothing, I am not working, and I will start Monday!

Unbelievably, it wasn't 'fucking' good enough! All of a sudden, she wants it done now! Soon I had Bridie on the phone, 'Why won't you do mum's kitchen for her'?! Then my nephew turned up that evening leaving paintbrushes and the like, so I could start first thing in the morning! Again, I explained my intentions, but they could not seem to grasp what I was saying! I started to feel insulted. Why will they not 'respect' my decision as a man? This is what I propose! Where is the problem! I stood by my decision.

My mum began to sulk. Then.... she took to the bed! Then.... she refused to take her medication. It was like there had been a death in the family, you could have cut the atmosphere with a knife!

On the Friday, I buckled, I decorated the fucking kitchen! 'Still' sulking my mum refused to acknowledge me while I was working. All I received was the odd cursory glance of disgust each time she passed by the kitchen door. It was an unbearable atmosphere. I felt like Huckleberry Fucking Finn, being forced to whitewash a fence! Later that day when I was finished, she made no comment. Full of resentment and feeling like an absolute mug! I went upstairs to get cleaned up. A little while later she barged into my bedroom and with a snarl demanded, 'Where's the brush'! I gave her a chastising look and said, 'I put it in the bin'. 'You.... did.... WHAT'!!? And then proceeded to go ape shit at me for being so fucking stupid!

I couldn't bear it a moment longer and declared, 'Fuck this, I'm going' and stormed out of the house. I was angry, hurt and confused. I wasn't sure where I was going, but I got as far as the shops! I knew I wasn't being too clever, but I did it anyway!

I hid the bottle of whiskey inside my jacket and walked back into the house. I ignored my mum and went directly upstairs to my room. I shut the door and pulled the bottle from my jacket, unscrewed the lid and took three large consecutive gulps from the bottle. I smacked my lips and wiped the back of my hand across my mouth and then repeated the process. I did half the bottle, put the lid back on, hid it in the drawer and then sat on the end of the bed feeling very, very, very, sorry for myself.

It only took around five minutes for the effects of my actions to kick in. I felt queasy. Wave after wave of nausea came over me. I began to feel hot and then had a strange sensation like hives. I became restless and fidgety and began to scratch at my skin. My feet felt like they were on fire. I pulled off my socks and started clawing at my bare feet. But no matter how much I scratched; I couldn't get any relief. I came over all faint and lay back on my bed hoping it would pass. But It didn't! It only got worse. I was conscious of the fact that my body temperature was increasing. I could not lay still or stop scratching (it was like I was covered in ants!).

I had been on Anti-buse, for 3 months, so it must have been building up in my system. I knew that if I were to drink alcohol while taking the drug, I would feel ill. However, in my rage, I had not really considered the consequences of my actions. I certainly had not expected a reaction as severe as this, but then again what idiot drinks half a bottle of whiskey in less than 5 minutes!

I started to become quite worried. I told myself, this is not good, you have seriously fucked up! It was not passing, if anything, I was feeling worse. I made my way to the bathroom and stuck my fingers down my throat, in an attempt to make myself sick, and thus rid myself of the alcohol! But it didn't work. I was just dry reaching.

I lifted my head from the sink and looked at my reflection in the bathroom mirror. I almost recoiled in horror. I had never seen a human being look 'that' red! My whole head was bright crimson, I was seriously beginning to panic, even the whites of my eyes were completely blood shot. There was no white to them at all. I staggered back to the bedroom. 'fuck, fuck, fuck', fuck, fuck....', I repeated it like a mantra. I deduced my blood pressure must be going through the roof. My head started to swirl, and my mind raced as I stood in the bedroom, startled, panicked and clawing at the relentless itching all over my body. I thought I was going to have a heart attack or a stroke! 'Fuck, ... fuck, what do I do'?

I had no choice! I felt like the world's biggest wanker when I phoned for an ambulance. I can assure you there is no way on this earth that I would have made that call, if I did not believe I was in serious trouble!

All the while my near-death experience is playing out upstairs, my mum is downstairs probably watching 'Emmerdale', and oblivious to what is happening. Despite everything that's been going on, she 'is' an old woman. The shock of an ambulance turning up, might give 'her' a heart attack! FUCK! I phoned my sister Bride and said, 'Don't panic'. She immediately panicked and raced to my mum's house. I honestly thought it was the end.

The paramedics carried me out of the house strapped into a 'chair' and with a blanket over me! I remember in my slightly comatose state feeling ashamed and embarrassed and hoping that the neighbours might not notice a big 'yellow' ambulance with flashing lights! I also remember feeling 'offended' when I heard my sister say, 'He is an alcoholic'! My mum was crying.

The paramedics wrongly assumed I was drunk! Bright red face, swaying, incoherent and stinking of whiskey, I think they can be forgiven. However, I was not drunk. I had only drunk enough for the medication to cause a violent reaction to the alcohol, but not enough so as I was unaware of my surroundings. 'Don't be sick in our ambulance'! they kept shouting it at me. They had zero sympathy and treated me with disregard and contempt, as if I were a park bench hobo. I was mortified and I was ashamed. But I didn't blame them. It was one of the most humiliating experiences of my life.

Over the years I have been arrested on countless occasions and this wasn't the first time I had ever been carted off in the back of an ambulance, but it 'was' the first time in my life I had been aware of what was going on while it was happening. In the past, I would be told what I had done! On such occasions it was as if the person telling me, were describing someone else. I would have no recollection and any shame I might have felt was only from not knowing! This was different. Even when we arrived at the hospital, the duty nurse was dismissive of me. When I asked if there was anywhere, I could lie down, because I thought I was going to collapse, she looked at me with disgust like I was a total tramp and said 'No' as a finality! I sat in a chair in a corridor amongst people who were, according to the nurse 'actually ill', whilst being violently sick into a cardboard 'gravy boat'! I'm nothing more than pure scum!

As soon as I was able, I got up from the chair and stumbled out of the hospital, avoiding eye contact with everyone in my path. Once outside I nabbed a taxi and went straight home and into the bedroom where I stayed for three days. I refused to talk to or see anyone. I lay on the bed; all I could think of was the blue rope. I knew there was no hope! When I eventually came out of the bedroom, I was quieter and more reserved than I had ever been before. I had given up! Things returned to relative normality, but no one noticed the profound change in me.

****

I stopped taking my medication. I knew it wasn't the answer to my problems. Instead, I carried on as I had always done and just pretended none of it had happened. A few weeks passed and then I received a 'gift from the gods', a £2000 tax rebate. I instantly knew what I was going to do with it, and I did.

I considered jumping on a train and heading for the coast for a long weekend, to get as far away as possible. I imagined booking into a seafront guest house, going to pubs alone and then bringing a carry out back to the room, where I could drink, hidden from view, undisturbed and to my heart's content. But I didn't! Because I didn't trust myself. I had a 'sense', a foreboding, that something bad would happen to me. I couldn't shake off the feeling that there was a permanent change heading my way. I just didn't know whether it was going to be good or bad, I just knew it was coming, I could feel it in my bones!

I hit the pubs. From morning till night and for eight days straight I drank myself into a stupor. Captain Morgan's for breakfast, Stella, Kronenbourg and double Jameson's with ice! I couldn't get it down quick enough. I spent the entire time in total black out. I was oblivious to my surroundings I did not know where, what or even 'who' I was.

On the sixth day I awoke in my bed at my mum's house. I got up and pulled on the same clothes I had been wearing since embarking on my mammoth spree. I splashed water on my face, grabbed my car keys and left the house before my mum had chance to verbally attack me. I drove to the corner shop brought some cigarettes and six cans of Kronenbourg and then drove to a local park, where I could sit in my car, smoke my fags, drink my cans and listen to the radio until the doors of the pub opened at 9.30am. I had about an hour to go!

Drinking in my car in the park was dodgy! I had to be careful I didn't get spotted by a dog walker, or the like, who might phone the old bill! Sometimes the police would pull into and cruise around the park whilst out on patrol, so it was a dangerous game to play! As I sat alone in a maudlin state, swigging from my can and watching the squirrels and pigeons going to and fro between the trees, I was overwhelmed with a sense of doom and pointlessness, and then my phone beeped! A text message from my mate Paul. 'r u working? Fancy a pint'?

I immediately perked up and became excited by the prospect of meeting and having a drink with my friend. I rarely met up, or drank with my friends these days, I could never stay sober or keep it together long enough to make or keep arrangements. It didn't help that Paul had his own demons to contend with, so due to our combined 'issues', we were often like to 'proverbial' ships in the night!

I drove into town to meet him. Not wanting to park directly outside the pub, knowing that at some point I would be returning to the car, probably hammered, I 'hid' my car a short walk away and around the back of some high-rise flats. In less than an hour of receiving McGillicuddy's text, I was sitting at a sticky table, in a smelly pub, drinking pints of Stella with my old friend. For the next two hours it was pint after pint of non-stop hilarity and belly laughs. I pointed out it was a shame that we didn't meet up more often!

Two hours was all it took for me to be completely out of it again! I was so drunk I had no choice but to leave! I suppose I had just been topping up from the previous days drinking. Paul knew I had my car with me, so he phoned me a cab, but I refused to take it. A couple of times he managed to get me in it, only for me to get back out again. He also tried to take my car keys from me, but I refused to give them up and even became aggressive with my old mate. I didn't want to leave my car behind or hand over the keys, I knew I would eventually sober up later that day and then I would be 'stranded' at my mum's house!

Having refused the taxi and having told Paul to 'fuck off", I staggered off up the road to where I had hidden my car. I don't know how long it took to walk the short distance to the flats, I have a vague recollection of staggering and taking both sides of the street. I have a vision of leaning against walls and holding onto railings in my attempt to stay upright and make it to my destination. By the time I made it to my car, I had experienced every emotion known to man! I think I may have been experiencing alcohol induced psychosis. I had started off happy in Paul's company, now alone I was angry with the world, all the wrongs I had suffered! Poor me, what a bad start I had had in life. My dad never bothered with me, my mum didn't like me and the only woman I had ever loved was repulsed by me. I was a disgrace and a liability to my son, even my friends shy away from me, poor me, what's the point?

I remember standing at the bottom of the high-rise flats and looking straight up at all 20 floors. Then I walked into the communal area at the bottom and pressed for the lift, I think I got out on the 7th or the 8th floor and stood staring out of the hallway window at the street below. I pictured myself running and jumping from the top of the flats and falling through the air, a matter of seconds and it would all be over. I remember a feeling of deviance wash over me. 'FUCK IT'! And fuck this life!

I took the lift to the top floor. I looked for a way onto the roof of the 20-storey block. At each end of the corridor there was a door leading to a final stairwell, I tried both, but the doors leading to the roof were securely locked. I pulled and kicked at the doors determined to get through. I remember doing running kicks at one and repeatedly falling flat on my back, undeterred and full of rage I continued in my endeavour to get through. I must have made quite a racket, yanking, barging, kicking and swearing at the doors. But they wouldn't give, I only succeed in wearing myself out, close to tears, I finally gave up. No way out!

At some point I made my way back down to the bottom of the flats via the lift and headed for my car. How long it took for me to manage to get the key in the lock is anybody's guess, but I would imagine it was quite a while! Eventually I managed to open the driver's door, got in, closed the door.... and passed out! Some while later there was a knock on the window. I opened my eyes and looked, 'you OK there sir'? Two police officers were staring at me through the car window. It was only four o'clock in the afternoon and I really didn't give a fuck!!!

I was arrested on suspicion of drink driving, I took umbrage to the accusation, because although I had managed to open the driver's door, I had given up trying to get the key in the ignition. Both officers were polite and courteous, but I took it upon myself (knowing I was fucked), to point out that we could all stop pretending to be 'friends' because we were not!

At the station I was asked to provide a specimen for analysis, I refused! 'You know that's an instant ban' said one of the officers! Not caring I just shrugged, 'Is it'. I was put in the cells to sober up. At 11 o'clock that night I was released and issued with a summons for court. On leaving the station I hailed a cab, picked up my car and drove to the nearest pub and carried on where I had left off. I remember driving to a pub in the town centre, parking 'directly' outside the front door, and then at 1am leaving the pub, getting back in my car and driving home!

Two weeks later at 10 o'clock on a Monday morning I appeared before the local magistrate. I was hanging! I had just done 3 days straight on the beer and I felt as rough as a badger's arse. It was true, I no longer cared, I had given up on life and was resigned to accepting my fate! Although I knew I deserved to lose my driving licence, if not go to prison, I still didn't want to! So, I formulated a 'defence' in an attempt to try and wriggle out of it. This was my defence; I am an alcoholic! I am receiving treatment for my problem! In fact, I take a medication called Anti-buse! In a moment of weakness, I attempted to drink half a pint of beer! The medication reacted badly with the small amount of alcohol and I became very ill, so I sought refuge in my car!

I made no attempt to drive the vehicle, in fact the keys were not even in the ignition. I do not drink and drive. No more than I rob banks! As I hadn't given a specimen, I thought, they have no way of knowing how much, if indeed any, alcohol was actually present in my system, plus I wasn't even driving! I remember thinking, I have a very good chance of getting away with this!

Before I was called into the court room, I visited the toilets and was violently sick as a result of the mother of all hangovers, I hoped I could not be heard as I repeatedly reached and puked the entire contents of my stomach into the toilet bowl. As a result, I entered the court looking drained of all colour and covered in a sheen of perspiration and then took my place on the stand confident that 'my defence', at the very least would cast doubt on the charge!

The defence read out the particulars to the court: 'Mr Delaney was discovered asleep behind the wheel.... blah blah blah'. 'When the defendant was asked to provide a specimen for analysis, Mr Delaney, 'laughing', proceeded to bend over, point to his posterior and said, ...'kiss my apple'!

Everyone in the courtroom turned their heads and looked directly at me! I hung my head in shame. I had no recollection whatsoever of saying it!! But like everyone else in the courtroom, I knew it was true! The judge 'wincing' asked, 'How do you plead'? Looking directly at the floor, I said, 'guilty'!

I lost my licence! And rightly so! I received a six month ban and a £215 pound fine. I was a menace to other road users; the court knew it and so did I! I left the court and headed straight for the pub. No car, no work! No problem!

****

Everyone had had enough of me, I had had enough of me, but still the madness continued. I woke up one morning with a large cut to my forehead and a massive black eye. I didn't think I had been fighting. I reasoned I had probably fallen over while staggering home from the pub. The truth was I didn't have a clue how it had happened. I told Jack I had tripped on a lead at work and had banged my head off a wall. He didn't look convinced and just said, 'Oh'. My sister Bridie on the other hand took one look at me and said, 'Right, that's it, I've had enough of this. You need help. I've lost my dad and my sister; I am not going to lose you too.' I was surprised by her reaction; it wasn't as if I had never had a black eye before! My sister phoned the local drug and alcohol services centre and demanded an emergency appointment. The same one I had been to four years earlier asking for help but was told I wasn't bad enough! An appointment was made for that afternoon.

I sat on a chair in the corner of a small consultation room looking every bit the train wreck that I was. I put up no argument or defence against being there. I felt bad when my sister become upset as she explained to the support worker that I needed help, or I was going to end up dead! She explained about my father and poor Kathleen. It surprised me when she told the bloke, if I was a horrible fucker, she would just leave me to get on with it, but said I was in fact a lovely brother! That I had tried and tried on my own to sort things out, but now I needed professional help, she 'demanded' I was put into rehab.

Much to my surprise the support worker agreed, he went on to explain that he would make an application requesting a placement, but first, I had to make an appointment to see a social worker! How fucking ironic! I had spent three years of my life studying to be a social worker, and now I had ended up 'needing' one, rather than being one!

I didn’t think much of the social worker, I would like to believe it was not sour grapes on my part. He was an Asian man and was around about my age. He was professional and nice enough, and he did secure the deal as far as the rehab was concerned. It’s just that I couldn't help feeling that perhaps there was a cultural barrier preventing him from being able to relate to my predicament. I'm not a fool, I know enough to know that just having experienced childbirth does not make you a childbirth expert! But I got the impression he had 'no idea' of what I had been through as every time I tried to discuss my drug and alcohol problem with him, he rather smugly nodded and said he understood, because he had given up cigarettes! I can remember sitting in his office, looking at him through tear filled eyes and thinking, getting scraped-up off the floor by the police at 2 o’clock in the afternoon is nothing like giving up cigarettes!

He asked why I thought rehab would work for me. I explained how negative and oppressive it was living at my mother’s house, that it was no good attending a weekly one hour appointment to discuss and 'resolve' my feelings, behaviour and alcoholism and then returning to all the negativity! I was never going to find the strength to drag myself out of the depths of despair that I was currently in. I needed to be removed from the restrictions of home and placed in a 'positive' environment to enable me to bring about positive and permanent psychological change.

It took a couple of months, but between the drug and alcohol services, my doctor and the social worker, I was offered a place in a residential rehabilitation treatment centre for alcoholism. I welcomed it! It was called Hope House.

Chapter Twenty-Six

A six-month programme. What would I tell my young son? He was the only constant in my life, throughout everything I had always maintained a close relationship and in my opinion a strong bond. I am not saying it like I have achieved something wonderful or great, I know it is what I'm supposed to do. I am not expecting a medal for it.

I also know I have not been the father I should have been and there are no excuses. But if I 'were' to proffer an excuse, then I would say I was dealing with a very difficult set of circumstances which I didn't fully understand. I still felt like I had done a pretty good job of hiding the worst of my drinking from him. I had to a certain degree succeeded in living the double life. On the occasions when my son had seen his father with a drink in him, and on the rarer occasions when I am ashamed to admit he had seen (the real) me actually pissed, I had always been jovial and playful, That is of course unless my mother had antagonised me and brought the mood crashing down around us. In fact, I recall Jack complaining once that he didn't like it when I was drunk because I kept hugging him and telling him I loved him. How different from when I was a kid! Nonetheless I had to tell him something because I was going to be away for 6 months!

6 months is a lifetime when you're a child. I didn't want his young mind worrying about where I was, nor did I want to burden his young heart with my adult problems. I just wanted him to be the much loved, happy, contented little boy that he was, but with a dad he could be proud of!

I didn't want him to think I might be in prison or that I suddenly no longer cared about him. I was also incredibly ashamed of what I had become. I didn't want to have to tell my 9yr old son that his father was weak. That his dad wasn't like other dads, because he's a loser. I decided the only fair option, the right option... was to tell my beautiful little boy the truth. Albeit a very watered-down truth. An age appropriate truth. I didn't want to scare him or confuse his young mind. I would leave out the horror stories. So, I prepared myself, knowing it was going to sting! No father wants to admit to his son that he is different from other men!

'Jack, you know sometimes I drink too much and well...act a bit... silly'! He didn't let me finish! Cutting me off he said, 'Yeah I know dad, you're an alcoholic. Mum told me'! I won't lie, it hurt! I was taken aback by this revelation. I think I was also relieved. My sisters said Louise was out of order for telling him. The truth is I didn't mind that she had. I understood. She had told him to protect him. Jack has always been a very bright kid; his mother and I have been truly blessed.

Me and Jack had a fairly frank and engaging discussion; there were no tears, I kept it very light-hearted. He is my son! He deserves a father who is honest with him (age appropriately). At the same time, I didn't want to leave him with the wrong impression. I explained how some people are allergic to peanuts (I have never liked this analogy) and eat them every day and some people are only slightly allergic to peanuts and just eat a hand full every now and again, 'like me'! Either way, it still causes an allergic reaction. I winced when I also asked him not to mention to his friends at school that I was an alcoholic, because sometimes people don't understand what it is, and they might think I am something that I am not. Plus, we all know how cruel kids can be.

I felt very uncomfortable asking this of my son. I felt as though I was asking him to lie for me! It reminded me of when I was a child and I would hide my dad's drinking from my friends. That's not what I wanted for Jack. But I was just trying to protect him, which I am sure sounds a bit rich. Too little to late! But it was necessary.

I didn't know it at the time, but something magical had happened when I had been honest with my son. He knew the truth about me. I could no longer dismiss or play down my drinking or brush it off as silliness. I could no longer 'kid' my kid, nor could I now, 'kid' myself!

****

The last drink! It had been seven horrendous and horrific years since the morning I had woken up in Rachel's bed and had decided to go for 'A' drink! Ignorance, 'luck'(?!) and a total lack of awareness as to what lay ahead, was the only reason I got through those seven years. Had I known the pain, humiliation, degradation and struggle that lay in store, then I fear I would have succumbed to the blue rope and I would not have lived to tell the tale.

I was due to go into rehab after the Mayday bank holiday weekend. The condition being that I had not consumed any alcohol for 3 days before admittance. This coincided well with my last dole check! On the Friday, I drew my dole money early and got the bus into town. I brought new socks and pants, some toiletries and a couple of cheap T-shirts from Primark's, and then went to the pub. I spent about forty quid getting completely shit faced!

It was my last chance! Would it really be my last taste of alcohol... ever! It was a mind-blowing concept! A very strange experience. I knew I needed rehabilitation, but did I really want it? Either way I knew I wouldn't survive without it!

I got back to my mother's house at around five in the evening, clutching my bag of pants and socks. She took one look at me and went fucking ballistic! 81yrs of age and she was that angry that she actually threw chairs around the kitchen! Jesus Christ, what have I done to this woman? She couldn't understand why I would get drunk when I am about to go into treatment. She clearly didn't believe (she had screamed as much!) that I would ever get sober. After all, I'm useless, just like my 'cunt of a father'! She had lived with it practically all her life, but she didn't understand alcoholism! But that was okay, because that made two of us.

It was a brutally depressing weekend at my mother's house. And it was in fact a relief when Tuesday morning came! I was surprised when my mother kissed me on the cheek and wished me luck, I picked up my suitcase, told her I loved her and took a taxi alone to the rehab.

****

42yrs old and 11 yrs after attending my first AA meeting I began the 6-month programme for alcoholism at the aptly named 'Hope House'. Unusually it was situated in my hometown! Generally, it's not normal practice to be 'placed' in your hometown, the thinking being that familiar places and people can act as triggers! However, I had argued (asked politely in fact), for an exception to be made, as I felt it was fundamental for my 'recovery' that I be close for my son. It had been granted.

I was tired, but I needed to change my life for the better. I needed to be a good father; my son deserved better than I had been able to give. Still I wondered if I was doing the right thing. There would be no hiding the fact I was in treatment; everyone would know I was a hopeless drunk! Of course, everyone already knew. It was the worst kept secret in town, and I was the last one to find out!

Nobody likes change (except buskers!). It unsettles people, even when they know that the change is positive and good. I think sometimes people can hold onto their problems/addictions for longer than they probably 'need too', because there is a perverse comfort in knowing. Knowing how it is, how it's going to be! Like the wife who suffers domestic abuse, who puts up with her abuser because she's scared to leave. Scared of the abuser, but also frightened of the unknown! Perhaps not the best analogy, but It may be 'easier' to stay put and just hope for the best, rather than taking a leap of faith into the unknown!

Likewise, I didn't know if rehab would work for me, for others, yes, but for me? I wasn't sure. I started (subconsciously) looking for excuses for not staying. But the only thing I came up with was, 'would they feed me enough'! How ridiculous! But then again is it? I had never been in a rehab before, so how would I know? It's the fear of the unknown that enslaves us. Just for the record, I was like Ray Mear's going into the jungle, I came out two stone heavier than when I went in!

****

Hope House was a large 1930s multiple occupancy dwelling with extensive and mature gardens. It had a modern single storey side extension which housed the staff offices and the large catering style kitchen diner. The rest of the house (the old building) was divided into ten bedrooms, a number of therapy rooms, and a TV room. On arrival I was appointed a keyworker called Anne. She was a very pleasant, but a no-nonsense type of woman in her late fifties. She was full of reassurances as she led me into the office and booked me in! She explained the house rules, including the random drug and alcohol testing (urine sample) and then showed me to my room. The room was sparsely furnished with a single bed, single wardrobe, dressing table, sink and a small wall safe for my valuables, not that I had any! There was also an ashtray! I think Anne saw the look of relief on my face when I saw it. 'Yes... you can smoke in your room', she said disapprovingly. 'but not in the rest of the house'! I remember thinking, that's because I am not allowed to do anything else!

Anne handed me my room key and a timetable listing all the compulsory group therapies. Weekends and evenings were free to do as I wished (almost!). Another rule was that I would not be allowed out of the house unaccompanied for the first four weeks. Anne told me to check the rota on the kitchen wall as I would be assigned cleaning duties, before adding, 'You get your own breakfast and lunch, but we have a chef called Camilla who prepares the evening meal. All clients are required to eat the evening meal together. Be careful, Camilla is a very good cook, everyone puts on weight'! 'Right, I will leave you to it, you need to be downstairs in the lounge for 1.15pm for psycho dynamics. If you need anything just ask'. After Anne had closed the door I lay on the bed, full of doubt, fear, and shame.

At 1 o'clock I made my way downstairs and stepped into a very comfortable-looking lounge, where I found a circle of green high-backed armchairs and the other residents of Hope House. Two women, Karen & Nicky, and three men, Gordon, Trevor and Donald. It felt like my first day at a new school! I introduced myself and took a seat. Due to my previous 'life' experiences and failed attempts to 'get sorted' it was not totally an alien environment to me, but still I felt slightly awkward. The six of us (all alkies!) sat in a circle of silence, until Nicky broke the ice and asked me where I was from.

For a bunch of failed (or not failed?) alcoholics, they seemed decent enough. I was surprised when Nicky mentioned this was her fifth stint in rehab! and Gordon and Trevor, their second! I admit it did not fill me with confidence, although I did not say as much. I knew that whether 'this' worked for me or not! Rehab was going to be a one-time only experience for me. At 1.15pm on the dot, the therapist, a lady called Coral entered the room, closed the door behind her and began the first of my group (talking) therapies. I didn't say too much in that first group session. I decided to just listen. It was interesting and I enjoyed it!

That evening I joined everyone in the kitchen for the evening meal. As I took my place at the table and sat down, the snob in me wondered who had previously eaten off my plate, who had used the cutlery before me. Who had drunk from that glass! It was a strange, somewhat uncomfortable and surreal experience to be sitting around a dinner table with a bunch of alcoholics in a rehab centre! But I would soon get used to it. Anne was right, Camilla was a very good cook. It didn't take long before I was at ease, and actually looked forward to the evening meal (Camilla's cheesecakes were legendary!).

On the third day I had a free afternoon, I phoned Bridie and asked her to come and get me! I just wanted to go home for a while! I suddenly wasn't sure if I was doing the right thing. A slight panic attack perhaps? Either way I felt overwhelmed by my current situation. Bridie reluctantly but dutifully picked me up and drove me to our mother's house. As we drove along, I could sense her concern as she asked me if I was okay, I lied and said that I was.

As soon as I walked through the door of my mother's house, I could feel the sickness that lingered and hung heavy in the air, infecting anyone who ventured too near, or stayed to long. It had always been there. Had I caused it? Or had it caused me? I was unusually quiet. I felt saddened. Not just for me, but for the whole family! After only one hour at my mother's, I asked Bridie to take me back to Hope House. I never again doubted I was doing the right thing. From that moment on I embraced my programme of recovery. That night I had the best night's sleep I'd had in years!

Each morning I would be up at 6am. I would make myself a coffee (sadly not strong and bitter tasting!) and smoke a couple of cigarettes in the garden with Trevor, who I had developed a rapport with. Then I would carry out my cleaning duties, shower, have breakfast and be ready for the day.

Charles Darwin said, 'it's not the strongest of the species that survive, it's the most adaptable'! It didn't take me long to adapt to my new environment, in fact I settled in quite quickly, it helped that I actually liked it! A feeling I struggled with at first. Am I supposed to like it? I felt safe, I got on well with everyone and I enjoyed the group therapies, (especially art therapy). I spoke to Jack every 'other' day on the phone, as I didn't want to hound, or bore him! And I also began to wake every morning feeling 'chipper'!

Being a binge drinker, I didn't struggle 'too' much abstaining. The positivity of Hope House, plus the constant threat of the random 'piss' test, helped my resolve. As I began to feel better and as the fog lifted from my brain, I also began to have very vivid and bizarre dreams concerning alcohol.

I woke one morning completely distraught; I was in a real panic! I thought I had been out drinking and was horrified of the consequences. I remember thinking, 'Shit what have I done'! Before realising I was in bed at the rehab. On another occasion I dreamt I was drinking with (the 1970s) Derek Griffiths from the children's programme Play School, he had a massive afro and a moustache and was dressed in seventies attire! I was really excited to be drinking with this icon from my childhood, but then I became annoyed because I had ordered a pint of lager and the barman had put 'ice' in it and ruined it! I was annoyed because I didn't have any more money for another drink, I remember staring at Derek (through the round window!) with hopeful eyes! But the fucker never brought me one!

The combination of rest, positivity, group work and healthy eating were beginning to pay dividends, I was starting to feel ...'alright'! Three weeks in and I woke one morning, and I didn't feel 'alright'. I didn't feel 'chipper' at all. In fact, I felt incredibly down. With the weight of the world on my shoulders, I had sat on the edge of the bed with my head in my hands and thought to myself, 'The honeymoon is over'! 'I was doing okay there for a while, but now I am doomed again'! 'I have been a fool to think I could ever change'! Then I had a moment of clarity. It suddenly dawned on me, that only a lunatic would wake every morning and leap out of bed ecstatic to be alive! Surely its normal to feel down sometimes.?

Feelings and emotions aren't a permanent state of being, they come and go. You can't have an up without a down! (hmm). That realisation alone lifted my mood, I was able to accept how I was feeling without having to dwell on it, knowing that it would pass. I didn't have to nurture the negative feeling into an unnecessary monster (negative action). I was slowly starting to learn how to handle feelings and emotions which I use to suppress with alcohol and drugs. I was starting to learn, who I was!

The first four weeks went quickly. Four weeks and I was then allowed out unaccompanied! All by myself! Although I had to be 'home' by ten! Strange, even though I now could, I hardly left the place!

The first time I did eventually venture out alone, I was on an errand to the bank. It may sound silly! But as I made my way through the town centre, I suddenly became aware of my 'vulnerability'! I had no desire or notion of taking a drink, yet still, I had an uncomfortable unease about me which I couldn't shift. As soon as I was aware of how I was feeling, I scolded myself for being so pathetic! 42yrs old, walking through the same town centre I had bowled through all my life and yet now I feel insecure, but I don't know why! As I ventured out on my own more and more, the sensation ceased, I was slowly regaining my confidence. It was a shock because I hadn't realised, I had lost it!

****

It was a Saturday morning, bright and sunny. With no other plans I decided to take the bus and go and pay my mum a visit. When I arrived at the house and she had opened the front door I was suddenly struck by how old and small she looked. The poor woman was 82yrs old and she had done nothing to deserve the life she had endured. She had put up with and suffered the effects of alcoholism practically all her life and yet she had rarely if ever drank! It was evident that now I wasn't drinking or living in her house, our relationship was improving, but I still found it stifling at 'home'. As nice as it was to see her, I didn't stay too long. ...I have always loved her!

As it was still early and the sun was shining, I decided to give the bus a miss and take a walk back to Hope House. As I made my way through the estate that I had grown up on, I contemplated my life. I had made a mess of things, I had been a fool, I thought back to when I had left school; how I had vowed not to be like my dad, not to be like them. And now, I think I may be worse! I can't do the most basic of things, a home, a relationship, they had that! Do people consider me a joke? Do they think I'm pathetic?

I push these thoughts aside because now there is light at the end of tunnel. I feel different, but then how different can I be in six weeks? Has there been a profound change in me? I think maybe there has! As I continued my walk, I realised I was fast approaching McGillicuddy's brothers house, I decided to give him a knock as I hadn't seen any of the lads for a while. As I did so, I wondered if it was a good idea, Andy's house had always been a bit of a party house, especially as now there was no longer a woman there to keep order. What might I be walking into? Although I felt different, I don't think I was entirely ready to let go of my old life completely (fear perhaps!). I still wanted (at some level) to be one of the boys. It was 11 o'clock in the morning when I knocked Andy's front door. He opened it in the same dishevelled and gruff manner as he always did. 'Alright how's it going', he chuckled as he gestured for me to enter. I stepped inside to find my mate Paul sitting at the dining table in a cloud of (marijuana) smoke and surrounded by beer cans, I could see the detriments of the previous night's cocaine use, neither of them had slept. Punk music was playing on the stereo in the corner of the living room. Andy resumed his place at the table and picked up his beer. Paul, genuinely pleased to see me, roared, 'Fucking hell, how's it going Pat', before trailing off to a whisper '...are you still in the rehab'? Both McGillicuddy's were throwing disbelieving and incredulous glances at one another as I gave them a rough outline of recent events.

I shouldn't have popped in! I felt uncomfortable. Perhaps I was being paranoid, but I felt like they were laughing at me. Maybe they were! We had been friends all our lives. As blokes we were all piss takers, in fact we were ruthless when it came to someone else's misfortune. The truth is, had the shoe been on the other foot... I would have taken the piss too! What had I expected? A fucking round of applause! Why or perhaps 'how' would they understand my situation. I left feeling incredibly foolish and headed for the town centre.

Andy's house is at the bottom of the estate, next to an alleyway which leads to the town centre and which also runs past the old Victorian cemetery situated on the side of the hill that over-looks the town. The same cemetery where my dad and my sister Kathleen are buried, (their plots lying side by side). Ashamedly, I hadn't visited their graves for some time, so I decided to cut through the cemetery and pay my respects. As I made my way to their graves,

I crossed horizontally through the cemetery along an avenue of trees. It really was a beautiful morning, I marvelled at the bright rays of sunshine bursting through the lush green canopy of the treetops. It was incredibly peaceful being alone in the cemetery. Never had I been surrounded by so many, yet bothered by so few! As I walked along, I listened to the birds and watched as they darted to and fro between the trees, it was almost heavenly. And then I was suddenly aware! An epiphany!

I am sober! And I am exactly halfway between Andy's house where he and Paul are sitting at the dining table out of their heads on drink and drugs - and where my father and sister are laying cold in the ground. Both their lives cut short by alcoholism. I am smack bang in the middle! Neither nor ...and it is beautiful ...and it is perfect! I knew then, I was on the right path, I was doing what 'I' needed to do. I was doing what was right for me.

I was happy in Hope House, which in turn told me I was in the right place. It had been seven weeks since I had last had a drink, and what's more I was okay with it! However, I had started to 'project'!

The idea had crept into my head that in the future, after Hope House was done and dusted, I might treat myself to the 'odd' joint now and again; surely that would be okay! I had been harbouring this idea for quite a while, when during one of the group therapy sessions, Trevor announced that he had been thinking about having a drink! Everyone in the group agreed it was a very bad idea! However, Trevor's honesty encouraged me to divulge my own thoughts about smoking pot once I was out of rehab. No sooner had I aired it aloud to the room, than I instantly realised just how foolish an idea it was. I would never be happy with the 'odd' joint. It would surely become a full-time habit! In fact, I had always smoked pot, 'alcoholically'. How long before I would be snorting the 'odd' line of cocaine and where would that lead me? My 'guard' would inevitably be dropped and then I would succumb to what I really wanted all along, alcohol!

I have never taken a drug as powerful as alcohol, for me there is no comparison. Everything else was just a lead up to, or a coming down from! I don't think it's unusual for people to 'believe' they are doing one thing, when actually, they are really doing something else! I was thankful, for Trevor's honesty! One-week later Trevor announced he was leaving. He said he just wanted to go for a drink and didn't wish to continue with the programme, I was shocked! I was also very concerned, as I knew he would regret it. I spent the best part of an hour, pleading with him in his room, as I watched him pack his things. I tried to convince him to stay, I tried to make him see sense. But it was pointless, he had made up his mind. Nothing I could say would change that. I knew this from personal experience. Trevor was a man on a mission. I had only known him for a couple of months, but we had got on well and I considered him a friend. I was sad to see him go; I was also worried about him. That's when I realised for the first time that I had put my family through hell. A true lightbulb moment! How many sleepless nights had my poor mother had worrying if I was dead or alive! How painful it must be to watch your child destroy themselves. I was truly sorry, for everything I had put them through.

Trevor started phoning me when he was drunk. It was very awkward; he would lament down the phone at length and talk gibberish. I didn't like to, but in the end, I had to blank his calls. I was after all an alcoholic in recovery! It had taken me a long time to accept the effect my drinking had on those around me. Those that I loved dearly.

I had constantly been told that I was selfish and uncaring, but it wasn't true. Alcoholism is a selfish illness! It is selfish by its very nature. The condition is selfish, not the sufferer! I once read a line in a book that has stayed with me, 'Illness is a lonely occupation'!

****

One to one counselling was also part of the programme at Hope House. It began in week ten and continued on a weekly basis, thereafter for the remainder of the programme, (with six more sessions after completion). I was dubious. I didn't really want to do it. I saw a film once where allegedly Sigmund Freud had said 'The Irish are the only race on the planet who are impervious to psychoanalysis'! Basically, I didn't see the point! As far as I was concerned, it would be a waste of time.

The truth was, I didn't know what I was supposed to talk about! It reminded me of being a little kid and having to go to confession. Being so young and innocent, I had nothing to confess, so like every other catholic child of that age, I made up some lies to tell the priest! I needn't have worried, because despite initially having my guard up, when I started counselling the truth came flooding out!

My counsellor was a little Irish woman called Mary, (so it ended up being difficult for either of us to get a word in edgeways!). After the preliminary exchanges and after Mary had outlined the counselling process, I kicked the ball rolling by saying, 'I suppose I should tell you about my background and how I ended up here in Hope House'? Mary smiled at me and said, ...'if you want to'! I told her off my childhood, I spoke of my parents and how I had at times felt marginalised by them and their social standing and how I had then felt guilty about it. I spoke of my alcoholism and how I felt ashamed of it, how I had been battling it all my life and couldn't understand how I couldn't be like other men; how I felt like damaged goods. I couldn't even do the basics like relationships and keeping a roof over my head. Even idiots have some where to live! My face lit up when I mentioned Jack, which didn't go unnoticed by Mary. I spoke of my pride and love for him, how I had been truly blessed. I then spoke of the unbearable shame of failing to be the father he deserved. My mum had said, if I loved him, I would stop drinking! Yet I think it was 'because' I loved him so much, that I couldn't stop drinking! I was too ashamed! I loathed myself for being unable to be the father and the man I should have been. I had to drink in order to bare the pain!

I did okay in my first counselling session, I managed to stop myself from blubbing on at least four occasions. Mary said she didn't think I was a bad father, she said I was a parent who suffered from alcoholism, and from what I had told her, I had done my best to protect Jack from my addiction. She pointed out my parents hadn't protected me from their problems. She said I was a good dad!

Surprisingly, a lot of people have said this to me ...but, I have always found it difficult to agree, I didn't pay maintenance for my son. It's difficult when you drink every penny. Mary pointed out that the financial side of things was only a small part of being a parent. We concluded (she reluctantly) that I had always been a loving dad and a caring dad, I just hadn't always been a good dad. My reasoning being I don't care what anyone says, if you're star shaped on the pavement, then you are not a good parent! It was something I was going to have to learn to live with. Something I was going to have to ensure did not continue to be the case. I hope my son is not embarrassed of me like, I was of my father.

My first counselling session had been a positive experience. Despite my previous concerns, I looked forward to my next one. That evening I decided to phone Jack, as I was really missing him. He was doing his French homework. I smiled down the phone when he started talking to me in French! I obviously didn't have a clue as to what he was going on about, so I called him, 'Air – sill – aye – nink – en – poop'! which made him laugh! It only seems like yesterday since I sat alone in the hospital delivery room, holding him in my hands and marvelling at his perfection. I am very proud of him.

That night as I slept in my room, I had the recurring dream again. Everything was white. The pond was again frozen solid and there was the same stillness and eerie silence as before. Around the edge of the pond stood the crowd of people, still too far away to determine if they were concerned or jeering. Only this time it wasn't me standing alone on the ice in the middle of the pond. Instead it was a small boy. I knew he was frightened, and I knew he looked bewildered, yet at the same time I could not make out his face. Again, I heard the faint but familiar, snap, snap of the ice beneath his tiny feet. I watched in terror as the cracks began to race and grow outwards and away from under him. I felt as helpless as the boy looked. Then suddenly without warning the ice gave way and the small boy dropped, I shot out my arm and grabbed him, I saw he was crying. And then I woke up. I never had the dream again!

I had a lot to think about in Hope House, a lot of soul searching! The group therapies were designed to challenge your mind-set; they were working! As well as looking forward to my counselling sessions I also looked forward to art therapy, it was by far my favourite of all the group works. We would have 30 minutes in which to draw, sketch or paint something and then each member of the group would then in turn place their 'art' at the front of the room, for the therapist to read (analyse); into its meanings and draw conclusions from the image. I always gave it great thought and often surprised myself by what I could produce in half an hour. In one group session I drew (with pastels) an Eskimo, fishing a hole in the ice! I drew it so you could see the ocean under the ice. The ocean was empty, and the Eskimo had no bait on his hook! He would never get anything out of it!

Above the ice and all around the Eskimo, there were glaciers and icebergs. The night sky above him was littered with stars and the northern lights were dancing and swaying all around him. But the Eskimo was oblivious to all the awe and wonder, because he was concentrating very hard and putting all his effort into the hole in the ice?

On another occasion I drew a scene from a childhood book I was re-reading, 'The Martian Chronicles' by Ray Bradbury (I had re-ignited my love of reading). In the first chapter, the book describes Mr and Mrs K and their Martian house. A rocket ship carrying the first manned expedition from earth, has landed near Mr K's home. Mrs K has revealed to her husband that she has had a dream and has stated that the earth man in her dream was, 'not' unattractive, in a 'strange' kind of way! Jealous and enraged, Mr K, dons a Martian war mask and carrying a Martian weapon goes to the landing site and kills the earth men!

My picture shows Mr K standing outside his Martian home wearing the war mask and carrying his 'gun'. To the right of the picture is a very large cylindrical shaped rocket ship and in the Martian sky above, can be seen the two huge Martian moons. When I presented my picture to the front of the room, Coral, the therapist chuckled! I was somewhat perplexed by her reaction to my picture, but thought no more of it, as I began to explain how my picture represented 'resistance to change'.

Mr K had killed the earth men. But it had been futile. The earth men had brought with them a foreign bacteria, for which the Martians had no defence. Eventually all the Martians were wiped out by ...chicken pox! Mr K's resistance to change had been pointless because it was going to happen anyway. Thus, representing my own resistance to change. How clever of me! I was really rather pleased with myself! Later that day while smugly admiring my picture, I was horrified when it suddenly dawned on me why the therapist had initially giggled at my 'Piece'! A large cylindrical rocket ship and two large moons! I had unintentionally drawn a massive cock and balls!!!

I enjoyed the talking therapies too; it was amazing what came out of the group discussions. In the thinking and behaviour group we were talking about strength. When I was asked my opinion, I said that we had all endured years of shite, to reach this point in our life's (rehab). That's strength! Not being able to stop at two pints down the pub, isn't!

I try not to think I will never drink again, it's too daunting. It seems as if I am setting myself up for a fall just by thinking it. For me to ever drink again is nothing short of suicide! But I now want to live! So, I just hope I won't. I don't want to let my son down. I feel sorry for him having an alcoholic for a father. Alcohol has turned me into something I never wanted to be; it has robbed me of a lot of things. Sometimes I still feel like the 'old' me. I think maybe I am in there somewhere, just below the surface scratching to get out, and then at other times, I doubt if there ever was an 'old' me. Sometimes I dare to dream what my life might have been like if I wasn't an alcoholic, who knows, maybe it would have been worse! I hope people understand that I am not a bad person.

The only group session I don't particularly enjoy is life skills and communication. Jane the lady who takes the group is nice enough, just not very good at it! She is totally out of her depth and it shows, (you, probably had a rubbish teacher at school who couldn't engage or control the pupils, well that's Jane!). She was very flowery and wishy washy; unfortunately, it just didn't work. During one of her group sessions she was discussing the dangers we might inadvertently put ourselves in while drinking and taking drugs. She was directing 'all' of the talking at the women in the group, when she said something along the lines of, '...and when he comes home from the pub, he might.... hit you'!!! As she said this, she turned and looked directly at ...me!

'What you looking at me for', I said in a very offended tone. It actually hurt my feelings. 'I've never hit a woman in my life'! I stated with a grimace, (well apart from Samantha outside the science block!). I hadn't imagined it. Everyone in the group had seen it too! Jane, realising she had got it horribly wrong, immediately tried to wriggle out of it, but without making any form of an apology!

When the group finished and as everyone was leaving the room, she spinelessly pulled me to one side and 'very' quietly made a hushed apology. I told her just because I am a white male and an alcoholic, doesn't mean I am a bully or a wife beater.... it just makes me a man who happens to suffer from alcoholism! I truly was offended. As I say, she was just a bit.... shit!

When the next week came around and we again had Jane for a group work session, she couldn't have been nicer to me. For this session Jane had decided she was going to go around the room and ask each person to say 'one' word that described exactly how they were feeling at that precise moment. First, she turned to Gordon. He shifted uncomfortably in his chair upon finding himself in the spotlight, he shrugged his shoulders and said, 'I feel... erm average'! 'Brilliant', declared Jane, 'That's, fantastic'!

She then turned to Donald, 'Donald, what word would you use to describe how your feeling right now at this moment'? Donald looked like a wide-eyed kid in a classroom who is just about to shout out the correct answer as he leaned forward in his chair and said, 'Normal'! 'Normal, that's very good Donald' she said patronisingly.

'And what about you Pat, what wor....'. I didn't let her finish and stated firmly, 'MORIBUND'! She suddenly looked like a rabbit caught in the head lights, totally at a loss, ... she didn't know what it meant! '...Sorry', she stammered nervously. 'Stagnant and without purpose, in a dying state, languid and morose, Jane'! I offered helpfully! 'erm...'!

Perhaps it was a bit mean. Perhaps I should have been a bit more gallant. Then again, perhaps I was just letting it be known that I was not an idiot. I was letting it be known when I was unhappy about, or didn't like something, as opposed to diverting my eyes to the floor, or skulking off to the pub to vent my disapproval. Perhaps it was progress! Still, no one likes a smart arse! All the therapies helped, even the shit one!

****

We had a new bloke start the programme at Hope House. Unlike the rest of us he was not an alcoholic. His name was Alan and he was addicted to crack cocaine! It had previously been agreed by residents and staff alike, that 'we' were a particularly nice group. So, Al's arrival had unsettled a few people, me included!

Selfishly, I worried how it would affect the group dynamics, I kind of liked things the way they were. Six alkies and a junkie! Would it work? I needn't have worried, Al was a really nice bloke. When he talked about his addiction, I could relate to everything he was saying. Likewise, Alan could relate to 'us' when we spoke of 'our' alcoholism. Addiction is addiction, the substance of choice, is, to a certain degree, irrelevant. You might be addicted to Jaffa cakes! If you are truly addicted to them, they will fuck you up! You will be at the end of your tether! You will be bawling your eyes out crying, you will not be able to imagine life, with, or without them. You may feel suicidal, hopeless and ashamed.

You will be driven to the gates of insanity as you try to figure out why you can't stop eating, the gorgeous, mouth-watering, little spongy, tangy orange-centred, chocolate-covered treats. Mmmm, Jaffa cakes! They do the twin packs now you know!!

Al had been with us for a couple of weeks, when during a group led by a therapist called Steve, he began for the first time, to open up about his personal life. I could feel his pain as he spoke through tear filled eyes, of the sadness of being apart from his wife and children. Alan and his wife had met as teenagers. 15yrs and two children later, she had left him for his best friend (ouch!), and now she was not letting him see his kids. I felt for the man, everyone did! It was all very personal, but he had aired it to the group, so it was fair game for everyone to offer an opinion. Most said they understood how he was feeling and offered reassurances that things would improve now that he was on the right path. Some were a bit more vocal and said the wife was out of order. Me, I said, 'Forgive her'. You could have heard a fucking pin drop!

'That's what I did Al'! 'Look, I'm not trying to stick the boot in Alan, I can see you're hurting, but I think you have to try and see it from her point of view'. 'I know you're a decent bloke and it's obvious that you love your wife and kids and reading between the lines I think she probably loves you too. But I think you have to be thankful that she supported you and stuck by you for as long as she did. It couldn't have been easy for her trying to deal with your addiction and bringing up two kids at the same time. Your best mate is a bit of a kick in the balls, granted! I would be more angry at him than her. As for the kids, well it sounds like she is just trying to protect your children. Not from you, but from your addiction.

Ask yourself this Al, would you leave your children with someone who smokes crack? I'm sure she no more wanted it to turn out like this than you wanted to be a crack head! Forgive her, let it go!

Concentrate on getting clean and getting your life back and be the best dad you can be'.

There was total silence and then Steve the therapist said, 'Hang on a minute Pat, I think Alan's situation is slightly different to yours, his is still raw'! 'And anyway, I don't think you did forgive your ex! I think you merely learnt to 'accept' her'. I immediately thought back to the utter rage I had once felt, I remembered a time not so long ago when I had only wanted to outlive her!

Change one word and it changes everything. 'I forgive you', it does have lofty connotations. Steve was right I had forgiven her fuck all! I had forgotten nothing! But I 'had' accepted her for who she was, I had also accepted she had never set out to hurt me, just like I never set out to hurt her or be an alkie in a rehab! In accepting her, I had also paved the way to be able to accept myself. Steve was right! I think he might also have been a little bit peeved at me for 'holding court' in his therapy session! Either way it was yet another light bulb moment!

****

After two months in Hope House I was allowed a night away, (and then every third week thereafter). This meant I could have Jack for the night at my mum's. Obviously I enjoyed it very much, it was excellent to spend time with my son. I also appreciated my mum accommodating us (as she always had), but I longed for the day when I had my own home, when I could be a proper dad! Just me and my boy. Jack, being quite inquisitive, had (naturally) begun to ask questions about Hope House. I surprised myself when over breakfast and having asked Jack if he would 'like my egg'! I had also asked, 'Would you like to come for a visit'? He grinned and said 'yeah'!

Initially I didn't want him anywhere near the place. I didn't want him infected by my disease. I had always tried to keep Jack and my alcoholism separate. I suppose I was like the man in prison, who does not want his kids coming to visit. He doesn't want them to see him incarcerated, kept behind bars like an animal, nor does he want them to be around people, ...who are, ... lacking in character! He doesn't want to sully any future memory his children will have of him. Its better if they are not part of it.

However, I had changed my mind because I was comfortable in Hope House. There were no white lab coats, no one walking around monged, everyone was sober and bright, it was actually, a very pleasant environment. I was also worried about Jack; fretting is probably a better term! His mum had just had another child and his dad was in rehab! I thought he might be feeling a bit left out. I reasoned if I showed him around and explained what I was doing, then it might ease his mind. It would reassure him that he was still the centre of my world.

I scheduled his visit for a Saturday afternoon, when I knew the house would be quiet. His mum dropped him off at two in the afternoon. I showed him round the house, I showed him where we had are 'talks' and watched telly in the evening, I showed him my room and the picture in pride of place on my wall that he had drawn for me (a dinosaur wearing a shirt and tie!?). I showed him the gardens and the hen house where 'Dorothy' lived! Then we sat in the kitchen chatting and I gave him a large bowl of chocolate ice cream! We had both enjoyed his visit, it was the right thing to do and we both felt better for it. After Louise had returned and picked Jack up, I had a moment of sadness, before realising just how lucky I was!

Jack wasn't the only visitor I received at Hope House. My sister Bridie and her new bloke Mick came to see me regularly. She was pleased I was getting the help I needed, and I was pleased she had met a decent man! My sister Evelyn came to see me too, and on commenting how nice it was said, 'I wouldn't mind a couple of weeks in here myself.... if I was allowed to have the odd drink that is, ha ha'! My mother and Connor didn't visit. My mum being old Irish and very old fashioned in her ways, said she didn't want to see me …'like that'! It was okay; I understood. My brother! I love my brother, I have always looked up to him, I just don't think he understood the nature of my illness, and why would he! I didn't! I think I reminded him of our dad and I don't think he believed I would change. And that was okay too, because I understood.

To my surprise all the lads came to see me too! Neil, Simón, Jim and my nephew Dan. McGillicuddy didn't; I think he was frightened that if he came in, then they wouldn't let him out again! It would seem my friends were coming back to me, perhaps they had never left, perhaps it was me who had been absent!

Jim had turned up on his new motor bike and wearing his (sexy) leathers, I heard him before I saw him! 'Fucking hell Delaney you look ten years younger', he said with a look of astonishment! 'Fuck off Jim, I've always looked good', I said grinning. It was nice to see my oldest friend; I was glad he had come. I made us both a cup of 'tea' and took it out into the garden where we could sit and smoke.

'So, when did you get the bike Jim'? Jim told me he had bought it two months earlier. It was a Honda Fire Blade, a powerful machine. 'Be careful Jim, those things are fucking powerful, it's not a matter of, if you have an accident, it's a matter of when'. Jim told me to: 'Shut up and stop being a fanny'! Then his phone rang! Jim immediately looked shifty and lowered his voice to a hushed whisper, 'Alright mate.... erm... yeah... what! Round the corner, ...sound, … ten minutes, okay nice one … cheers bruv'. Jim looked at me wincing and shrugged his shoulders! I couldn't believe it, 'For fuck sake Jim, ...I'm in a fucking rehab'!

I couldn't help but laugh at his audacity. With a massive grin Jim said, 'Sorry, Pat', and then changed the subject by saying, 'Anyway, any birds in here? You shagging any'? 'Nah, relationships aren't allowed Jim, if you get caught getting involved ...as it were, then they throw you out'. Jim just grinned again and said, 'Yeah'! 'Well that just makes it all the more exciting Pat'!!!

Despite his tactlessness, Jim's visit had left me in a good mood. After he left, I chilled for a while and then joined Nicky in the TV room to watch an episode of 'Breaking Bad'. Possibly not the most appropriate viewing for a couple of alkies in rehab, but we watched it anyway. During this particular episode there was a scene were one of the main characters is doing drugs with his girlfriend. When he wakes up in the morning his girlfriend is dead in the bed next to him. I briefly knew a man who woke up one morning and found his girlfriend dead in the bed next to him. I didn't mention it to Nicky.

****

My mum phoned to tell me her friend Jean Ellis had died; she was 84 and had cancer. It saddened me; I had always liked Jean. She used to call everyone duck! I used to give her and my mum a lift to bingo in the early days, (before I got really bad)! I don't think I ever heard the woman swear or say a bad word about anyone (unlike my mum!). The news that she had died made me think of when I was in America and I had received the letter from my mum. The one that didn't say very much, apart from she had been to bingo with Jean, but they didn't win! It just reminded me of home! The mundane and the ordinary. The familiar. The simple pleasure of 'being'. I have been so wrapped up in trying to get myself straight, I have forgotten, 'the normal'! I will miss Jean, (I never knew her middle name was Beryl!).

My mum will be 82yrs old next week, she lives alone now that I'm in here (rehab). Jean was a very good friend of hers, my mum is upset and invariably thinking about her own mortality. She will be going up to bed tonight all alone, in an empty house. I am not happy about it, but I am powerless to do anything. I worry.

Jack is on his summer holidays from school. I can't take him anywhere because I'm skint and in here. His mum is working, so he has to attend sports school. I am not happy about it, but I am powerless to do anything. I worry.

I could leave rehab. That would sort out both problems but unleash all the old ones. I love them both with all my heart! I wish I was a better father and a son (I'm not quite ready to be a holy spirit!). Do I dare imagine a time when life will be good, when I will feel that I am fulfilling my roles and obligations? A time when I will be content, a time when my opinion matters and is considered and respected? Will I have someone to share it with, someone to confide in, someone to understand; someone to point out when I am not being wise, but without condemnation or judgement? Or will I always be like this? Will I always have to fight to keep my sanity?

I had another counselling session with Mary. We talked about my mum and Jack. I told Mary how my mother had always been negative and abusive towards me. I also explained that she loved me very much and I her. As I was telling Mary, I thought of an abuser, who one minute tells you your worthless and then the next tells you they love you! Perhaps I am being a bit harsh!

Mary said, 'You' have to stop allowing her to do this to you. She might not change! But you will and you are.' Mary asked me to give it some thought. How can I stop my mum, from being my mum?! It's all she knows! If I don't drink, that would probably be a good start. It would take away her leverage. I could stop being a pain in the arse, that would help too. I need to stop being so needy and reliant on her. I have to let go of the apron strings! Sounds easy now I am not living in her house. It was very difficult having to absorb all the negativity and hatred, it drained me to the point of not wanting to live. However, I have to take responsibility for my part in it all. My alcoholism! My reluctance or incapability to stand on my own two feet (easier said than done at certain times!). I am not trying to present myself as blameless, far from it. I think what I am trying to say is, I needed kisses not kicks.

I haven't been very well. Sometimes I have been very unwell! But now I am starting to feel better, stronger. Yet every time I mention my mother, I feel like I am a child again. (my son lives with his mum, ...and I live with mine!). I started to feel uncomfortable, so I told Mary I didn't want to talk about my mum anymore! I said I would rather talk about Jack and my alcoholism. Mary said, 'I think perhaps you need to talk about your mum'! Shrugging my shoulders, I said, 'But I feel a bit pathetic going on about my mother all the time'. Mary said it was important to talk about my feelings, 'If you don't, then how would anyone know if you needed help?' She then said, 'It's the squeaky wheel that gets the oil'! I grinned, 'That's excellent, do you mind if I use it'? Still grinning, I then said, 'My mate Simón told me he got reprimanded for being late for work. The boss said, 'You know Simón, it's the early bird that gets the worm.' To which Simón replied, 'Yes, but it's the second mouse that gets the cheese'! It was Mary's turn to grin.

'Okay then' said Mary, changing tack, 'What would you say to someone, who has 'your' problem'? It was a good one, I had to think for a while before I answered. Then I said, 'I would tell them that 'alcoholism is the symptom of an underlying problem'. 'I would also tell them that it's not their fault, that they should not feel ashamed'. 'Just because you have a drink problem doesn't make you any less of, or a bad, person'! Mary nodded. I continued, 'I would say that, living a sober life might seem like an impossibility, but it isn’t. You can live the life you deserve, the life that you are entitled too, if you work hard enough for it and don’t be frightened to ask for help'! Mary smiled and said, 'That's excellent advice, Pat', before glancing at the clock on the wall behind me.

It was nearly the end of our session. Mary said, 'You have a lot to think about Pat. I would like you to give some thought to what we have talked about today, I think it will do you good'! 'We didn’t really get chance to talk about your son today, so I am going to give you some homework, which we can discuss next week'! I physically shrank away from her when she said the word, 'homework', which made her smile again. 'Okay' I agreed reluctantly. 'Good, I want you to write down some examples of the things Jack might say to you, if he had a voice'. I was immediately offended and protested, 'He has got a voice, he can talk to me about anything.' But Mary shook her head and said, 'No, he's a 9yr old boy, he can’t say the things to you that perhaps he would like to, he doesn't know how. You’re his father and you’re an adult'! Mary read my face and said, 'It may well be a painful exercise, but I believe it will be a very worthwhile one'! She was right, it was painful, the next morning I wrote this:

“What would Jack tell me if he had a voice? That he's glad I don't drink anymore because it scared him and made him unhappy and it made nan unhappy too. He didn't like it when me and nan argued. He wishes he could see me more. He wishes I had my own house (like other dads) so we could have more time together, just us. He wishes I had a good job, so we could do more fun things and go places. He wished we lived together. He wishes me and his mum lived together so he could have us both all the time. He wishes I would visit him more at his house (I never go there; he always comes to me). He doesn’t like me when I am drunk!

“What will Jack tell me when he is older? You were a good dad and I always felt loved? You didn't bother with me as much as you could have done and sometimes, I felt alone. Why didn't you pay for me or help mum financially? If you loved me, you would have given up the drink and drugs long before you did. Why didn't you come to see me more, I only live across town? Why weren't you more involved? I sometimes felt uncomfortable and embarrassed by you. I'm glad you stopped drinking!"

Being forced to think about how my son might view and feel about my problems was upsetting. It reinforced the belief in me that I was indeed 'no good'. As a result, I wanted to be alone, away from the rehab, away from my alcoholism, away from everyone. So, I decided to go for a walk. Not far from the rehab is a park, I used to go there sometimes as a child and I had in the past taken Jack there to feed the ducks, when he was a toddler. I have always thought it a beautiful, tranquil place, a stark contrast to the industrial town it is nestled in. The walk was doing me good; it lifted my mood and cleared my head. I strolled up through the park past the old Victorian boating lake and the weeping willow trees and on towards the old museum house situated at the top end of the park. It was a bright but fresh afternoon, I was in a world of my own, just mulling things over, as I ambled past the museum. Unbeknown to me, there was an exhibition on at the museum and as a result the south facing windows had been covered in mirrored glass, but I hadn't noticed as I was too busy taking in the beauty of the park.

As I walked past the windows, I glanced in their direction and noticed a little old man staring at me. He was short and stocky with slightly slumped shoulders; he wore a half smile on an otherwise weary looking face, and he had short cropped snow-white hair. I did a double take, stopping dead in my tracks. The wind knocked out of my sails. I was horrified! Because It was me!

I stood silent and opened mouthed as I stared at my 'full' reflection. I couldn't believe how old I looked. I felt a sudden pang of sadness come over me, as I realised in that moment, that I had wasted the best years of my life on drink and drugs. All the time I had been fighting, or succumbing to my demons, life had been marching on regardless. I looked like a man in his late sixties! Disheartened, I turned away from the museum and as I did so I noticed a young lad who was wearing skin-tight jeans and a black leather jacket. He was taking the opportunity to check his appearance and coif his abundant jet-black hair, (just like the fonz)! 'What a fucking cock'! I thought bitterly to myself as I about turned and began 'shuffling' my way back to the sanctuary of Hope House!

Without ever really considering it (until now), I suppose I had in my mind still believed I was a twenty something young go getter, who was just taking some time out.... to work on himself! My walk had forced me to concede I was no longer the carefree young man, I had perhaps imagined myself to be. I'm now an old man, before my time and with 'white' hair! And at this moment, I don't have a lot going for me!

For the first time in my adult life I am experiencing true sobriety. No drink, no drugs, which is great. But I am also faced with the stark reality of my situation! I am becoming very aware of the things I have done, the things I haven't done and the things I need to do. Bridie said it is like I have woken up out of a coma and everything has changed! Only now do I truly see the mess I have made of things. I hope I can put most of it right. Stopping drinking is easy! Yes, I did just say that! The difficulty is staying stopped!

My sister Bridie is having a surprise engagement party next week in Swindon. I love my sister, but I can't go! It's too soon, the truth is, I'm still too vulnerable. If it were here in town, then I could go along for an hour, but if I travel to Swindon I will effectively be trapped and surrounded by people drinking, with no means of safeguarding myself, or escape! I hope she will understand. Now I think about it, I rarely attend family do's. And even if I 'do' attend a 'do', I'm normally standing on the side line of whatever it is that's going on. I have always been different.

Alcohol-ism! Alcohol is in the bottle, the 'ism', is in me! Alcohol-ism! I have been in rehab 12 weeks now. Monday will be the start of week 13. It's a 24-week programme. Anne, my key worker says I need to start thinking about leaving, and what I can put in place to ensure I don't relapse. Steve the therapist said it would be a good idea to think about the sort of person I would like to be. This is what I came up with:

Sober, decent, independent, reliable, dependable, happy, caring, tolerant, strong, admired, loved and loving.

How do I achieve this, how do I achieve the goals that will change my life?

CHAPTER TWENTY-SEVEN

I WAS ASLEEP, WHEN I HEARD MY PHONE RINGING. Waking up I raised myself up on one arm and in the darkness reached across to the bedside cabinet for my phone. The illuminated screen told me it was midnight and it was my sister Evelyn phoning! Receiving a phone call from the family at midnight while you're in rehab, can't be good news! My mum!? I answered the phone, 'What is it Evelyn'? 'Right don't worry it's okay', she said. 'Is it mum'? 'No, everything's okay, don't panic, listen to me, its Jim, he's okay, but he has been in a bad motorbike accident'!

Evelyn explained that Jim had hit an oncoming truck and was in a 'critical' but 'stable' condition in Addenbrooke's hospital. I was in shock, stunned, I sat on the end of the bed, I didn't know what to do! A few moments passed before I phoned Simón and told him what Evelyn had told me. After an initial pause on the phone he said, 'Right I'm going straight up there', I said 'Pick me up on the way'! I knew the staff at Hope House would have something to say about me going out at midnight, but I really didn't care.

We arrived at Addenbrooke's at 1.00am and were shown to a waiting room by a member of staff. Upon entering we were greeted by Jim's devastated family. His wife and his mother were both in tears. His sisters were in shock. A little over two years after burying Tony (Jim's only brother), they were again faced with tragedy and the very real threat of losing their only other brother, husband and son!

Jim had sustained life threatening and life changing injuries. He had broken nearly every bone in his body. The collision with the truck had been so forceful that his bike had all but disintegrated and Jim had been catapulted nearly a mile down the road. I think it was only down to the fact that Jim was such a big bloke that he had even survived the crash, a lesser man would have perished at the scene. Jim had been placed into an induced coma to prevent the risk of further injuring himself in his fragile condition. He had already undergone five operations in an attempt to save his right arm by the time me and Simón had arrived, with more surgery planned for when his condition improved. Me and Simón were allowed to see him. I think we were both taken aback by how 'okay' he looked, if that makes sense. He looked like he was just sleeping. It was a comfort to see him and know he was in good hands. We returned to the waiting room and tried to offer encouraging words of support to his poor wife and mother, but not wishing to intrude too much on such a personal family matter, we left. Both mine and Simón's spirits had been lifted after having initially feared the worst.

Now alone we discussed the affects Jim's injuries would have on his psychological wellbeing. 'This is life changing stuff, Simón, Jim's going to need a lot of help, it will destroy him, we have to stay strong and be there for him'. Simón agreed that we, as his friends would do whatever it took to help him through the tough times ahead. 'He might end up in a wheelchair'! To lighten the heavy mood I said, 'I will do anything... but I won't wipe his fucking arse, no matter what. You know why? Because the fucker will make a full recovery and one day we will be standing in the pub and there will be some beautiful looking bird standing there and Jim with a smug grin on his face will say, 'Pat, do you remember that time when you used to wipe my arse!!!' And I will go bright red, so she will know it's true'!!! Me and Simón both laughed, but only to hide the awkwardness of how we really felt. We were both extremely worried about our friend.

I got back to Hope House at 4.00am. I was tired and restless, but I could not sleep. I kept picturing Jim's family sitting in the waiting room at the hospital. My heart went out to them all, poor Jim. At the same time, I couldn't help but think, that could easily have been my family wondering how and what they were going to tell my son. Eventually I feel asleep.

I woke up still tired and still worried. The situation was bad! With a heavy heart, I forced myself to shower, get dressed and to go downstairs and join the others. It was a strange morning in Hope House, I was treated with suspicion by both staff and clients alike. Going out at midnight and returning at 4.00 am, when you're in a treatment centre doesn't look good. It was no surprise then when I was asked by Jenny and Sarah, two senior staff members, to come into the office. Sarah spoke first. 'Why did you go out, and where did you go'? it had been said as an accusation. I explained about the phone call from my sister, how she had told me about Jim's accident and how I had phoned Simón, who in turn had picked me up and we had gone to the hospital.

Jenny and Sarah exchanged quick glances; they weren't convinced! I suppose in their line of work they had both heard every conceivable excuse and sob story known to man. Sarah pressed on accusingly, 'Why didn't you phone the on call and let us know'? I looked her straight in the eye and said, 'Because it was midnight, I've just been woken up and told my mate has been in a serious accident. I was seriously worried, I didn't have time to think, I just went'! 'Look, I know I'm in treatment and I know it's important, but so is my mate Jim. I was going to the hospital, regardless of what anyone said'. They again exchanged glances only this time holding each other's gaze for a moment longer than they had before, they weren't sure. Jenny came straight out with it, no messing! 'Did you have a drink last night Pat'? I let out a sigh, I felt like a naughty schoolboy, my shoulders slumped as I said, 'No Jenny I didn't'!

I wasn't as offended as you might imagine, what else were they to think. Jenny stared at me and said, 'You know you're going to have to do a piss test don't ya'! 'yeah I know Jenny, it's okay, I understand'. And I did understand. I just really wasn't in the mood for fucking rules and regulations or for pissing into a little plastic cup to be presented to the office for that matter! Rules and regulations! I still 'had' to take part in all the group works, although I found it difficult to engage in any of the discussions, I couldn't concentrate. I was unusually quiet.

The next day having 'passed' the urine test and with the 'permission' of Hope House, me Simón and Neil Duncan drove up to Addenbrooke's hospital to see Jim. He was still in intensive care but was thankfully in a stable condition. Simón had spoken with Nicola, Jim's wife. She had told Simón that the doctors had briefly woken Jim out of his induced coma, he had looked around the room, smiled at her and said he was sorry, before the doctors put him under again. It was a good sign! Simón said Nicola was understandably very upset, she was also annoyed with Jim for being so foolish. What was she to tell the children? The poor woman was beside herself with worry.

The three of us, (me, Simón, and Neil), all took it in turns to go in and have a few moments alone with Jim. My oldest friend! I was at a loss as what to say or do. I rubbed his hand and gently patted his head, aware that if he were to wake up, he would probably say, 'What you doing, get off me you fucking mug'! I told him to be strong and that I would help him any way I could through the tough times ahead. As the three of us made our way home in the car, I pointed out that Jim was not out of the woods yet. He was very lucky to have survived but, 'This is serious'. We all agreed and were determined to do whatever it took to help our mate to get through this. That night I slept a little better.

The next morning Simón phoned me. I could barely make out was he was saying because he was crying,

'Jim's dead' !

There was a moment of silence. I didn't respond. I didn't speak. My brain refused to process what I had just heard. I did not compute! It did not make sense. Poor Simón was inconsolable, he had never lost anyone close to him before, he had never been touched by the hand of death. When my father had died, I was a boy, I was just a child. When my sister passed, I wasn't much older and when the Geordie had died, I was half the world away. I was somewhat removed. I was somewhat detached from the grief. This was different. This was raw. It cut through me like a knife. I was stunned into complete silence. After a moment I managed.... 'How, why'?

Through short gasps and sobs, Simón informed me that our dear friend had passed away at 2.00am that morning having suffered a heart attack brought on by the trauma of his injuries. His body could no longer cope. Despite the efforts of the doctors they were unable to save Jim.

This wasn’t real. This wasn’t happening. Jim’s poor wife! His poor mum! The kids! In that moment I recalled when my father had died and the realisation that I would never see him again. It now hit me like a ton weight when I realised, I was never to see my friend again. I didn't cry. I didn't sob, instead I 'Wept' for my friend. It’s different somehow isn't it!

Through the daze I realised it was 9.00am and time for group work, obviously I would not be going. Instead I dried my eyes and headed for the office to tell them I would be going to see Jim's family. In my mind I dared them to tell me otherwise. When I entered the office, Sarah and Jenny both took one look at me and instantly knew, ...they both looked straight at the floor, I sensed their unfounded shame. I told them Jim had passed, I could see they were both embarrassed as they stole a quick glance at one another and then at me before again lowering their heads to the floor and mumbling their apologies.

My phone hadn't stopped ringing since Simón's call, bad news always travels fast. Everyone was in shock. My sister said she would pick me up, but I phoned a cab instead not wanting to wait. I made my way to Jim's sister's house, dreading the scene that awaited me. Donna (Jim's sister), opened the door and immediately burst into tears. I was at a loss as what to do, even though I was aware I needed to hold it together for the family's sake. As I entered the house, I was met with vacant looks of disbelief, the hugs, tears and handshakes and offers of condolences that I had expected. Still I managed to keep it together. Then I entered the front room.

Jim's poor old mum was sitting at the living room table. I walked across the room and hugged her tightly and kissed the top of her head. She turned to face me and held up a picture of her two sons and said, 'Oh, Pat. Why did He have to take them both'? It was pitiful. In that moment, it was too much for me. I broke. I turned and walked away. I had to!

As soon as I was outside the house, I began to sob uncontrollably. Jim's devastated family had their own grief to contend with, they didn't need to bare witness to mine. I left and went back 'home' to Hope House and the sanctuary of my room.

By 1 o'clock my phone had stopped ringing. Half my friends have probably gone to a pub the other half are probably in someone's house drinking and taking drugs. In short, everyone including my family and Jim's, have got on it. Alcohol serves a purpose; it numbs the pain. It makes life bearable. But I can't do it. My friends and my family all know this, so out of respect for me they will not be inviting me to join them. So, I am on my own. Forgive me if this sounds like selfish thinking at such a sad time as this, but it's true. I am painfully aware that I am no longer part of the gang. It is now 8.30 in the evening, I have sat alone since 11.00am this morning, grieving for my friend. Thinking how difficult this must be for his family, his wife and his children. I am totally gutted for Jim. The rest of my friends will all be raising a glass, recalling fond memories and toasting his life, no doubt with a sentimental tear in their eyes. I can't do that. I can't be part of the ritual, of the coming together and sharing in the grief and in the taking comfort of the mutual bond of old friends. I am not invited. I am alone. Me and Jim have been friends since we were seven years old. We went to school together, worked together, drank together, pulled birds together. We went to America together. He was like a brother to me. I had assumed we would become old men one day, perhaps sitting on a park bench, wearing flat caps and bickering and agreeing on nothing, just like we always had. He was genuinely pleased that I was getting help and sorting myself out, but I can't take part in toasting his passing with our friends. That's hard! I am really going to miss my friend.

****

I will be seeing my son at the weekend, what a gift! His first priority is his mum, always has been and always will be, as it should be. Dads are dads, but mums are mums! I've never felt so alone!

For the next two days I hardly left my room at Hope House. I didn't take part in any of the group work sessions or activities, I really didn't feel up to it. Anne, my key worker, paid me a visit. She said she was sorry for my loss and understood that it was not an easy time for me, but rather forcibly insisted I re-join the group work sessions. I had no choice; I also knew she was right. That afternoon I reluctantly joined the thinking and behaviour group run by Steve.

It was awkward for everyone, so I apologised to the group as I felt 'my grief' had somewhat taken over the proceedings. I was mindful of this, so did my best to remain silent. Nobody else spoke either. Steve asked, (in front of the group), if I would like to talk about Jim? He said, 'I think it's healthy to talk about death. We have a reluctance in this country to acknowledge it'. I looked around the group, most people nodded their approval. So, I told them of my shock, I told them what an excellent bloke he was and how women loved him, which was great because I always got her mate! I told them some of our escapades, working on building sites, going out on the piss, when we bounced at the party in America (Jesus, Mary and Joseph!). It was the first time I had smiled in two days! I explained how we were like brothers.

'I think it's not until somebody dies that you realise, just how excellent they are and how much of a big part of your life they actually inhabited. It's the unthinkable reality isn't it! DEATH. We all know it's coming. It will happen. It's just hard to visualise'! I was glad Steve had asked me to talk about it. It helped. Maybe it helped the others too. Maybe it brought home to them just how precious life really is. It shouldn't be wasted or taken for granted?! At my next counselling session Mary asked how I was coping? 'Well obviously it's been very difficult, I feel sorry for him. He should have lived to a ripe old age because that's the natural order of things, that's what should have happened'. I saw his family at the hospital just before he died, they all looked helpless and sick with worry. I couldn't help but think that could have been my family sitting there. Then I felt guilty for even thinking such a thing at a time like this. 'me, me, me, it's always about, fucking me, I'm tired of being an alcoholic. I'm tired of working on my problems, its fucking boring me! I just wanna be fucking normal, Mary'! Mary said, 'There's no such thing as normal, it doesn't exist'.

Neither of us spoke for a while and then I said, 'I can't help thinking some people think it should have been me that died and not Jim. I'm the one whose life is shit, I'm the one who is in a fucking rehab centre. It's me that used to collapse in the street so out of my face, I didn't know where or who I was. I'm the one who use to get behind the wheel of a car so drunk I could barely stand up'! I feel like a total shitbag for even thinking it, let alone saying it. I feel guilt'. There was another pause with neither of us talking. Then I said, 'I'm glad I am sober Mary'! 'I'm glad I can mourn the death of my friend in a dignified and respectful manner'. 'At the beginning of this session, you asked me how I was coping. Well I think I am able to process and cope with what has happened, far better than if I were stocious and wallowing in self-pity'! I let out a deflated sigh and said, 'What's wrong with me Mary'? Mary sat forward in her chair, smiled and said, 'There's nothing wrong with you, Pat. You just happen to be an alcoholic'. 'Yeah, I know Mary, but couldn't, I..... just happen to be something else'!

Over the next few days Neil, Simón, and my nephew Danny became regular visitors to Hope House. Most evenings we took over the garden and the kitchen as we struggled to sort out Jim's eulogy and the delicate matter of who was going to be carrying the coffin. We even managed to joke around a bit, roasting each other on Jim's behalf.

A week after Jim's death, I received an unexpected phone call from his wife, Nicola. She told me she was at the chapel of rest with Jim's mum, 'if' I wanted to come and see him. Obviously, a difficult call. I felt obliged to say, 'Yes'. The truth was I wasn't sure if I wanted to go or not, I hadn't quite made up my mind. After the call, I thought about when my dad and Kathleen had died. As I was young, I had been given a choice as to whether or not I wanted to go and see them. I remember how as a son and a brother I had felt it was my duty to go and pay my last respects. I reasoned Jim was family too. As a man it was my duty to go and see Jim one last time. In fact, it was more than that, it was an honour to be asked.

At 4 o'clock in the afternoon I arrived at the chapel of rest. Jim's wife and mother were sitting in the front foyer. To see them both sitting quietly together, looking so bereft, so lost, was heart-breaking. I felt for them both and didn't know what to say that hadn't already been said. Nicola let out a little whimper, composed herself, stood and said gently, 'You can go through if you like', indicating to a little room at the end of the corridor. I nodded politely and made my way along the corridor and into the room.

The room was painted in soothing lilacs and smelled of incense, while gentle, calming, background music played at a low audible hum. As I entered, I saw my friend's open casket, for the briefest of moments I hesitated before I approached. Poor Jim, he looked serene. He was wearing the suit he had been married in. I noticed photographs of his children had been lovingly and carefully placed in the casket all around him. I placed my hand on his, and just like my father and sister before him, it was cold to the touch. I stayed for a while talking to my friend, despite my grief I had a brief moment of feeling foolish, because I sensed, I knew, he was already gone. I said my last goodbyes and left the little room.

I returned to the foyer and offered some words of comfort to his mother and his wife, but I can't remember what they were. As I began to leave and make my way out of the front door, I met Jim's sisters coming in, for a brief fleeting moment. I felt a pang of guilt, like I had intruded on a very personal matter.

As I walked back to Hope House, alone with my thoughts, I considered how brutally tragic it all was. I have just visited Jim in the chapel of rest. I was drinking tea and laughing with him the other week and now he is dead. I've always been glad that I went to see him.

When I arrived back at Hope House I was 'expected' to join

everyone at the dining table for the evening meal! I hadn't told anyone where I had been, and I was too emotionally drained to argue or to explain. So, I took a seat without protest. I couldn't nor did I have any intention of eating. Then to my astonishment, Donald barged into the kitchen with a face like thunder and threw himself down in the chair next to mine. He began slamming his cutlery around and was actually pouting, like a disobedient and petulant child. Karen asked, 'What's the matter Donald'? To which he stomped, 'It's not fair'! as he huffily crossed his arms against his chest. 'It's my neighbours' birthday and 'I' am not allowed to go for a coffee with her, because I have to sit here, with you lot and eat my dinner'!

I couldn't help myself and said in a rising and disbelieving manner, 'What's that Donald, you can't go for a coffee and a bit of fucking cake'! 'you do realise that you're in a fucking rehab centre, that 'you' signed up for, presumably because your life is so fucking shit, that you can't manage on your own. You do fucking realise that don't ya'!! I tell you what Donald, you want to have a serious fucking word with yourself '!

You could have heard a pin drop. Everyone was staring at their plates. I hadn't meant to sound so aggressive, but I really couldn't be bothered with his silliness. 'Can you pass me the water, please Nicky', I asked politely. She smiled as she handed me the jug.

Thirteen days later, Jim Sweeny was laid to rest with his brother Tony. Hundreds attended the funeral; I don't think the town had ever seen anything like it. I was pleased he had such a good turnout; it's comforting for the family. It made me think of my mum. She is 82yrs old, she has outlived nearly all her friends and family, I wonder who will be at her funeral?

Me, Neil, Simón, my nephew (and Jim's friend), Danny, and both of Jim's brothers in law, paid our friend the final and ultimate honour of carrying his coffin to his final resting place. I knew life would never be the same again.

Chapter Twenty-Eight

Two months later I completed my 6-month rehabilitation programme at Hope House. I left with a certificate, a £40 gift voucher and a new vigour for life! I emerged a very different man than the one who had arrived 6 months earlier. Truly sober! Nothing stronger than a cup of coffee in 6 months. I had once thought it an impossibility, now I had proved to myself that it was not. What's more I liked being sober! I had finally accepted, what I had known all along. I embarked on a new beginning; a new life much better than the old one. I was about to enjoy a new freedom that I had previously not dared to even dream of!

Upon leaving hope house, I was technically (actually), homeless. Moving back to my mum's (even as a stop gap) was not an option and despite having been on the council bidding list for some time, I had still not, as yet, been offered a place. So, when Hope House offered me the chance of 'second stage' supported housing I happily accepted. This would mean I would stay under the umbrella of Hope house for longer than I had expected and until I had secured a council flat of my own. As a result of this decision I moved into a small two-bedroom terrace house, sharing with a skinny 27yr old rock god, with long lank hair which went all the way down to where his arse should have been! He had also been a client of Hope House. His name was Zach.

My first impressions of Zach were not good! In fact, my heart sank when I saw the state of the house. I asked myself how anyone in recovery could live in such filthy conditions. I also wondered how Hope House would allow it. With little choice, I spent a week (angrily quiet) cleaning the house, while Zach hid in his room, playing his guitar and his Xbox. So, I'm dad! I had thought to myself. Zachary being every bit the teenage son I had not asked for! Despite this, I chose to say nothing and just clean the house. I didn't want to walk in and start shouting the odds, thus starting off on the wrong foot. I instinctively knew it would be a waste of time anyway, so I decided to lead by example and shame him into following suit!

I was quietly chuffed when I realised it had worked, and from there on in, the house sparkled! I soon realised my first impressions of Zach had been wrong, he was in fact a decent young man with a good heart. Nor had it gone unnoticed by me that he had been to rehab and had begun to sort himself out by the age of 27, I had 'waited' until I was 42! We actually got on very well and became good friends, we enjoyed good conversations putting the world to rights and trying to outdo each other whilst watching, University Challenged! (as we liked to call it!).

Zach, being the wannabe rock god, lived for his guitar! Playing a little myself, we even on occasion 'jammed' together, presumably much to the annoyance of the neighbours, although they never complained! Perhaps it was because the neighbours knew our house was for 'alkies' and the like, coming out of rehab! (or maybe it just sounded alright?!!).

One morning over a cup of coffee Zach began to tell me his story. He had grown up estranged from his dad and had been raised by his mother and grandfather. He had a hard time at school, struggling with conformity and suffered a brief spell of being bullied and then at the age of fifteen, his dad came back into his life, much to the annoyance and frustration of his mother. I couldn't help but raise an eyebrow when Zach told me his dad was a skate boarder.... who liked to drink, smoke weed and snort coke. Like most young boys, the impressionable young Zachary, hero worshipped his father, to the point of going to live with him. Zach thought his dad was super cool, because he let him drink and smoke weed with him. They became more like a couple of mates rather than father and son. Soon Zach was snorting coke with his dad too, then the arguments started! They ended up having a fight and Zach realised his father was a very selfish individual, who was in fact more childlike than the young Zach. His dad threw him out!

Hurt by his perceived betrayal, his mum refused to take him back, so at the age of sixteen he had found himself homeless and living in a tent around the back of an Asda's supermarket. With this last piece of information, I couldn't resist saying, 'Wow, I've always wanted to go camping'! Zach just shook his head and continued with his story. He said it was at times frightening, 'You had to be careful and keep your guard up, you had to watch out for idiots'! 'Sometimes it was okay, almost enjoyable, it was sort of freeing in a way. Occasionally I would sneak into Asda and steal a bottle of whiskey! I had some good times too, although at times, it was really cold'!

Zach continued talking, he told me he went off one day and when he returned, someone had set fire to his tent! Probably for a bit of a laugh. But it was the only thing he had in the whole world! After that it was sofa surfing, hostels and a steady demise into the dark world of hard drugs. Zach confided in me that when he had been offered a place in Hope House, he had no intention of giving up drugs, he just saw it as some where warm to sleep! But after having been in there a couple of weeks, he started to change, he started to like the idea of being clean! He told me it had been two years since he had used or took a drink. He then apologised for the state the house was in when I arrived! 'To be honest, Pat, I was struggling a bit, I had been living here on my own for almost a year and I didn't like it. I felt isolated and retreated more and more into my room until I was hardly living in the rest of the house at all. You moving in, well I wasn't sure at first, but it has actually done me a lot of good'!

I won't lie, as he was telling me this I was thinking to myself, 'Well, you could have come out of your room and helped,' but I didn't say it, the truth was I couldn't but help admire the man. Sharing a house with Zach was good. I liked it. Things ran smoothly. In fact the only time I ever got the hump with him was when I would be doing the washing up in the kitchen sink and would end up with a very fine, very long, rock god hair wrapped around my hand. That use to piss me off! They were everywhere!

Zach had a girlfriend and would sometimes stay at hers. He was also working towards trying to rebuild a relationship with his mum, so on the occasions when he would be away, I would have Jack to stay at the house. It wasn't perfect. I definitely wanted better. But it was a start! At least I was sober, and I was getting to see him.

****

It hadn't gone unnoticed by me that Jack was growing up fast, it was a joy to be part of it. He was soon to be leaving junior school and was busy rehearsing for his last school play. He had landed the role of 'King Herod'. I had been invited to witness the showbiz extravaganza along with his mum and his maternal grandmother! I was really looking forward to it.

The day of the play, I received a phone call from Louise, saying she and her mother wouldn't be going, because they had both come down with the flu! 'Oh no, that's terrible,' I had feigned down the phone. The truth was, I was sort of glad they were not going. Not out of malice, but because I still felt a little uncomfortable in the presence of Jack's grandmother. I suppose, understandably, the woman doesn't like me very much!

On the afternoon of the school production of 'King Herod', I proudly took my seat in the audience amongst all the other doting parents and awaited the treat in store. The lights dimmed, the curtains opened, and the music rose up from somewhere behind us. From the side wings, children spilled out onto the stage, all of them searching the audience for a familiar face. I beamed with pride as I watched Jack do the same. When his eyes meet mine, he returned my smile, and then like a true professional took his (rightful) seat on his throne and got on with the job in hand!

Obviously, the play was rubbish! They always are! The brainchild of a well-intentioned, but ultra-silly, super-excited teacher, getting totally carried away and thinking they are Steven bloody Spielberg! The play was quite long and apart from the stage, which was well lit, the rest of the hall was quite dark (and warm), and as a result a lot of the parents (mainly dads, I noticed), had begun to slump in their chairs and slowly nod off! (except me of course!). It was during a 'slump' that Jack delivered the killer line he had been practising for weeks in his mum's living room and my kitchen! He jumped up out of his throne stamping his foot very loudly on the stage floor, threw out a pointing hand and then roared at the top of his voice, 'Take them away'!!! It caught half the audience (dads) by surprise, jolting them upright in their seats and snapping them out of their slumber! I grinned from ear to ear and marvelled in sheer delight at my (not so little anymore) boy. Just me and him! In that exact instant, as I looked on bursting with pride and pure love, I knew that all I had been through had been worth it! It's great to be a dad!

My mum didn't come to the play! as I didn't invite her! She has begun a decline, her behaviour is at times odd, bordering on the bizarre. I was worried she might do or say something to Louise or her mum and spoil it for me, so I hadn't asked her to join us (more guilt)! She is becoming increasingly confused. Today she asked me if I had seen my father, was he in the pub? She then confused me with my brother. When I (wrongly) corrected her she said, 'For God's sake, one minute you're Patrick, and the next you're Connor'. 'You wanna make yer mind up, you stupid looking cunt!' Smiling, I apologised, saying, 'Sorry mum, but my memory isn't what it used to be.' She gave me a cursory look!

Having only one kidney she is prone to urinary infections which can send the poor woman a bit doolally. But I am starting to think it might be something a bit more serious. Twice I have found the TV remote in the fridge and I have also found it wedged in the phone base in the hallway. It's not good. It would seem it's my turn to worry! I love my son. I love my mum.

****

Christmas came and went, by comparison it was a good one. I had managed to get a few shifts here and there in the run up, so was pleased I could make a fuss of Jack and his little brother. Christmas was also good because I didn't have to worry about making a fool of or disgracing myself in front of the family. I didn't have to worry about offending or upsetting anyone! Nor did I have to worry about making sure I had enough of 'something' or worry about what I was going to do when 'it' ran out!? It was a very liberating feeling!

Instead of getting off 'my trolley', I cooked dinner for seventeen (disappointed, ha ha) people, and then watched as they nearly all got drunk. This may sound a bit 'rich' coming from me, but I don't like being around drunk people, I find it almost offensive nowadays! It makes me feel uncomfortable! I don't begrudge anyone having a drink, far from it, good luck to them. If I wasn't an alkie! I would be doing the same. I think the 'issue' is that I see myself in them, and I don't like it!

I enjoyed Christmas because I knew once it was out of the way, I had the new year to look forward to. The start of the rest of my life! It excited me and I was keen to get on with it. I didn't have the same silly notions as when I had previously stopped drinking. I didn't naïvely believe I was going to become a 'millionaire' or live some sort of super existence. I was now, older, wiser and calmer. I realised that being sober was just the beginning. It meant I now had the same chances as everyone else, I could deal with 'whatever' life threw at me!

It was the end of March before the council offered me a first floor one bedroom flat. I had hoped I would be offered one near to where my son lived, but he lives in quite a nice area, so council flats were few and far between; the pickings were slim! Instead, I had been offered a flat on the same estate I had grown up on, just around the corner from the house I had been born in and where my mum still lives.

I was ecstatic, I was over the moon, it was the next big step in my recovery which would propel me to 'normaldom'!

It was also the first time in almost 20yrs (since I had lived with M in fact!) that I was to have somewhere I could truly call home, my own front door! I viewed, signed for, and received the keys to the flat all on the same afternoon. I was extremely grateful. I felt like I had just won the lottery, I couldn't stop smiling! I couldn't wait to get started and turn it into a nice comfortable home for me and for when Jack came to stay. I was happy!

Happiness tends to be short lived! So keen was I to get started that I arrived at 'my' flat at 7am the next morning! I wanted to measure up for carpets and curtains and contemplate colour schemes, magnolia and white perhaps! The truth being, I was so excited I just couldn't stay away!

As I crossed the road, reaching the pathway that led down to the main doors of the block, I heard music blasting out from the flat below mine! Immediately alarm bells began to ring in my mind. As I approached, I thought to myself, 'You have got to be fucking kidding me'! The day before when I had viewed the flat, it was so peaceful and quiet you could have heard a 'sparrow fart'! (as my father use to say!). 'Jesus Christ its only 7am', I had said to myself, before trying to rationalise what I was hearing. ‘Okay, it’s a beautiful sunny spring morning, it’s a Saturday! Perhaps whoever lives there has woken in an exceptionally good mood and is spring cleaning with their windows open whilst also enjoying listening to their music’! ‘After all, people are entitled to 'turn it up' now and again, right’? Please God let it be that! And so, the battle began!

Although I had yet to meet them, I tried to give the downstairs neighbour the benefit of the doubt. It was hard. The noise was nonstop! I went to bed listening to Alexander O’Neil, I woke up listening to Alexander O’Neil! I don’t mind admitting I felt like crying! This can’t be happening to me, not now, not after everything I have worked for. Could this be any worse!

After just one week of living at the flat, I arrived 'home' one day and found a young homeless woman sitting on the steps outside my block. She was a bizarre looking cretin. It’s hard to describe her, she wore a type of bandanna on her head and it looked like she had what appeared to be about a week’s worth of washing (blankets included) wrapped around her person under a bed sheet! She kind of reminded me of those knitted dolls your mum might have had in the bathroom in the late 70s, that hid the toilet roll!!

I'm not a snob, nor am I a heartless man, but my first thought was... 'You can fucking get gone'! You can imagine then my bitter disappointment, when I discovered she was the one that had been bombarding me with Alexander 'fucking' O’Neil! I recoiled in horror and physically shrank away from her. She lived in the flat below me! To say I was devastated is an understatement. However, I am not an idiot! The woman clearly had mental health issues. So, I rationalised that she had as much right to live there as I, and she also had the right to live her life as she saw fit, as I mine. I decided then that I would try and reason with her.

The next time I saw her, I politely introduced myself as the man upstairs, (would she think I was god?). I then explained the issue regarding the noise. I told her I did not wish to prevent her from enjoying her music, but perhaps we might reach a compromise. Perhaps there was a noise 'level', that would suit us both. Then for good measure I added that I had a brand-new pair of headphones (Zach gave them to me!), still in their box, if she wanted them. 'Nah, you're alright, maybe when I get my new stereo though, …yeah'! '.... You got a pound I can have'? I said I didn't! Then she said, 'Well have you got a fag then'? I said I didn't! To which she replied, 'But I've seen you smoking'!

I had been in my flat for about a month when I finally met the equally as noisy crackhead who lived upstairs! A very pleasant young man, but who had a tendency to smash his flat up, usually around 2.00 or 4.00am when he was drugged up to the fucking eyeballs! During such episodes he would also make alarming screeching noises which to me sounded like a couple of seagulls fighting! I have tried on numerous occasions (when trying to explain to someone) to mimic the noises he made, but have found it impossible to do so, I didn't even come close! I am not ungrateful, but I can't stay here!

****

I nearly drove the council housing officer mad with my daily calls! But tough! This was serious, I had found myself on dangerous ground! I needed to get out of there before I snapped. I had come too far to throw it all away now. I was not giving up without a fight. The biggest barrier to getting moved was that I had to wait a year, for my secure tenancy to come through (as yet, I was not 'technically' a council tenant!). A whole year!! It was a daunting and harrowing prospect. However, I'm sober, I can deal with it!

A month after moving in to my 'dream' home, I had my very last counselling session with Mary. I took my seat opposite her, as I always did and when I was settled Mary innocently asked, 'And how are you getting on in your new home'!

Poor Mary looked startled as I began to rant and rave. 'The council have fucking stitched me up, Mary'. 'I can't believe this has happened to me'. 'My neighbours are pure bastards, Mary' 'Do you know what some cheeky fucker suggested? They suggested I wear fucking earmuffs, in my own fucking home, Mary. Can you believe that! Do you know what I said? I said, 'And shall I get a little pair for when my son comes to stay'!!

I hadn't even stopped for air and was halfway through another rant when I suddenly stopped, mid-sentence and gasped... 'Huh'. Wide eyed I drew in a dep breath. Mary shot forward in her chair looking very concerned and in an alarmed manner said, 'What'?! I was stopped dead in my tracks by the sudden realisation. I stared right into Mary's eyes and said, ...'I've got a new set of problems'! With that, we both burst out laughing! 'Yes,' said Mary, 'You have'!

Giving up drinking doesn't mean I will no longer have any problems. I will always have problems, I have always 'had' problems. The difference is now I can deal with them ....in an 'adult' fashion! The good thing is, for once, my new problems are not because of me. They are because of others. I have no control over others. The only control I have, is how I respond to them. I was going to miss Mary. She asked me how I felt now the counselling had come to an end? I told her I felt okay about it, good in fact. A beginning a middle and an end, it's how it's supposed to be, its right isn't it! It's not really the done thing, but I gave Mary a big hug and thanked her for helping me to see 'the woods and the trees'!

****

Two years! I thought the housing officer was going to have a nervous breakdown, I was relentless in my quest to get the matter resolved. As much as possible he avoided answering my calls, but when he had no choice but to take the call, I would hear the dread in his voice! I wrote letters. I kept a noise diary. I went to see my local MP, who was very sympathetic, but useless. Going against my own moral code of conduct I even reluctantly agreed to the council installing recording equipment in my flat in an attempt to gather evidence! I was extremely uncomfortable with this phase of developments, because where I come from it 'really' is not the done thing. What's next? Packing Jews onto a train? I really didn't fucking like it! I had grown up on the estate; you don't 'grass' on your neighbours. If you have a problem, you tell em to their face, like a man! But this was different, because they were actually driving me mad, it was impossible to tolerate! I had tried to reason; I had tried to be reasonable!

In my attempts to be reasonable I had hammered the loon's door (downstairs), one night and had roared through her letter box for her to 'turn it fucking down'. To my utter astonishment she had opened the door, and with not a bother on her, asked, 'Are you an actor in EastEnders'? To which I replied, 'Yes, I am.... and I need to rehearse my fucking lines, so could you please 'turn it' the fuck down... please'! That night I went to sleep listening to.... 'Give me the reason to want you baby....' by Alexander O Neil.

Also in my attempt to be reasonable I had found myself out on the landing outside my flat at 2.00 in the morning in just my underpants (nobody wants to see that!), arguing with the crack-head from upstairs and a couple of his mates about all the shouting and hollering coming from his flat. ' ...And stop screeching like a fucking seagull', I roared in anger!

I had startled him by catching him off guard; he hadn't expected to be challenged at 2.00am and in front of his friends. He looked for a moment bewildered as what to say, and then having seemingly come up with a valid excuse, tried to blame the noise on 'Fifi', his cat! I gave him a look of utter contempt and said, 'But I just heard it shout 'fuck off' mate'!

I had come too far in my recovery to throw it all away, one wrong move from me and suddenly I would be the bad guy! I could not let that happen and that is why I had agreed to the recording equipment. A few weeks later the housing officer came to my flat with the good news. He excitedly told me, 'we' now have enough evidence to send both of your neighbours 'warning' letters.

'Letters, fucking letters, ... with all due respect mate, sending a letter to a lunatic or a crackhead, is not going to stop them from being a lunatic or a crack-head is it'? 'And you're not going to evict them, not that that's what I want anyway, but you're not going to'. 'So, the only viable option is to move me'! The housing officer said, 'Well, you know it's not that easy... because... well'.

I cut him off, and said, 'I am a human being! I have the right to live in peace without being harassed and tormented on a daily basis, by my neighbours. It's like a ticking clock or a dripping tap, in fact it is nothing short of water torture. I'm going to put this in writing for you! It isn't a silly childish threat, I'm only human and I can only take so much. At some point I 'will' snap! When that happens one of two things will take place, either I will say, 'Fuck it' and pick up a drink, or I will say, 'Fuck it' and batter my next-door neighbours'!

The housing officer, shifting from one foot to the other said, 'Well Mr Delaney, attacking your neighbours is not a good idea is it!!' 'No, its not', I replied, 'But out of the two options, I would rather batter the neighbours, because I have a chance of coming back from that.

If I pick up a drink, I am fucked. I will end up in the gutter ....and all this will be forgotten and everyone will be 'urgh'! look at that bloke in the gutter, and the crack head and the loon will continue with their shit lives, But mine and my son's lives will be destroyed. Do you understand the seriousness of what I am saying, mate'?

The housing officer said the only realistic way I was ever going to get moved to another property was on medical grounds and I would need a letter from my doctor to support such an application! So I spent the next 3 months trying to get in to see a doctor, only to eventually be handed a leaflet from the receptionist saying that the doctor would not write letters concerning housing matters as it was not in their remit to do so. It was a fair comment, although it did nothing to help my plight!

It really was a daily battle, but It wasn't all bad (just almost) during these two years. I had managed to get myself back into work (construction! Beggars can't be choosers!), which was good on two counts: firstly, I had wages and secondly, I was out of the flat all day! Also, since I had started to do the right thing in life, I was overwhelmed by the amount of help I had received, it not only amazed me but also humbled me! (people are good!). My sister Bridie gave me her old car, (her and her husband paid for the insurance!). I was thankful for but embarrassed by their generosity. The things we take for granted! When my sister handed me the keys for the car and after I had said thank you a million times, I said, 'I will now be able to take Jack to a drive through McDonald's for the first time in over two years'!

Not only did having a car help for work and for having Jack at weekends, but it also made it easier to get to the odd AA meeting. I had decided that although I had no intention of doing the steps or getting a sponsor, it wouldn't hurt to keep my hand in! A constant (weekly) reminder of what I was! And, more importantly, what I am, couldn't hurt! Especially now that I had (completely) finished with Hope House. I soon realised the people at AA were exactly my type of people. I felt at ease in their company. At each, and every meeting, I was reminded of some aspect of my past, sometimes painfully so. It helped keep my head on straight!

Jack was doing really well and turning into a lovely young man! He was growing up faster than I would have liked. It would be a bum fluff moustache and a, 'What have you ever done for me', before I knew it. But I didn't mind. It was a joy to watch him grow. He was just about to start high school, I couldn't believe it, my little boy going to high school!

He was really excited by it all, whereas I was worried sick! Even Louise, told me to stop fretting. I know I look at him through rose tinted glasses, but he genuinely is a nice kid! He is leaving the lovely little world of his junior school and going into the lion's den of the big school, full of horrible little bastards! As I was so concerned, I decided to have a word with him and give him some fatherly advice!

I sat down next to him on the sofa and said, 'Not everybody in this world is as nice as me and you son! So, watch out for the wrong-uns! And remember if anyone starts acting like a gimp... kick em in the nuts'! To which he replied, 'Stand up then'! ...Some kid, huh!

I had also, at around about this time, begun a dangerous flirtation with gambling, not uncommon among alcoholics in recovery. It had begun as the odd scratch card here and there and the odd pound on a horse on a Saturday, as something to do!

But as someone, who suffers from alcohol-ism! The 'ism' being the real problem, it had quickly spiralled out of control. I had nipped across to the shops one evening to get a loaf of bread and had decided to pop into the bookies opposite. I had thought because I was in no hurry to return to the unbearable conditions associated with my flat! And I had, to my delight, won fifty quid! Result! A couple of nights later I again popped over to the shops, only this time I lost fifty quid and had no bread!

And so, it began! From a pound on a horse to a hundred pound in the machine! Sometimes I won big, but more often than not I lost! Either way it didn't make me happy. As soon as I put the first pound in the machine, I was fucked! Just like as soon as I took the first drink! It was a bit of a surprise to discover I could be a complete dick, ...without drinking!

I soon realised that for me, gambling had nothing to do with, and was not about, the money. It was about acting out old patterns of behaviour! When stressed! Later, automatically! At no point did I ever phone anyone up and say, 'Guess where I'm going'! No. Instead I skulked off to the bookies with money I could ill afford to lose and engaged in high risk behaviour! I was chasing the, Weh, Woo's! because that's all I had ever known! It was drinking without the alcohol and as soon as I placed the first bet, I was powerless to control it. In AA, they say, don't take the first drink, because it's the first drink that gets you drunk! Not the sixth or seventh! I applied the same logic to gambling! Don't place the first bet and you can't lose! I made a vow to stay out of the bookies, and I did! And my happiness returned, 10-fold, (ha ha!). It had been an expensive lesson in monetary terms but worth every penny! As I live my sober existence, I am learning the do's and don'ts!

****

Another Christmas came and went, and I was still in the flat from hell. It was very depressing, I was climbing the walls, convinced I was going to get dragged down and contaminated by the madness all around me. Another Christmas completely ruined by the crack head's ....'cat'!

My son had shocked and delighted me, by asking his mum without any prompting from me, if he could spend Christmas with his dad! Much to my surprise she had said yes. Needless to say, I was 'well' chuffed! I had by now gotten into the habit of letting the crack head know when my son was staying, in the hope he might do the right thing and hold it down. Sometimes he did and sometimes he didn't. In an attempt to reach some mutual understanding, I divulged that I had been in rehab and that I was not judging him as I did not have the right! I suppose the truth of it is, he no more wanted to be a crack head than I had wanted to be an alkie!

I didn't 'hate' either of my neighbours, I didn't think I was better than them. I just couldn't live among them! I explained that this was to be the first Christmas I had ever spent with my son, so it was very special and important to me. I just wanted a peaceful Christmas Eve and Christmas Day with my boy! 'You can go as mad as you want New Year, because I won't be here', I said finally. Christmas Eve, I thought the ceiling was going to come through! I really am not trying to sound hard or as if I am some kind of tough guy, but the crack head still doesn't realise how close he came to getting the kicking of a lifetime! I felt like a complete wanker for 'not' battering him. I was enraged, because my little boy was with me! But I couldn't do anything about it, because my little boy was with me! I was starting to feel embarrassed in front of my son!

I was on the verge of snapping; I could feel it in my bones! I went to the doctor and asked him to give me something, because I was going to lose it and soon! I explained my situation to the doctor. How I had come out of rehab, excited about my future. How I was devastated when I realised I had been 'hoodwinked' by the council, how I had been even more devastated when I realised I was going to have to sit tight for 12months to get my secure tenancy, before I could even begin to try and get out of there. How the housing officer had said, I needed a letter from my doctor, but how I had been informed the doctors would not do it because they are not social workers. I even said that I understood, that it made sense! I told him how my programme of recovery had stopped dead the day I moved in to the flat, I was on dangerous ground. I also explained how in my neighbour's defence they had never been rude to me, I did not think I was a cut above, but living there was dangerous for me!

The doctor asked, 'Out of a matter of interest who is the woman that lives downstairs'? When I described her, he rolled his eyes and said, 'You're joking'! He fucking knew her! He knew she was a nightmare! 'And who lives upstairs then', he enquired. When I described the crack head upstairs, he said, 'Yeah I know him as well'. The doctor looked genuinely gutted for me! With that he spun round in his chair and began tapping away on his keyboard, staring intently at his computer monitor. 5 minutes later he turned to me again and handed me a letter and said, 'Give that to the housing. I have recommended they move you, before you relapse or there is an altercation between you and your neighbours. If you have any problems come and see me. In the meantime, here is a prescription for diazepam, which should take the edge of things for a while, so hopefully there will be no 'fisty cuffs'. Good luck Mr Delaney'!

I couldn't believe it, nor had I been expecting it, but if it wasn't for that doctor I would probably still be there now! Or in prison! Or in the gutter! Or in the grave! It took him less than five minutes to change my life!

****

To get a new place I had to bid online for properties with the council. Four months after getting the letter from the doctor and I was still in my flat. I was beginning to give up all hope, as every time I placed a bid I came second or third, which might as well be last! I was starting to think I would never get out of the asylum! And then one day quite unexpectedly I came first! I was stunned. I couldn't quite believe it was over! It all happened quickly, so quickly in fact it almost frightened me! Within two weeks I had moved out of the flat from hell and into my new one!

I absolutely love it! It's very peaceful and if you listen very, very carefully you might just hear '...a sparrow fart'!!! I now have the best of neighbours, friendly, courteous and polite. And the icing on the cake? It's just around the corner from my son's house, exactly where I wanted to be all along! I truly feel like I have won the council flat jackpot. Plus, Jack loves it here. I love it here. I look forward to coming home at the end of the day! I look forward to my boy coming to stay without having to worry about lunatic neighbours that do excellent seagull impressions or who look like toilet roll disguisers! It's perfect! It feels as though a huge weight has been lifted off my shoulders. I feel relived and I am extremely grateful!

Nothing ever stays the same. It wasn't just me that was on the move. The whole family were at it too! It's strange but for decades we were all held fast, wedged in place, anchored to the estate and the family home where we had all grown up. It was where we belonged, it was who we were. Not one among us had ventured more than a few miles away from base point! Then within a matter of months everything changed. My brother brought a rather large pile in Cambridge! Evelyn moved to a lovely garden city a good 20 miles away. Bridie moved to a village just outside the town and, also brought a second home in Spain, and I had won the council flat 'lottery'! And then there was my poor old mum.

My mum had been getting steadily worse. She looked small and frail and was becoming increasingly more confused. As a family we all took turns in staying with her overnight at the house. No one begrudged it, but the truth is, it was hard work.

As her condition worsened still, she started to wander. A neighbour had found her on her way to the bus stop at 6.00am saying she was off to work. At other times she would be trying to leave the house at 3.00 or 4.00am saying she had to pick the kids up from school. It was a real worry.

My mum was eventually diagnosed with Alzheimers. Although heart-breaking and very sad, it wasn’t really a shock, because we already knew. As hard as we all tried, it got to the point where it was impossible to be with her 24-7, so with little choice social services became involved and it was decided the best option was sheltered accommodation. It wasn't what we wanted! We wanted her to see out her days in the family home. But it wasn't about what we wanted; it was about what was best for her.

It was a difficult time for my family, we drip fed her information about the move to sheltered accommodation which she was happy to go along with, which in turn was a clear indicator of just how far down the road her dementia had taken her! If she had been of sound mind, had she still been the strong woman I knew as mum, she would have dug her heels in and told us all to 'Fuck off'! But bless her she didn't!

52yrs she had been in that house. Sadly more bad memories than good. Although the right thing to do, it was still a sad, somewhat strange occasion the day we moved her out. She was excited, like a child going on an adventure. She helped put things in boxes and made cups of tea, but she didn't fully understand what was going on. The transition from the house to her one-bedroom flat was surprisingly uneventful. She seemed to take it all in her stride. Once she was settled and comfortable, I went back to the house and began the agonising task of clearing out and 'throwing away' the years of clutter that she had accumulated. It felt harsh and insensitive, like a betrayal.

Having spent most of the weekend stepping on my mother's memories and with the house now clear I decided to make a start on the sheds. As I pulled the door open my eyes immediately fell upon the 'blue rope' hanging on the wall! How could I have forgotten? Startled, but motionless, I stared at the rope before me, void of all emotion. I was going to hang myself with that rope! That was real. It had been a real consideration once upon a time ago. Thankfully that's all in the past now, no longer do I have such selfish thoughts. With a shudder I pulled my eyes away and looked around the huge pile of stuff that needed clearing, this time my eyes fell upon the 'robin' on the back wall of the shed!

It had been there all my life. A 2ft high chalk drawing of a robin redbreast, drawn directly onto the brickwork (like a cave painting!), my sister Kathleen had drawn it when she was a little girl. That must have been 40 years ago or more. A reminder that she was once here, she was once a part of this family, this household. Instinctively I pulled my phone from my back pocket and took several photos of it, aware that if I didn't, then I would never see it again!

My mum settled into her new home. She is doing really well and looks great for an 85yr old woman. She now gets the care she needs. She is thoroughly spoilt! And I am glad!

Chapter Twenty-Nine

It's been five years since I last took a drink, even longer since I felt the need (or the want) to use recreational drugs. I think it's fair to say I don't have a particularly wild or exciting life, but nonetheless I do have a good life! I am a free man.

I am there for my son. I am there for my mother. Finally, I am of use. I am comfortable in my own skin. It's a nice feeling! For the first time in my life, I have peace of mind. The funny thing is, I didn't know I didn't have it, ... until I got it!

I used to feel ashamed, but now I don't mind being an alcoholic, I have learnt to accept it. It's okay, as long as I don't take the first drink. In fact, I love being sober. I cherish it and value it above all else. Because without it... I am nothing, I have nothing! Which in turn means I can give nothing!

It only took a lifetime, but I am happy, and I am grateful. I want to live! I am looking forward to the rest of my life. I am looking forward to watching Jack grow and become the fine young man I know he will be. I even like the idea of being a Grandad one day!

****

So that's me. I live on my own in a one bed flat, and I love it. It's raining outside and there's nothing on the telly, but that's okay. I don't mind. Sometimes I feel very lonely! I have family and I have friends, but I don't tell them how I feel, because I am embarrassed by it, but that's also okay, because I know it will pass!

Sometimes I stare at my reflection in the bathroom mirror and marvel at my ever-ageing face. The creep of old age is upon me. But that's okay too, I'm not worried, it's normal. Despite what I see staring back at me I can't resist blowing myself a kiss, and why wouldn't I .... I still got it!

I am tired now, so I am going to go to bed. I would climb the wooden hills to Bedfordshire, but I haven't got any! Instead I will simply slip into the next room. I need an early night, because the letter on the living room table informs me I have an important appointment to keep tomorrow morning. I love it when appointments are first thing, because then I can have the rest of the day to myself! Which is good news because tomorrow night I've got a date! ...Wahoo!

THE NEXT DAY!

I get up early, make myself a strong coffee and read the letter again. I have to be there for 9.00am. Good! I shower and shave and get dressed. And then head off into town. Despite the wind and the rain last night, it is a beautiful sunny morning.

Along the way, I stop off at a shop for a packet of cigarettes for myself and a paper for my mum, who I will nip in and see later. As I enter the shop, I can't but help notice the young girl behind the counter is very pretty, but I don't let it show for fear of embarrassing us both. I ask for the cigarettes and the newspaper and give over the money. Then, as she hands me my change, she stares at me for a moment and says, 'Oh my God, you have got two different coloured eyes'! And then gives me a gorgeous smile. I can't help myself and grin from ear to ear. It's been a long, long time since anyone has noticed my eyes. I leave the shop knowing today is going to be a good day.

I arrive in the town centre and having parked the car, walk along the street to my appointment. As I walk up the steps of the building and towards the huge old oak doors, I stop briefly and smile. I am reminded of being 6yrs old again. My mum has taken me to the Children's Annex and as we walked up the steps towards the old Gothic style doors, she had looked concerned. I had held her hand and said, 'Don't worry, mum, I will be alright'! 6yrs old and I had reassured her!

I push the heavy door open, enter the building and walk up to the reception desk and give my name. The receptionist tells me to take a seat in the waiting area. I have no sooner sat down when a door adjacent to the one I have just walked through opens and a young woman steps through and says, 'Mr Delaney'? 'Yep that's me, I offer cheerfully. She indicates for me to follow her, not that there is any need, as I have been here before and knew where to go. She stops at a door halfway down the corridor and says, 'He will see you now'.

The first thing I notice as I enter the room is a large swathe of sunlight, spilling through the sash window to my right, which illuminates the room in a glorious soft yellow glow. I marvel at the dust motes contained within as they float, bouncing aimlessly through the air. The man behind the desk doesn't look up as I take the seat opposite him. I sit for a moment in silence, while he continues to scrutinise the paperwork in front of him. Feeling slightly awkward and wanting to break the uncomfortable silence I say, 'Give it to me straight doc. Don't pull no punches', and let out a little chuckle.

Dr Calow looks up from his documents but does not return my smile. So, I now I feel a little foolish. 'Ah, Mr Delaney, err mm, yes, I have the results back from the tests we did last week'. He then just stares at me. 'Okay, so what are they saying', I ask, matter of factly. The Doctor looks pained as he says, '.... It's... not good news, I'm afraid'. I am at a loss? What's not good news?

I notice the man steal himself, he slightly grimaces and appeared to wince before just blurting it out, as if saying it quickly would make it less painful, 'I'm afraid are results show that you have a rare and rather aggressive form of cancer called Sarcoma'! Now it is my turn to blurt, '...but I feel alright!?'

He looks slightly embarrassed and awkward as he continues, 'Erm, now there are therapies that can alleviate some of the discomfort you may experience and we have things in place that can offer you ..and indeed your family, support. Perhaps these leaflets may be of some help....'.

He had diverted his gaze. It may sound mad but, in that moment, I actually felt sorry for him! And then the penny dropped! 'How long'? The doctor lifted his eyes to meet mine, 'It's difficult to say, 3 to 6 months, maybe longer ...you may wish to start thinking about putting your affairs in order. I am very sorry Mr Delaney'. I felt like I had just been hit by a truck. Bizarrely, as I got up to leave, I thanked him.

I hadn't seen it coming! It's true I had been feeling tired and run down lately, but when I got up this morning I assumed the doctor was going to tell me the usual; quit smoking, cut down on your pork life and do some exercise! But not this. I was numb.

I don't recall the walk back to my car or the route that I took to get there. As I got in and closed the door the sound it made seemed suddenly final and ominous. I sat for some while behind the wheel motionless just staring blankly ahead. Awash with emotions. Why me?

I felt cheated, almost angry, I felt fear and then I felt an overwhelming sense of loss. I continued to sit motionless behind the wheel, disconnected from the world around me and then, at some point, my mind drifted and I thought of all that I had experienced and all that I have enjoyed and all that I had learnt, … .and then strangely, just for a brief moment, I didn't feel so bad.

What am I going to tell Jack? How am I going to tell Jack? It's hard to imagine that I am not going to be around; that I won't get to see my boy grow, get married and have a family of his own. I love him with all my heart; I hope he will be okay.

I'm not ready to die! I toy with the idea that there has been some mistake, but I know in my heart there hasn't! What about mum. 'They' probably won't tell her when I die, they won't want to upset her. I don't want to upset her. What do I say to the family?

Jack has let slip (as kids do!) that there is a surprise party for my birthday in five weeks' time. This will probably be the last time we will all be together as a family. Perhaps I will tell them after that? Funny, but I don't want to spoil the party! I can't believe this is happening, not now. I don't want to go.

****

After I am dead you can cut me open and have a root around. You will find my brain, my heart, my lungs, all that stuff will be there. But you won't find anything labelled, mind, spirit, or soul!

The very things that make me who and what I am, do not exist. But I existed, they existed in me!

Patrick Delaney
07 - 04 - 1972
07 -04 - 2019

JACK

TOO OLD TO BE A CHILD AND TOO YOUNG TO BE A MAN. The boy cuts a solitary figure as he stands alone, respectfully silent by the graveside. He kneels and gently places the bouquet he has been carrying upon the grave and then he re-reads the inscription upon the stone.

'Sweet are the memories that never fade'

He stays in this moment for a short while and then stands and with the back of his hand gently wipes away a tear. Then, deep in thought, he smiles to himself at some distant happy memory. Despite everything the boy is nearly always smiling. He seems to have been born with a naturally cheery disposition. He has also been born with two different coloured eyes, one green one brown.

THE AUTHOR

Pat Maloney is 48 years old and the director of a small building company. He lives alone in a one bedroom flat somewhere in the South East of England

He enjoys a peaceful existence and continues to remind himself, with each new day, just how fortunate he is to be surrounded by good family and good friends.

He has been sober for six years.
Here Comes the Son is his first book.

****

Thank you Sara and Toni.
If it were not for your patience and guidance, the book would still be a stack of papers under my bed.

*****

This book is obtainable from Amazon